# AUTISM AS CONTEXT BLINDNESS

PETER VERMEULEN, PHD

# AUTISM AS CONTEXT BLINDNESS

FOREWORD BY BRENDA SMITH MYLES, PHD

PUBLISHING
P.O. Box 23173
Shawnee Mission, Kansas 66283-0173
www.aapcpublishing.net

©2012 AAPC Publishing
P.O. Box 23173
Shawnee Mission, Kansas 66283-0173
www.aapcpublishing.net



Vermeulen, Peter, 1962-

Autisme als contextblindheid. English

Autism as context blindness / Peter Vermeulen ; foreword by Brenda Smith Myles. -- Shawnee Mission, Kan. : AAPC Publishing, c2012.

p. ; cm.

ISBN: 978-1-937473-00-6 ; previous ISBN: 978-90-7612-9 (Acco), 978-90-6445-547-6 (EPO)
LCCN: 2012937637
"Translated from the Dutch, Autisme als contextblindheid, c2009"-- T.p. verso.
Includes bibliographical references.
Summary: This book presents a whole new way of looking at autism by considering the impact of the context in which the person lives and where interventions are delivered.--Publisher.

1. Autism spectrum disorders--Treatment. 2. Context effects (Psychology) 3. Autism--Treatment. 4. Asperger's syndrome--Treatment. I. Title. II. Title: Autisme als contextblindheid. English.

RC553.A88 V47 2012
616.85/88206--dc23 1205

Translated from the Dutch, *Autisme als contextblindheid* © 2009

Previous ISBN: 978-90-7612-9; 978-90-6445-547-6

Cover design: Peter Vermeulen
Photographer: Peter Vermeulen



This book is designed in New Century Schoolbook.

Printed in the United States of America.

# Table of Contents

# Foreword

Many think that the world becomes more comfortable and meaningful when we can systemize (thank you, Simon Bar-on-Cohen!), categorize, quantify, and simplify. While we associate these terms with the autism community, in reality, it is neurotypical people who have attempted to break life into more easily defined components using the aforementioned strategies. For example, we have identified evidence-based practices (EBP) – interventions that are effective for individuals with autism spectrum disorders (ASD). We have attempted to task analyze activities so that they can be taught element by element. In some cases, the interventions and activities seem to have developed a life of their own. And as a result, they are not considered within the context of autism and life in general.

Over the years, attempts have been made to broaden our understanding of the world – to provide a different perspective. Leo Kanner and Hans Asperger helped us understand that individuals we have identified as being on the autism spectrum exhibit different ways of being and thinking. Building upon the work of Kanner and Asperger, Lorna Wing pioneered the understanding that ASD is a complex exceptionality. Bernard Rimland challenged a misinformed society to look beyond a simplified etiology of ASD and accept that the "cause" of ASD is multifaceted. Eric Schopler, Gary Mesibov, and Ivar Lovaas showed that our children have learning potential. In particular, Schopler and Mesibov married the concept of ASD and the nature of an iceberg – illustrating that the "behaviors" demonstrated by an individual on the spectrum are so much more than what we observe. Rita Jordan, Patricia Howlin, and Tony Attwood each has furthered our knowledge. More recently, Ruth Aspy, Barry Grossman, and Shawn Henry have linked "the autism" to interventions and have developed a comprehensive planning process to help ensure that we recognize the limitless potential of learners on the spectrum (thanks to Lee Stickle for highlighting the important concept of "limitless potential").

One critical area that has been missed, or only addressed in a cursory or tangential manner, by these important researchers and practitioners, as well as by many others whom space precludes mentioning, is the topic addressed in this book – *context*. This book communicates in a very professional and highly readable manner the importance of context to life success. In so doing, Peter Vermeulen reminds us of something very basic yet very complex – what we do, what we say, how we act or react, how we interpret, and so forth, is based upon context. And he cogently goes on to explain that an intervention, strategy, or support system is much less than it should be if we do not consider the context in which it will be used.

Very simply, Peter Vermeulen's book is a game changer. I believe that his book creates a foundation upon which we can build life success for individuals with ASD.

– Brenda Smith Myles, PhD

# Preface

Through years of evolution, the human brain has become an efficient information processor. Paradoxically, as advanced as the human brain has become, it cannot completely understand itself. Despite years of study and advanced technologies, we do not fully understand how the "typical" brain works, much less how an autistic brain works. In 1996, I wrote the book *Autistic Thinking*. Since that time, the community of autism has become familiar with the term *autistic thinking,* but the importance of this type of thinking for the way we meet people with autism is still largely misunderstood.

Recently, there has been an increase in autism awareness. Various treatments and interventions have surfaced: Social Stories™, the use of new technologies (computer, smart phone apps), early intervention, pivotal response training, structured teaching, counseling, and even autism-specific job coaching. But even with these advances, it is difficult for many to understand the autistic thinking style. In brief, there is a lot of know-how but still a profound lack of know-why.

> *Cheryl is a woman with autism who had difficulty going against the wishes of others. She found herself accepting invitations to events she did not want to attend. She found it difficult to make decisions on her own and often allowed others to make choices for her.*

*Cheryl's parents decided to enroll her in assertiveness training where Cheryl learned that she could have and voice her own opinion. Unfortunately, her social behavior became unacceptable as she relentlessly argued and demanded her own way, even when she knew she was in the wrong. Her assertiveness training taught her to oppose the opinions and decisions of others. She understood her assertiveness training on an autistic level:* ***Being assertive means saying "no."***

*Billy was a 12-year-old boy with autism whose mother attended one of my seminars. Billy refused to wear his dental retainer. His parents tried to prepare Billy for using a retainer. They thoroughly explained the process of being fitted for a retainer; they showed him photographs of retainers and of people wearing retainers. Still, Billy refused to wear his retainer. Billy's mother wrote, "We tried a reward system to encourage him to wear the retainer, but nothing has helped, and our dentist doesn't have any ideas to offer. Billy is afraid he will swallow the retainer. Please help us find a solution."*

*Reward systems are appropriate in certain situations, but in this instance a reward system was useless because a reward system focuses on willful behavior. In Billy's case, his behavior was based on his fear of swallowing the retainer.* ***In his way of autistic thinking, anything that is in his mouth can be swallowed.***

Both of these examples show how we often look at behavior without focusing on how people with autism perceive and understand things. Sadly, intervention for individuals with autism spectrum disorders (ASD) is still too focused on behavior and only minimally on the way of thinking that leads to the behavior. That is the reason for this book.

In *Autistic Thinking*, I wrote that one of the challenges of autism is a lack of the ability to connect details into a bigger picture. Since that time, it has become clear that people with autism can, in fact, see relationships between things (for example, the relationship between a facial expression and an emotion or the relationship between a word and its meaning) and that they sometimes can see the big picture – certainly, when we ask them to. So, if relating things and seeing the big picture is not the problem, what is? My quest began there.

*Autistic Thinking* was based on a definition developed by the well-known psychologist Uta Frith. As I looked back on Frith's definition, I noted that along with the term *drawing together information*, the word *context* was also used. Up to that point, I, along with many others, had understood only part of Frith's definition. I began to research what context would entail and how the human brain processes context. I made some surprising discoveries. Recent research in areas such as neurology, psychology, philosophy, and artificial intelligence has shown that context plays a central role in the way the human brain processes information, and especially in those areas that are involved in autism, such as processing social information. This made me realize that using context might be a challenge for the autistic mind. I call this *context blindness.*

I contacted Professor Frith and explained my perspective on context blindness. She reacted positively, and we carried on some interesting conversations – in London, in Vlaanderen, and by email. I was encouraged by her positive feedback on the idea of context blindness, but she also raised some deep questions. Thus, what was originally meant to be an update to my previous book, *Autistic Thinking,* grew into a completely new book.

The present book stresses the aspect of autistic thinking that has been mentioned, but has not been described critically and in detail. *People with autism have difficulty with context.* We can only understand context blindness if we know what it is to see context and how the human brain processes and uses context. Therefore, this book is not only about autism, but first and foremost about context sensitivity in the non-autistic brain. It is my hope that the reader will learn about the brain, both the autistic and the neurotypical.

Explaining how the human brain works is not simple. Context is a vague and slippery concept, and autism is a very complex disorder. I have tried to explain even the most theoretical and academic topics such as the neurological underpinnings of context sensitivity and the theoretical aspects of context blindness in an accessible way, with examples and anecdotes to make them more understandable. Much of the information is based on research. A number of studies and experiments are described in detail. For all others, I have constrained myself to a reference in the endnotes, which also contain technical and specific remarks and additions. The endnotes are meant primarily for people who are interested in the scientific background of the book.

This book is about context. But, of course, it also has a context itself. People with autism, their parents, caretakers, and scientists are those with whom I have shared my ideas and whose questions and remarks helped me to further develop those ideas. I am especially grateful to Uta Frith for her help, her critiques, and, above all, her willingness to give her attention to my questions during a time at which she was incredibly busy with her forthcoming retirement. I also benefited from conversations with Professors Ina van Berkelaer-Onnes, Rita Jordan, and Ilse Noens. Also, Roger Verpoorten, an experienced autism consultant, made me think about the role of context in developing different concepts. My colleagues at Autisme Centraal in Gent, Belgium, gave me food for thought on more than one occasion through their difficult questions and remarks about context blindness. We had very fruitful discussions for which I am thankful. I am also very grateful to the AAPC team, especially Keith Myles and Brenda Smith Myles, for taking the risk to publish a book that was tough to translate and that was written by someone unknown to most people on the American continent. I extend my sincere gratitude to Ruth Aspy and Kirsten McBride from AAPC Publishing for meticulous editing, and Kate Rankin, author of *Growing up Severely Autistic*, for her help with parts of the translation.

And finally, there is Det, who for the last few years listened to my constant nagging about context, but could, luckily, place it in the correct context. She helped me to sort my thoughts, to sharpen them, and to put them on paper. I would be context blind if I did not see Det's contribution to this book.

*Special Note*

Throughout this book, the word *autism* is used as synonym for autism spectrum disorder (ASD). Although there are some advantages to arguing for the use of various labels within the autism spectrum (e.g., Asperger Disorder), in terms of understanding the basic problem – as described in this book – of all people with an ASD and in terms of treatment, a broad definition, encompassing the range of disorders within the spectrum, is most appropriate. Thus, wherever the word *autism* is used, it means *autism spectrum disorder*.

# Introduction

Why can a book also be considered a weapon or an umbrella?

How do you know if a garbage bag is art or just a plain garbage bag?

What does context have to do with autism?

- What is a nice birthday present for a good friend?
- How do you pronounce *wind*? And *does*?
- How much milk do you pour in a cup of tea?
- What does it mean when someone says *no*?
- Are you allowed to touch someone's hair?
- How many pages are there in a book?
- What do you do when the bell rings?
- What is the best thing to do when someone raises their hand?
- What do you put in your suitcase when you go on a trip?

No doubt you can answer each of these questions. But what if you were asked to give the one and only correct answer? You would probably reply: "There is no single correct answer." What might be a nice birthday present for one of your friends could be quite inappropriate for another. What you pack depends on the destination and length of your journey. In other words, the only correct answer to each of the questions might be: "It depends," meaning that it depends on the situation. Another word for *situation* is *context*. The answer to the questions above depends on the context: the friend whose birthday it is, whether the recipient likes milk in his tea or not, where and when that bell rings, and what bell it is. Would you go and open the door when the bell of your doctor's office rings while she's taking your blood pressure?

Context is very influential. Similarly, the context, this time the sentence context, influences how you pronounce the word *does*.

John does not like hunting.
John loves hunting and likes to shoot does.
John is a hunter, but he does not shoot does.

Your retina receives exactly the same information (the letters *d-o-e-s*), but this information can have different meanings, depending on the context:

Does = conjugation of the verb *to do*
Does = plural of doe, a female deer

Words that have different meanings and pronunciation, although sharing exactly the same spelling, are known as homographs. Their meaning and pronunciation can only be derived from the context.

Similarly in the case of homophones. A homophone is a word that is pronounced the same way as another word but differs in meaning and (sometimes) spelling. The best known examples are the words *know* and *no*. If you hear someone say these two words, their meaning only becomes clear from the context, as in the following sentence:

I know no other examples of homophones.

Actually I do. You probably remember the famous song "Do-re-mi," sung by Julie Andrews and one of the hits from the musical and movie *The Sound of Music*. Andrews, Maria in the movie, sings this song to teach the notes of the major musical scale to the Von Trapp children, the way some teachers still do to their students. The names for some notes are homophones and can have different meanings in a context outside of music:

Do, a female deer (doe); Re, a sunbeam (ray); Ti, a drink or meal with bread and jam (tea) …

In summary, depending on the context, hearing "do" could mean a musical note or a female deer.

And then there are homonyms, words that are identical in sound and spelling but different in meaning. For example, the word *bank* can have many meanings, such as slope, a financial institution, a group or series of objects arranged together in a row, to incline, to rely on, and so on.

Most languages contain hundreds of homonyms, homographs, and homophones. There is a lot of ambiguity in language and, yet, in most circumstances, the human brain copes quite easily with these ambiguities. Most of the time, we are able to choose from all the different meanings exactly the meaning that is correct because we use the context to solve the problem of ambiguity.

The ambiguity of meanings is not confined to words and language. Ambiguity exists in almost everything we perceive with our senses. Nothing in our world seems to have an absolute, fixed meaning. It's not just words that can have different meanings, so can simple objects we come across in daily life. Take the book you are reading at this moment, for instance – a book can only be a book, you say. It cannot be a trampoline, a toaster, a ladder, a weapon, or underwear. When we see a book or hold it in our hands, there is only one definition: This is a book: One can open it and read it.

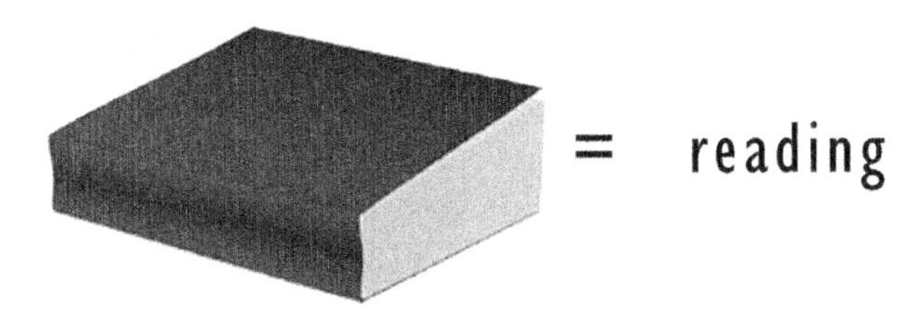


It seems that way, but as with words, the perception of a book can result in different meanings. Imagine you keep a book on your bedside table because you like to read before sleeping. After you have read a few pages, you turn off the light, close your eyes, and try to fall asleep. However, just as you start nodding off, you hear a buzz. A mosquito! You switch the light back on, and the first thing that comes into sight is ... your book. In this context, the book suddenly acquires a completely different function. Instead of being something you read, it becomes a tool to kill that annoying insect. In this case, the book could be defined as a weapon. In other contexts, a book can have many other functions: You can use it as a step to reach something (OK, it must be a thick book), you can use it as a press or as a support for something.

Admittedly, the number of different uses for a book is not infinite. Seeing a book as a toaster or a trampoline will not be very useful or successful. However, it is clear that the meanings and functions of a book can be quite diverse, and this is true for almost everything we perceive. The various meanings of objects, words, human behavior, and events are context dependent.

Through its evolution, the human brain has learned to take context into account because it is context that helps us to give meaning to the stimuli our brains receive. Context is essential for making sense of the world around us. It helps us to know how to react and how to choose an appropriate gift for a friend, for instance. Contextual information about that friend (Who is he? What does he like or dislike? What did we give him last time and how did he react? On what occasions do we buy a present – Christmas, a birthday, a wedding ...?) will influence the meaning of "a nice gift" and, therefore, our choice. If human brains did not take these variables into account, people would receive even more useless, silly and tasteless gifts than they do now!

It is April 9, 2008. In a street in Antwerp, a painter is making a large painting on a concrete wall. The painter is not just any painter – he is the internationally renowned Belgian artist Luc Tuymans, whose works have been exhibited in some of the most famous galleries in the world. His painting, a replica of one of his famous works, is part of an experiment for a cultural television program examining the influence of context on people's appreciation of art. In 48 hours, a total of 2,858 people walk by. Only 197 of them, a little over 4%, look at the painting with any interest or attention. Most people just walk by blindly.

It would have been interesting to ask the passers-by what they thought of the painting. I am sure that most people would not have deemed it a masterpiece, but an ordinary mural or even a piece of graffiti. However, if they were standing in front of the same painting in an art gallery or museum, those same people would probably be admiring or discussing the work. At least they would not just walk past it; certainly not if they knew it was a "Luc Tuymans." Different context, different meaning. If we are in a museum or art gallery, we expect to see art, and we know we are looking at art. Context not only affects the significance we give to things, it also influences our attention. In the case of the Tuymans experiment, the surroundings played a role in people's (lack of) attention and reactions.

Even when things are put in a gallery or museum people do not always recognize them as art. In 2004, a custodian at London's Tate Modern Gallery threw away a garbage bag filled with papers, thinking it was garbage. Only the next morning did it become clear that the trash bag was actually a piece of art, made by the German post-modernist Gustav Metzger. The custodian had assumed it was just a bag of garbage.

Three years earlier the same happened to a work by the popular contemporary British artist Damien Hirst. In that case, it was a collection of empty bottles, cigarette packets, full ashtrays, and paint tins, reflecting the chaos of an artist's studio. Both works were in a context that identified the objects as "art," but the cleaning staff were not aware of this.

These rubbish-as-art anecdotes illustrate again that nothing has a fixed meaning, but they also make clear that besides the exterior context (the surroundings), our inner context (what we know, expect, and remember) influences and changes the meaning of what we perceive and encounter. If you don't know that a bag of garbage is part of an artwork in a gallery, then it is only what it is – a bag of garbage.

*Nothing in the world has an absolute meaning. A bag of garbage is not always a bag of garbage. Sometimes it is art.*

If the context had been clearer, the mistake by the cleaning lady at Tate Modern could have been prevented. Embarrassed Tate officials later declared that they could have roped off the work to avoid confusion.

These examples should convince you of the importance of context in human information processing and make you hungry to find more examples and to read the rest of this book. In the remainder of the book, we will examine what context is and how it plays a crucial role in human perception, in language and communication, in social behavior, and in human reasoning. In the last decades, research in a variety of disciplines, from philosophy to psychology to computer science, has revealed surprising and remarkable facts about the role of context in several aspects of human functioning. Indeed, a good sense of context contributes significantly to our adaptability and our survival skills in a world without fixed meanings. For instance, as we shall see further on, taking context into account is crucial for distinguishing what is relevant from what is circumstantial. Contextual sensitivity is equally vital for understanding other people's minds and behavior. A lack of contextual sensitivity results in misunderstanding the meaning, not only of human behavior but also of many events and even objects, and hence results in logical but inappropriate reactions, as was the case with the cleaning crew at the Tate Gallery.

This is where autism comes into the picture. The behavior and reactions of people with autism are mostly logical but often at the same time seemingly a little inappropriate, because they are out of context. When the front doorbell rang, the mother of a seven-year-old boy with autism asked her son to open the door. He opened the back door instead of the front door ... His reaction was logical; he did exactly what his mother asked him to do: He opened a door. But his choice of door was out of context.

As I will demonstrate, research into the role of context has shown it is crucial in exactly those areas that are known to be affected in autism: social interaction, communication, and flexibility in thoughts and behavior. It seems plausible, then, to propose a hypothesis of autism as a form of context blindness.

Autism is a developmental disorder and characterized by three main areas of difficulties, commonly referred to as the triad of impairments: difficulties with social interaction, (social) communication, and (social) imitation, the latter resulting in difficulty dealing with change, adherence to certain routines, and restricted interests. These difficulties and problems are common to all people with autism, but the way they affect each individual and their impact on daily life are very different. Differences among people with autism are as great as their similarities. Autism has always existed, but was only recognized and labeled as a distinct condition halfway through the 20th century when, almost simultaneously but independently, two physicians described the disorder: the American (though born in Austria) child psychiatrist Leo Kanner and the Austrian pediatrician Hans Asperger.

Since then, scientists all over the world have studied autism extensively; in fact, autism is one of the most studied disorders in the world. Since Kanner's and Asperger's descriptions, parents, professionals, and scientists have been searching for an explanation of this puzzling disorder. Some of the proposed explanations are nothing more than "armchair theorizing," and some are based more on myths than on facts; for instance, the theory that claimed that autism is caused by "refrigerator mothers" who coldly rejected their children.

Fortunately, most of the theories that have stood the test of time and peer review are based on hard scientific work. Studies in the fields of neurology and genetics have revealed that autism is caused by genetically triggered brain abnormalities, and psychologists together with neurologists have developed theories about the difficulties and differences in the autistic way of information processing in the brain.

Although, from time to time, we will make a little excursion into the area of neurology, we will focus mainly on the psychology of autism: how an autistic brain works, how people with autism perceive the world around them, and how this affects their behavior.

The quest for a neuro-cognitive explanation of autism has resulted in three major hypotheses that are now recognized worldwide: weak central coherence, theory of mind, and executive dysfunction. These three theories[1] have done a great deal in increasing our understanding of autism "from within":

- The theory of "weak central coherence" asserts that people with autism have difficulties in seeing "the big picture" and in coherence.
- According to the "theory of mind" account, people with autism have difficulties with the attribution of mental states (what people think, feel, wish, know, etc.) to themselves and others. This has recently developed into a theory that claims that people with autism are good at understanding events organized and caused by rules and systems (systemizing) but are less effective at understanding events caused by human agents (empathizing).
- The theory of "executive dysfunction" hypothesizes that autism is the result of deficits in flexibility, planning, and other higher cognitive functions for organizing and controlling reactions.

Although these theories have considerably improved our understanding of autism, none of them succeeds in explaining the whole picture. In other words, none of them can plausibly account for all the behavioral characteristics of autism. For instance, the theory of mind approach explains very well the social and communication difficulties, but it is hard to find a logical connection between a lack of theory of mind and rigid behaviors or resistance to change. What is more, all three accounts put forward rather high-level cognitive functions as key variables in their explanation of autism, ignoring the fact that autism also affects perceptual and rather basic cognitive functions (think of the sensory and attention problems in autism). For example, how can one explain the sensory problems in autism as an effect of a lack of theory of mind? Ina van Berckelaer-Onnes, a Dutch professor in educational sciences, once made a striking comparison: Explaining autism as a consequence of a deficit in theory of mind is like saying that an intellectual disability results from the inability to calculate square root.[2]

The three theories are known as cognitive accounts of autism. They try to explain how people with autism think and how they process information in the brain. It is said that autism involves specific cognitive deficits, or a different cognitive style. This is undoubtedly true, but from what follows in this book it will become clear that autism not only affects more complex, high-level cognitive processes (such as the ability to attribute intentions and feelings to people or the ability to make a plan), it also affects, possibly even more strongly, primary and low-level processes in the brain, processes that operate mainly at unconscious and preconscious levels.

Maybe what the famous cognitive scientist Douglas Hofstadter[3] said about artificial intelligence applies equally to a cognitive account of autism: not cognition, but subcognition; everything that happens in the brain in less than 100 to 200 milliseconds is interesting. As I will describe, a great deal of the influence of context on human information processing takes place within this short time span, and many of the effects of context on sense-making are processed at unconscious or preconscious levels, more at the level of perception than at the level of cognition. Of course, it is impossible to tell where preconscious perceptual processes end and more conscious cognitive processes begin. Low-level and high-level processes are inextricably linked, and perception is a cognitive process.

Later in this book, I will describe how perception guides our thinking but how, simultaneously, our thoughts guide perception. Despite the difficulties in separating perception from cognition, everyone can intuitively distinguish unconscious and preconscious aspects of information processing from more conscious aspects: You don't have to think consciously about every letter or word you see in this book, yet your brain processes all of them in order to understand the text on a conscious level.

Like my book *On Autistic Thinking*,[4] this book is about the autistic mind, but this time I will focus more on unconscious and spontaneous cognitive processes that underlie and precede the more conscious, high-level cognitive processes in so-called autistic thinking. For instance, I argue that people with autism do have a theory of mind but that their social cognitive abilities are not activated by the more basic subcognitive processes that activate them in people without autism.

It is not my intention to present a new cognitive account of autism, certainly not at a time when there are reasonable arguments to suggest that there is no single explanation of autism. With the hypothesis of autism as context blindness, I want to stress the importance of context and its role in the subcognitive processes affected in autism. This subcognitive account should be seen as supplementary to the existing cognitive accounts of autism. The next-to-last chapter in the book provides details about the relationship between context blindness and the three main cognitive theories of autism.

My interest in the role of context in autism is not merely theoretical. It is practical – probably even more practical than theoretical. If autism affects preconscious brain processes, perhaps even more than the conscious ones, this sheds new light on some common practices in the treatment of autism. I will describe some of the consequences of context blindness in the way we communicate with and relate to people with autism and in some of the widely used treatment and intervention strategies. I will argue that some of the techniques used in social cognition and social skills training programs can have only limited effect because they ignore the important role of contextual sensitivity in, for example, emotion recognition and social problem solving. It will become clear that within the scope of our current knowledge and techniques there are limits to what we can change about autism and that we should focus on creating autism-friendly environments rather than on trying to cure or correct autism itself. However, let us not anticipate too much but start examining this interesting concept of context. What is context?

## Endnotes – Introduction

1. For an overview and description of these three theories, see Rajendran, G., & Mitchell, P. (2007). Cognitive theories of autism. *Developmental Review*, 27(2), 224-260.
2. Van Berckelaer-Onnes (1992), p. 14.
3. Hofstadter (1988), p. 651.

# Chapter 1
# Context

What is context?

Why do we understand words
whose meaning we have never learned?

Why does the sentence "The pet walks barking
through the garden and chases the cat"
make you think about a dog?

Why does the back side of playing cards influence
the risks we take when playing cards?

## What Is Context?

It is difficult to give an exact definition of context. Everyone knows intuitively what it means, but when you look at actual definitions, you will find that they differ quite a bit from each other. It cannot be a coincidence that the meaning of the word *context* is dependent on ... well, the context in which it is used.

In archeology, for example, context refers to an environment in which a historical object has been found: the exact place of the excavation, the environment in which it was found (water, type of soil), and the relation to other objects. For an archeologist, an object without context is meaningless.

Another field in which context is often mentioned is history. You probably have heard of historical context, which refers to circumstances that help us to understand a certain event or a certain person from the past. Context is so important in history that a historical account that includes a person or item that is out of place chronologically calls into question the entire message. This is referred to as an *anachronism* – to situate an object, person, or event in the wrong time or context. The cartoon series *The Flintstones* contains a humorous anachronism – dinosaurs interacting with human beings. (Dinosaurs were extinct before humanity took the stage.) In the case of *The Flintstones,* the anachronisms make the cartoon fun. In more serious forms of history, however, correct historic context is critical.

## History of the Term *Context*

The term *context* has its own intriguing historical context.[1] *Context* comes from the Latin word *contextus*, the past continuous tense of *contexere*, which means "to weave" or "entwine." *Con* means "inter" and *textus* means "woven," hence the words "textile" and "texture," but also the word *text*. For the Romans, *contextus* meant "connection, strong relation, interdependence." It is a little bit odd, but although the word derives from Latin, the Latin language did not originally contain a word for context. In the fourth century, a related word, *contextio*, appeared. It also meant "put together," "joint," or "composed" but was closer to the current meaning of the word *context*. The word *contextio* referred to the pieces of text around a text that one wanted to study or interpret. During this time, the Bible was translated to Latin, and in order to understand these writings, one had to understand the context well.

The meaning of context as "the text before and after a text of interest" is, even after 16 centuries, still the first meaning of the word found in dictionaries. The *Merriam-Webster Dictionary* defines context as:

> **1:** the parts of a discourse that surround a word or passage and can throw light on its meaning
> **2:** the interrelated conditions in which something exists or occurs: environment, setting <the historical *context* of the war>

Linguistically, the word *context* has almost the same meaning as *co-text*, the text that accompanies a passage. With the interpretation of ancient texts such as the Bible, the word *context* appeared in the 16th and 17th centuries in a variety of European languages: *contesto* (Italian), *contexte* (French), *context* (English), and *Kontext* (German).

Through the years, the meaning of the word expanded, although still in relation to the interpretation of texts. In a broad sense, the word *context* not only referred to co-text but also to the intent of the author of the text.[2] Still later, in the 19th century, the context was understood even more globally. To understand the text well required considering not only the surrounding text and the intent of the author but also the historical context, the cultural context, the place in time – in short, all circumstances in which the text originated. When circumstances were not taken into account, it was, and still is, referred to as "taken out of context."

Nowadays, the word *context* is not only used in the context of the interpretation and understanding of texts. Context also clarifies, for instance, the meaning of music. In 1952, the American experimental composer John Cage composed a piece called *4'33'* ("four minutes, thirty-three seconds"). The remarkable thing about this composition is that the score instructs the performer not to play his instrument during the entire duration of the piece. In other words, no music is actually played on stage. This doesn't seem to make sense, but the composition makes sense when you put it within the context of the avant-garde art movement of that era. That is, avant-garde artists such as Cage tried to push the boundaries of what was accepted as the norm, such as – in the case of *4'33"* – a musical composition should be performed by musicians playing their instrument. Cage did not intend to compose a piece of silence, although most people perceived it as such. The piece claims to consist of the sounds of the environment that the listeners hear while it is performed. Without the context of these avant-garde intentions of the composer, Cage's composition is rather meaningless or at least difficult to understand and appreciate.

*Context is the guide in our search for meaning.*

Throughout history, the notion of what constitutes context thus expanded. Today, context applies to whatever we want to give meaning to: text, images, music, objects, or events. Context no longer refers to the surrounding pieces of text; it can refer to anything. Think about the historical context, the political context, the cultural context, the socio-economical context, etc.

In short, the meaning of context has expanded, but its function remains the same: Context helps us to give meaning to and understand things and events. We could say that context is our guide in our quest for meaning. When we don't know the context of something, we easily misunderstand it.

In 2006 a photo on the Internet caused a lot of consternation. The photo pictured a Japanese toddler licking an ice cream cone in the shape of a penis. People reacted: This was shocking! They were questioning the moral standards of the Japanese population. However, for Japanese people and anyone with knowledge about Japanese culture, it was all serene, because they knew the context. The picture was taken at the Kanamara Matsuri festival. This festival, also known as the festival of the steel phallus, is held each spring at the Kanayama shrine in Kawasaki, once popular among prostitutes who wished to pray for protection from sexually transmitted diseases. The penis, as the central theme of the event, is omnipresent in decorations, in a parade, and even in the candy, vegetables, and ice creams that are being served during the festival. The festival even has a honorable goal: It is used to raise money for HIV research. This context sheds an entirely different light on the photo of the toddler.

## Where Does Context Begin and Where Does It End?

Context helps us to understand what we see, hear, feel, smell, etc. That much is clear by now. But where does context begin and where does it end?

The context of a word is the sentence in which it appears. In turn, that sentence is part of a paragraph. The context of that paragraph is the chapter, which is part of the larger context of the whole book. And in order to understand the book, we need to see it in the context of the author's ideas and intentions. For a full understanding of the author, we need to know more about his life, which is situated in a certain temporal and geographical context ... we can continue endlessly, adding still other contexts.

Context seems to have no final end. How far do we need to go in this infinite contextual space in order to understand something? How do we know which of all these different contexts we need to use? Well, it is kind of a mystery, but the fact is that the human brain effortlessly succeeds in using only the context that it needs to understand something. So, nobody starts reading the full biography of an author in order to understand the book he has written (until it seems necessary ...). We only use the context we need. How we do this is not a complete mystery. Let me explain it with an example.

What does the word *convalescent* mean? I hope you don't know the meaning, otherwise this example won't work. (Please, don't look it up in a dictionary now!) As an isolated word, it is difficult to grasp the meaning of *convalescent*. Luckily, we seldomly encounter isolated words in our world. Words have a tendency to group together in sentences, articles, and books. So, what happens if you read the word *convalescent* in the next passage of the story *The Man of the Crowd*, written in 1840 by Edgar Allen Poe:

*"Not long ago, about the closing in of an evening in autumn, I sat at the large bow window of the D-Coffee House in London. For some months I had been ill in health, but was now convalescent, and, with returning strength, found myself in one of those happy moods which ..."*

That makes it a bit easier. Maybe you are not completely sure yet, but you will probably think of meanings like "recovering," "getting better," or "regaining one's health." In order to find these meanings, you didn't have to take a wild guess. You inferred the meaning from the context, more precisely the sentence around *convalescent*: First he was ill and now his strength returns. That sentence is the immediate context. Of course, there is also the wider context of the whole story and even the whole oeuvre of Edgar Allen Poe.[3] Between the immediate context (the sentence) and the wider context (Poe, his oeuvre, and even the whole 19th-century Romantic movement), there are also many different contexts: the paragraph, the chapters in the story, the whole story. So, around the stimulus that we want to give meaning to (psychologists name this *the target stimulus*, in this case the word *convalescent*), there are many layers of context.

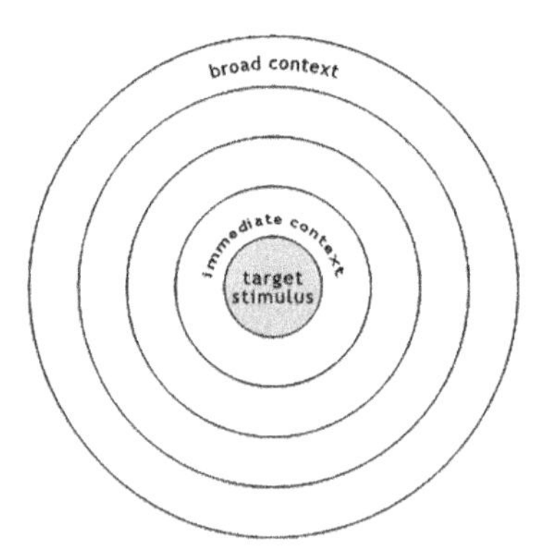


Context is a collection of different layers around the one thing that we want to give meaning to.

We only start using the wider or broader context when the immediate context does not offer us enough clues to find the correct meaning. When the sentence around *convalescent* is not enough, then we start looking further. In search of the meaning of *convalescent*, we do not start to study the oeuvre and life of Edgar Allen Poe. We will not look far away, when we can find the answer nearby. This is logical. Our brain works according to the law of least effort.[4] Not that it is lazy. It is efficient.

## External and Internal Context

There is another differentiation in context, a differentiation that will be important when autism is discussed later in this book (especially, the role of context in memory).

When we use the word *context* to refer to *the situation*, we are usually referring to the *external* context. This is the physical and social environment of the target stimulus, such as the sentence around the word *convalescent*. There is also the *internal* context, the context in our brain: our ideas, knowledge, experiences, feelings, and so on, stored in our long-term memory.[5] You might be able to understand the meaning of *convalescent* even without the external context of a surrounding sentence, because you had studied Latin and had knowledge of Latin words. On top of that knowledge, you "know" that difficult words often have Latin roots, so you might remember that the Latin word *valescere* means "getting better." In this case, both the internal and the external contexts help us to find the meaning of the word *convalescent*.

In theory, we can distinguish the internal and external contexts, but in reality they are inseparable. So, when you have to dig deep into the internal context of your memory to find the translation of the Latin word *valescere* and you even have doubts, the external context will quickly take away that doubt. Your vague presumption of the meaning of "getting better" will immediately be confirmed by the external context of the sentence around the word. It also works the other way around: Based on the external context of the sentence, you get a vague idea of what *convalescent* might mean, but with the help of the internal context of your knowledge of Latin, you will be certain.

Cooperation between the internal and external contexts is (along with the law of least effort) a principle that helps us to select from the infinite number of possible contexts that are available to us. Not only are there many layers and elements in the external context, there are also an infinite number of ideas in our brains, the internal context. External context helps us to select from all of these ideas.

An interesting experiment of Diederik Aerts and Liane Gabora[6] explores this. Aerts and Gabora asked people to read one of the following sentences:

The pet chews on a bone.

The pet received training.

Did you see the type of pet he has? This explains why he is such a weird person.

Aerts and Gabora then showed their test subjects a list of pets such as hamster, parrot, dog, goldfish, canary, cat, spider, hedgehog, and snake, and asked them how typical these animals were as a pet.[7]

The **external context** (the sentence) appeared to have significant influence on the answers given by the test subjects. In the context of a sentence like "The pet chews on a bone," people primarily thought of a dog or a cat and hardly ever thought about a canary or a goldfish. This makes sense, because goldfish that chew on bones are very rare and possibly have some sort of disorder! The test subjects did not think of a dog or a cat with the sentence about the weird person, but thought of snakes, spiders, and hedgehogs.

External context influences which concepts are activated in our brain. For example, in the sentence "The pet walks through the garden," you probably activate concepts like cat, dog, or rabbit. In the sentence "The pet walks barking through the garden and chases a cat," you probably only think of a dog.

At this exact moment, while you are reading this book, there are external influences on your mental context. The text or context is primarily activating your concepts and ideas about psychology, thinking, or perception, while everything that you know about cycling, historical battles, brands of toilet paper, or Italian cuisine are not being activated in your brain. It is possible that because of the description of the experiment by Aerts and Gabora you suddenly thought about your goldfish that you forgot to feed. That is yet another example of the influence of external context on the internal context.

Conversely, the **internal context** can influence the aspects of the external context on which your attention is focused. Somewhere in your brain there is a concept of book. The concept includes the characteristics of reading. When you see a book, you typically first pay attention to the title. Immediately, you classify the book into one of two categories, "might be interesting to read" or "no interest in reading." To reach this conclusion, you did not need to feel the paper or check the book binding, which a bookbinder's critical eye would notice. For a bookbinder, the type of paper and binding of a book may be more interesting than what is inside the book. Who you are, what you know, what you want, and what interests you all influence what attracts your attention in the external context. In the chapter on context and perception (Chapter 3), we will explore more deeply the influence of context on attention.

Internal and external contexts influence each other continuously. The external context, the situation, changes and influences our ideas, expectations, and feelings – in short, our mental state. At the same time, this mental state determines the aspects of the external context on which we focus the most. It does not make sense to ask which is first, the external or the internal context? This would be the same as asking the chicken-or-egg question, as we will see in the next chapter.[8]

## Significant and Incidental Context

Not everything in a context is equally relevant. This has led psychologists to make a distinction between significant context and incidental context.[9] **Significant context** contains the parts of context that have an influence on the meaning of something, like the word *barking* in the sentence "The pet walks barking through the garden." **Incidental context** incorporates all the other things that were present coincidentally yet were not immediately relevant to the meaning. For example, the color of the ink in which the sentence "The pet is walking barking through the garden" is printed is a part of the incidental context. It is not immediately relevant.

Why is there a different category for context that is incidental? If the context is incidental, then is it unimportant? No. It may be difficult to believe, but even incidental context can influence our determination of meanings and our reactions, even if we are not aware of these influences. For example, in an election, the room where people are voting has an influence on their voting behavior, without them being aware of it. People voting in schools, for instance, are more likely to vote for a candidate who supports extra school spending, no matter what their political allegiance is.[10] Similarly, the back side of playing cards has an influence on the level of risk-taking in a gambling game, even though we do not usually pay much attention to them.

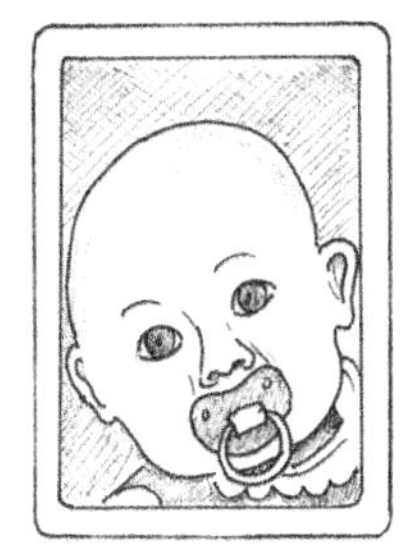
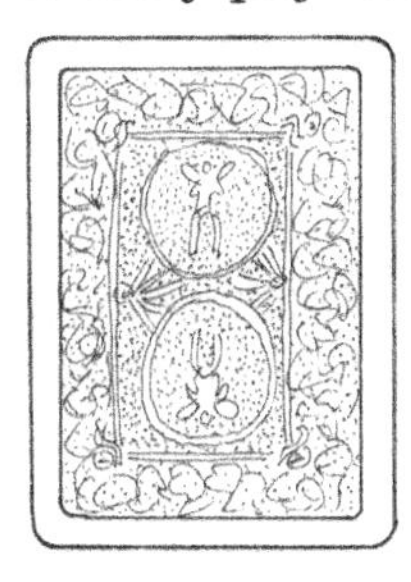

Test subjects who received a deck of cards with a picture of James Bond on the back took more gambling risks than did those who were given cards with a neutral background. When using cards with a picture of a baby on the back, people tended to take fewer risks.

Kokinov,[11] a Bulgarian professor of psychology who studied these types of effects, has proven that small changes in seemingly irrelevant elements in the context can have an influence on different cognitive processes. Kokinov demonstrated a contextual effect of incidental factors on the solution of problems such as gauging someone's age or estimating rental prices of apartments. In the case of apartment prices, it appeared that the color in which the rental price was shown had an effect on the perception of the rent being cheap or expensive. The lesson to the consumer is to be aware that even the color of ink is influencing whether a rental property is worth the cost of rent required. Numerous incidental effects that we observe unconsciously influence our interpretation of information. Smart advertising makes intentional use of incidental contextual influences.

## Summary

The endless collection of elements that we call context can be subdivided in the following ways:

- Immediate, close-by context, and broad
- Internal and external context
- Significant and incidental context[12]

With what we know by now, we can try to come up with a definition of context with which we can work in the rest of the book. Certainly, it will not be an all-inclusive definition.

A technical definition, one used by psychologists and scholars, could be stated as follows:

> Context is the set of elements within the perceiving person (affective and cognitive, as well as concepts in long-term memory and short-term memory) and of elements in the spatial and temporal environment of a stimulus (close by as well as far off) that affect the perception of that stimulus and the meaning given to it. This influence can be direct, explicit, and conscious but also (and mainly) indirect, implicit, and subconscious. Contextual sensitivity is the ability to discover within that collection of elements contextually relevant information and ignore contextually unimportant information.

Here is a more concise definition:

> *Context is what is going on in the environment, outside and inside our brain, that influences our way of giving meaning to things. The ability to select elements in the context that are useful and meaningful and to use them is* ***context sensitivity****. The neurotypical human brain is, inherently, context sensitive.*

By the way, when you Google the term *context*, you might discover that context is also a brand name, and the name of a convention. For those who do not have an urge to Google, there is the endnote.[13]

## Endnotes – Context

1. See Peter Burke (2002) for an excellent description.
2. In Latin named *scopus*, which is the origin of the English word *scope*.
3. Burke (2002) uses the terms *microcontext* and *macrocontext*.
4. According to researchers from the Carnegie Mellon's Center for Cognitive Brain Imaging, more precisely the group around psychologist Marcel Just. Just contributed significantly to the brain research in autism.

5. The literature mentions other terms as well. For instance, Phillips and Silverstein (2003) use the term *stimulus context* for the external context and *task context* for the internal context.

   Phillips, W. A., & Silverstein, S. M. (2003). Convergence of biological and psychological perspectives on cognitive coordination in schizophrenia. *Behavioral and Brain Sciences*, 26, 65-138.

6. See Aerts and Gabora (2005a, 2005b).
7. The literal instruction did not ask for a judgment about the probability of concrete exemplars, but subjects were asked to estimate the frequency of a specific exemplar.
8. This the reason why some authors (e.g., Bradley & Dunlop, 2005) see context as a process rather than a product.
9. For instance, Smith (1988) differentiates between *meaningful* and *incidental* context. Baddeley and Woodhead (1982) use the terms *independent* context (the context that does not have an influence on sense making) and *interactive* context (the context that is used in the process of giving meaning).
10. Berger, Meredith, and Wheeler (2008).
11. The Distant Context Effect (DICE) of Kokinov and Raeva (2004).
12. Scientists, known for their interest in classifications and subclassifications, have identified even more categories. The following list of different kinds of context was developed by scientists from Vanderbilt University in Nashville (Park, Lee, Folley, & Kim, 2003):
    a. Perceptual context (more or less similar to what I called the external context):
       i. The context within the target stimulus (for instance, the color or size of something)
       ii. The spatial context, the spatial aspects of the stimulus array
       iii. The temporal context: stimuli that appear before or after the target stimulus
    b. The cognitive context (more or less similar to what I named the internal context):
       i. What is stored in long-term memory (what could be called the wider internal context)
       ii. Task-relevant information in working memory (what could be called the immediate internal context)
    c. The socio-affective context: the emotions of the moment
13. ConTEXT is also the name of text editing software and an annual convention in Columbus (USA) focused on speculative fiction literature (SF, fantasy, manga, horror, etc.) and related games, comics, and films.

# Chapter 2
# Context in the Brain

Why is the back of our head as important
to seeing as our eyes?

Why is seeing not the same as taking pictures?

How is it that you do not think that people shrink
when they ride away or when they walk away from you,
and that things do not change color
when moved from sunshine into shadows?

Which do we see first, the trees or the forest?

What are the characteristic differences in
information processing for individuals with autism?

Why is Waldo difficult to find in the *Where's Waldo?*
books, and why can we not immediately find the differences
in the pictures when told to "find seven differences"?

How is it that when a gorilla appears in a group of
basketball players, almost no one notices the gorilla?

How are the human brain and a symphonic orchestra
similar? And what happens when there is no conductor?

Where in the brain is context sensitivity located?

Perception and giving meaning is primarily done by the brain, and, as we have seen, the neurotypical brain is inherently context sensitive. But where is context sensitivity located in the brain? How do contextual influences affect our perception? How and when does our brain use context? These questions are the focus of this chapter.

We will focus mainly on visual perception, seeing. The influence of context on visual perception has been extensively researched. Because a book is something that you process with your eyes, an explanation of the role of context in vision is more suitable to use in this book than would be an explanation involving the other senses. With examples about hearing, you would need a CD to accompany the book. With examples about smells, it would become quite difficult, not only to produce the book but also to read it, especially in a crowded train or subway. Although this chapter is exclusively about visual perception, the context obviously also has an influence on other forms of perception: hearing, feeling, tasting, and smelling.[1]

## Perception: Two Misunderstandings

The role of context in human perception becomes clear when we correct two misunderstandings about perception. These misunderstandings are the following:

1. Perception is a process in which we get impressions from the outside world and process them in our brain. In other words, seeing is like taking pictures or shooting film.
2. During perception, we assemble all the pieces into one. In other words, when we see a lot of trees, we decide to see a forest.

These two misconceptions are not totally separate from each other. They may be combined as follows: To see is like processing various visual stimuli that enter your brain via the eyes **into a meaningful whole**.

What do you see? It's easy; you think, "a car," of course.[2] What happened inside your brain to make you think *car*? The following is a brief description of visual perception.[3]

After passing through the pupil, images appear on the retina, at the back of the eyes. The retina, a sort of projection screen, contains receptor cells shaped like rods, which differentiate between light and dark, and cones, which register color differences. Although it is inside the eye, the retina is, in fact, part of the brain. From the retina, the information travels via the optic nerve to a part of the brain that is called the thalamus.[4] Next it travels farther to the back of your head, to the visual cortex. It sounds strange, but seeing is primarily something you do with the back of your head.

The visual cortex contains different areas (the extrastriate visual cortical areas). The most well known are V1, V2,

V3, V4, and V5. Research shows that the different areas have a sort of hierarchy. Information from the thalamus ends up first in the primary visual cortex, the V1. The range that a brain cell (neuron) in the V1 can observe, the receptive field of that cell, is relatively small. These cells only fire, in reaction to small parts of the world like color, orientation, and movement, when there is light in that small range of the visual field. From the primary visual cortex, the information travels farther to the other areas (V2, V3, etc.). Neurons in higher stations (V1 being the lowest and V5 the highest) have a bigger visual range. For example, neurons in V4 fire up when "seeing" complete objects.

From V1 there are two main routes to the other areas. There is the back route (dorsal), also called the "where route." Information that follows the where route helps us perceive movement and positions. The where route travels to the parietal area of the brain (put your hand on the back side of your head and move it up until you almost reach the vertex, below that lies the parietal area).

The second route, the front route (ventral), is the route that helps us recognize objects and other things. It is called the "what route." This route leads to the temporal part of the brain, which is on either side of your head (under the skull). Whereas the what path helps you recognize a car, the where path helps you see that the car is coming towards you. When that information reaches the higher areas of the brain, it is compared to the information already stored in the brain. Your brain then tells you, "Oh, it is a car!"

Are you dizzy from this explanation? It's rather complex, but what did you expect from an organ that is the result of thousands of years of evolution? The following illustration may clarify things.

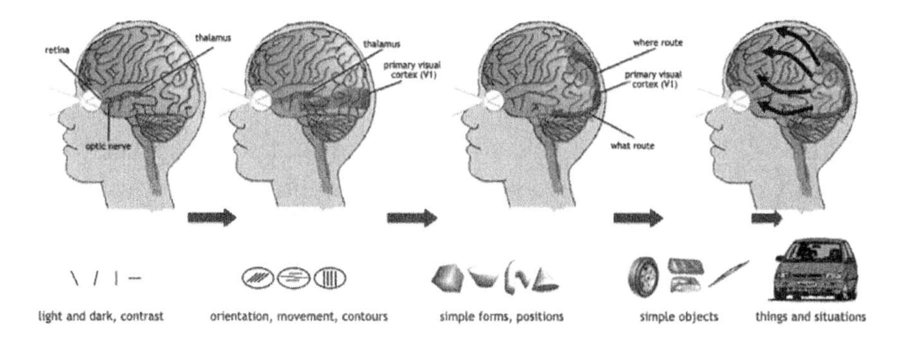


To summarize, when you see something, the various small pieces of information are processed to increasingly larger pieces in different stations of the brain until you finally get the whole. That whole is then compared to the knowledge already stored inside your brain to give you the opportunity to make meaning of what you are seeing. You can then give what you are seeing a name, and can react upon it.

## The Brain: More of a Director Than an Observer

The brain does more than just receive information and put together the pieces of the puzzle we see. The brain is very active during perception. It not only receives the information, it also manages it. In cinematic terms, the brain is not just an audience. It is a director.

The previous drawings show only half of the story, which is the process scientists call bottom-up. This means the process goes from below to above, from a low level to a high level. Applied to perception, information that reaches the brain through the senses is first processed in lower stations (which specialize in processing simple pieces of information), then in higher stations. Bottom-up information processing refers to the process directed by the stimuli in the world outside the brain. These are stimuli-driven processes.[5]

Simultaneous to the bottom-up processing, there is also top-to-bottom processing. Scientists call this top-down. Top-down refers to processes that are controlled by ideas and concepts in our brain and are called concept-directed processes.[6] Top-down is about the influence of complex information present in higher stations of information processing on the simpler processes in the lower stations. Your knowledge of an object influences your perception of, for example, the color or the shape of the object.

*In perception our brain is not an observer but a conductor. It organizes our perception actively.*

You know that a white piece of paper is white, and because of that, a white piece of paper appears white in sunlight as well as in shadow, while the color your eyes register is different in the two cases (white in sunlight and light grey in shadow). However, when the sun disappears behind the clouds, you will not get the impression that the blank paper simultaneously changes color.

When you say goodbye to your best friend as she rides away on her bike, your friend and her bike will get smaller in the projection on your retina. However, you will not have the impression that you are observing your friend actually shrinking. Your knowledge that people do not shrink instantly, unless in Walt Disney movies,[7] influences the processing of height in the lower stations.

The American psychologist Ulric Neisser was one of the first to describe this top-down process.[8] Neisser was irritated by drawings such as the ones above, which portray perception as a linear and straight process. The assumption that the brain only receives information from the senses (the bottom-up process) is, in large part, based on laboratory research. In real life, our brain does not wait for the senses to send information when they get around to it. Our brain is continuously exploring the environment, searching for information that can be helpful to us (for taking the right road, for eating, for finding a girlfriend, for getting a promotion at work, etc.).

Because of this continuous exploration, the perception becomes focused. This means that some sensations that are coming in bottom up capture our attention whereas others do not. For example, when you urgently have to go to the bathroom, you focus on stimuli related to toilets and ignore other aspects of your environment. You may even not notice that beautiful lady or that handsome guy.

The end product of this perception, what we give a meaning to, is possibly more dependent on what we want to do and on what we want to find than on sensations that are picked up by our senses. When you urgently have to use a toilet and you see a restaurant, to you the restaurant at that moment will mean a place to use the restroom. In the eyes of someone who is hungry, that same restaurant will mean a place to eat.

In the model developed by Neisser, stimuli influence our ideas and expectations,[9] but our expectations and ideas in turn determine our perception. This is why we can select and actively pick up and focus on certain stimuli. Thus, seeing is far from a passive process of getting impressions or taking pictures. It is an active process in which the brain is continuously filtering, checking, summarizing, distracting, zooming in and out, and so on. That process is not linear or straight (from stimulus to meaning) but is rather the way Neisser described it: a cyclical process, bottom-up and top-down, hand in hand.

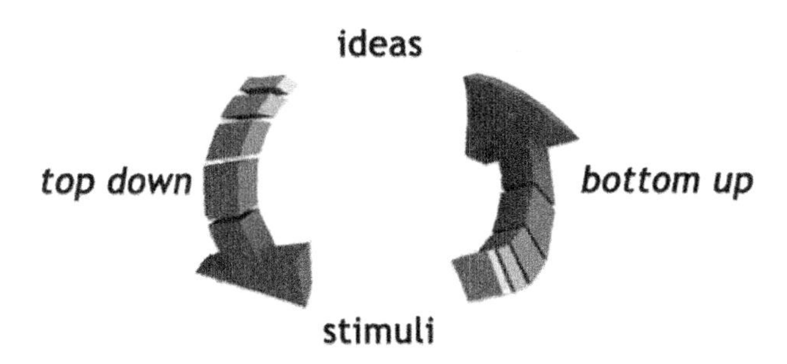


Perception is not a straight process of input and output, but a continuous exchange mechanism between ideas in our brain and sensations from the environment.

This was a lengthy explanation to show that internal context actively influences our perception. As mentioned before, what you know, want, feel, think, or expect also determines where you focus your attention and which meanings you assign.

Here is another example of how internal context influences visual sensations. What do you see?

Three black lines of different forms are what most people would think they are seeing, and they are correct. Now pronounce the first five letters of the alphabet in your head and then look back to the drawing. What do you see now? The three lines are no longer random lines but together form the outline of a white letter E.

The influence of top-down processes on visual perception has been proven in scientific research more than once, mostly using unclear images like the E above, but also by using visual illusions that involve knowledge and expectations in the way we determine the meaning of things. (We will discuss illusions in Chapter 3 on context and perception.)

The influence of the internal context on perception means that what we have learned helps us understand what we perceive. That learning effect can evolve very quickly. What do you see in the image below?[10]

Picture with spots.

When you see this picture for the first time, it appears to be only a collection of spots. Your perception is primarily focused on stimuli: You only see spots. When you read the explanation in the endnote[11] and look back, you will see the subject of this image. The information in the endnote will be neatly stored in your memory, making certain that your perception becomes more concept focused, which will result in a rather different meaning than a couple of spots.

Let's return to our brain. The bottom-up process traveled from the retina to the thalamus, to V1, and from there to other higher visual areas (V2, V3, etc.). But where is the top-down process located? It is located in different places, but a major part is manifested in the feedback that higher areas of information processing give to the lower areas. Areas of the brain that play an important role in top-down processing include, among others, those located in the frontal lobes, primarily in the prefrontal cortex (the parts of the brain that are located on the side of your forehead).[12] These areas communicate with the higher visual areas (V2 and above), which, in turn, give feedback to the primary visual cortex (V1).

Thus, we must correct the picture on page 46. A more correct illustration would be as follows:

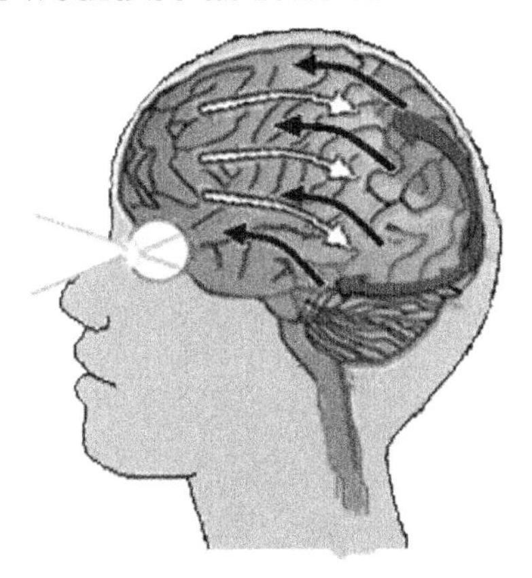

During perception, bottom-up (black arrows) and top-down (white arrows) processes occur at the same time.

## First the Forest, Then the Trees

In top-down processing, both the internal and external contexts play a role. Because it is true that external context influences perception, it cannot be true that we assemble all the details until we recognize the whole picture. That misunderstanding was corrected a century ago by a group of German psychologists, which included Max Wertheimer. These psychologists resisted the idea that perception consists of a variety of different impressions that we neatly assimilate or put together. According to this school of thought, the perception is not an accumulation of impressions, but the result of an organized body of impressions that is more than the sum of its parts. That organized body of impressions is better known under the German word *gestalt*.

There are a number of principles, or gestalt laws, about how our brain organizes impressions into patterns and larger parts (e.g., the law of similarity). The mind groups similar elements into collective entities or totalities. For example, in the following graphic, you see sequences of black and white spots rather than just black spots and white spots.

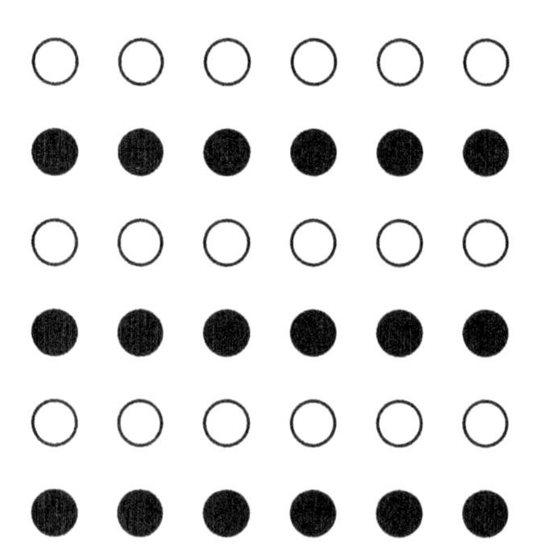

People think that we recognize a forest because we encounter a lot of trees together: first the trees, then the forest. But it appears that the brain does not work like that. Rather, the opposite is true: Because we recognize the forest, we know that we are looking at trees.

A recent theory about perception stresses this opposite process: the reversed hierarchy theory of Israeli researchers Shaul Hochstein and Merav Ahissar.[13] Hochstein and Ahissar built on earlier formulations of, among others, Irving Biederman[14] and David Navon,[15] who in 1977 wrote, "We can recognize a global scene without being influenced by the details, but we cannot recognize details when we have not seen the whole."

According to the insights of these scientists, we do not see the details first, followed by the complete picture, but the other way around. In the blink of an eye, we see the essence of a scene (the context) by a very fast, subconscious transfer of information to the higher areas in the brain.[16] When this scene recognition reaches our conscience, we notice the details, using top-down processes, which are slower and more conscious. For the remainder of this book, it is important to note that the quick process that leads to recognition of the context takes place subconsciously or, as psychologists call it pre-attentively.[17] This means that we do not have to specifically focus our attention on the context.

This process happens quickly. How fast? Well, we recognize most scenes or categories of objects within 100 to 200 milliseconds. To understand that level of speed, know that it takes twice as long to blink your eyes (between 300 and 400 milliseconds). Saying that we make an evaluation of context in a blink of an eye is an underestimation of the speed of our brain: We do it twice as fast!

This was proven by Mary Potter of the University of Massachusetts Institute of Technology (MIT) in the mid 1970s.[18] Potter showed test subjects sequences of 16 pictures. The subjects were asked to react when they saw a certain scene, for example, a picnic. The test subjects could do this without any problem, even when they were shown eight pictures per second, or one picture every 125 milliseconds. We receive information about context in a very early stage of the perception process, and we are unaware of it.

*We recognize a context in less than 200 milliseconds and only after that the details. First the forest, then the trees.*

Contexts generally contain a lot of information. How does our brain process so much information in barely one fifth of a second? The brain makes a quick scan, not a detailed picture or description of the context. The quick and preconscious recognition of a scene is a sort of rough sketch of the situation or the context.[19] You can compare it with a vague and blurred picture, as is shown on page 107. The recognition of a context is not an exact science; it is comparable to an estimated guess or surmisal.[20] In order to make this estimated guess, a vague impression will do. We do not need all the details. Therefore, we don't notice them immediately.

## Detail Blindness

Skipping the details is very useful. To begin with, our conscious mind has a limited capacity; it can only keep between 5 and 9 pieces of information in short-term memory and is only able to consciously process 60 bits per second.[21] It would require too much of our brain to take all the nitty-gritty into account and to analyze it. In most cases, the majority of details are not important for what we want to do (take the correct road, go to the toilet, eat, find a girlfriend, get promoted at work, etc.). In other words, in the first instance, we are blind for details and we only start noticing details when we intentionally look for them. Look at the following picture:

From *Evening Party Game*. Scarbourough, UK: E. T. W. Dennis & Dons Ltd.

This drawing is from a series of pictures from the 1930s, in which there is an error that you have to find as quickly as possible. At first glance, there is nothing wrong with the picture. To find the error, you have to make a more focused search and consciously look at the details. It often takes quite some time before we note a faulty detail in drawings like this. If after a long search you still cannot find the error, the endnote will help you out of your misery.[22]

So in our everyday perceptions, there are many details that we do not see. For example, imagine you are on your way out for the evening, and a man on a bike asks you for directions. It is quite likely that afterwards you will not remember what kind of shoes the man was wearing or what color his bike was, although an image of it entered your retina. (Admittedly, if you are a woman, there is a bigger chance that you will have observed the shoes.)

Our detail blindness is the source of many games, such as image searches like *Where's Waldo?* in which you have to search for Waldo, a young man with glasses wearing a red-and-white striped sweater, a cap, and a walking stick in a very busy drawing. Additionally, "find the 7 differences" picture searches in newspapers and children's magazines address the detail blindness of the human brain.

## Change Blindness

Sometimes we do not notice even more significant things. When the man who asks you for directions disappears from your sight and is replaced by another man, different in posture, height, clothing, and voice, the probability is high that you will not notice the difference. It sounds unbelievable, but in an experiment by psychologists Simons and Levin,[23] half of the test subjects did not notice the change.

This phenomenon is known as change blindness. Our brain does not notice changes quickly, because it is more efficient to not remember everything we see. Our short-term memory is, as mentioned, a bit restricted. Additionally, changes, especially sudden changes, statistically rarely happen. A book does not instantly change into a rubber duck, the soup in your bowl does not suddenly change into vanilla ice cream, and your neighbor does not, without warning, turn into former U.S. President George Bush.

Change blindness is not exclusive to everyday situations in which you experience dynamic, moving information. It even works with pictures and illustrations. For example, look at the following photograph for two or three seconds and then turn to the next page.

Picture of tower.

Simons[24] went further in proving change blindness. He asked people to watch a video in which several actors were playing basketball. The test subjects were asked to count the number of passes between the teams. Halfway through the video, a woman in a gorilla suit appeared and stood between the groups of players, looked at the camera, beat her chest, and walked calmly off screen. The whole show lasted for nine seconds. Half of the test participants did not see the gorilla! Some who saw the gorilla in the second showing of the video did not believe that it was the same film.

Not seeing the details and changes appears to be a mistake of our brain, but that is the price that our brain gladly pays for efficiency. To process all details would require too much energy and is, most of the time, not useful.

What has changed?

Many people with autism say that perception takes a lot of their energy. Possibly this is because top-down perception (first the situation, then the details) does not work well for them, and because they perceive primarily bottom up, from the details to the whole situation. In image searches like *Where's Waldo?*, some people with autism perform much better than people without autism. This may be because they are not bothered by the whole of the situation and see first the details and much later, and with conscious effort, the whole situation. This is just the opposite of people without autism.

In a well-known test for recognizing autism, the *Autism Diagnostic Observation Schedule* (ADOS),[25] children are shown big pictures that they have to describe. One of the pictures presents a scene with all kinds of vacation activities, such as sunbathing, waterskiing, swimming, sailing, and beach games. Children with autism generally begin summing up and describing each separate activity but fail to mention that the picture is about vacation. People without autism do not have to *assemble* a situation or a context; that is accomplished within 200 milliseconds. It is likely that people with autism must assemble situations and contexts.

*In the documentary film* Autimatically, *Michelle tells how she recognizes her living room.*[26] *Contrary to people without autism, Michelle does not recognize her living room in the blink of an eye. She first sees totally separate things: a flower, a VCR, a TV, a figurine on the mantle, the CD rack, and so on. Only when she makes a conscious effort does she succeed in assembling all of these impressions into a living room. Michelle also immediately notices when something has changed in her living room, even if it is only a slight detail.*

Most people without autism do not notice that type of change in details. It's not that people with autism cannot see the whole, but they have to do it more consciously than do people without autism, so this happens far more slowly. Remember that we first see the forest and only after that the trees. In the next chapter, the influence of context on the early stages of perception is described more fully, but for now we can conclude that context plays a very important role in the top-down processes of the brain.

## The Brain as a Symphonic Orchestra

The influence of context on information processing is not restricted to the top-down processes in which the higher located stations (like the prefrontal cortex) influence information processing in the lower stations (like the V1). There is already a top-down process within the very low levels of information processing.[27] We saw that the projections of neurons from the retina of the eye go to a part of the brain that is called the thalamus. This is, let's say, the very first stage of the processing of what we see. As a matter of fact, of all the connections in the thalamus, only a small number are busy with projections from the retina. More than half of the connections in the thalamus are involved with giving top-down feedback from the next station in the processing, the primary visual cortex. Even in the first phases of perception, there are already top-down effects. Thus, the influence of context happens at stages where we are not yet aware of what we perceive.

In addition to the top-down process is contextual influence even *within* the stations themselves, involving not connections *between* areas but *within* the same brain area. Researchers have discovered that visual neurons in the primary visual cortex (V1) are not only sensitive to characteristics within their receptive field, but also to the global context of a scene. In other words, the firing of a neuron is not only dependent on the area for which the neuron is responsible (the receptive field), but also depends on stimuli outside the scope of that nerve cell. Apparently, brain cells are also influenced by what other cells in their neighborhood perceive. This has led some scholars to introduce the term *contextual field*[28] as distinct from *receptive field*.

*Contextual field* refers to the influence of context on the firing of neurons, which has been demonstrated for different aspects of visual perception, such as movement and color. Contextual effects at low levels also operate on other senses: hearing, touch, taste, and smell.[29] It seems apparent that our judgment about the intensity of the tastes sweet and sour, for example, depends on context.[30]

When you want to experience a contextual effect in the area of touch, specifically in the perception of temperature, try the following test. For one minute, keep your left hand in a bowl of hot water (not too hot, of course!) and your right hand in a bowl of ice water. After one minute, place both hands together in a bowl of lukewarm water. The left hand and the right hand will experience the temperature of that lukewarm water differently.

Contextual connections in the brain play a role among and between areas as well as within areas. These connections influence not only the activity of individual neurons but also that of a group of neurons or brain areas. This is fully in line with recent ideas about the brain. For a long time, it was thought that the different areas in the brain each had their own specific and autonomous function.

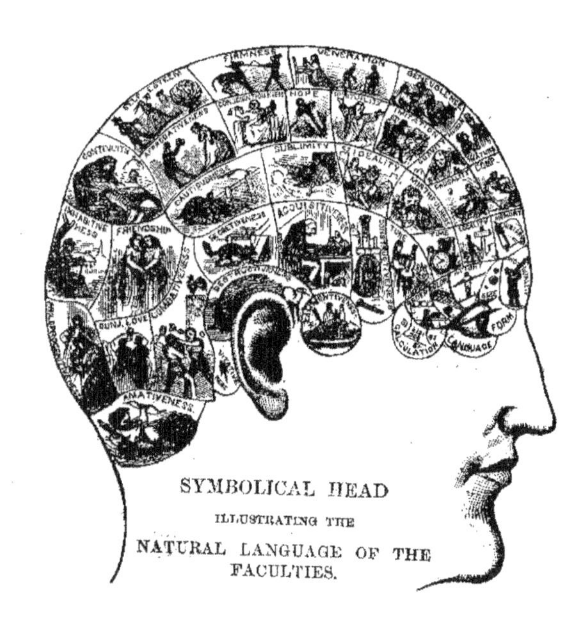


In early times, people thought every area in the brain had a different function.

That different areas in the brain have their own specialization is more or less true. On the left side of the brain are language, logic, and reasoning. The right side of the brain houses spatial insight, music, and visual imagination. By examining which activities people with injuries to specific areas of the brain could no longer perform, it was deduced that specific functions take place in certain parts of the brain, like the visual cortex or the speech area (the area of Broca). Today, cooperation and connections between areas of the brain are believed to play just as important a role, if not greater, than specific areas of the brain. To understand the sentence "The number eight looks like an hourglass," the brain uses language areas as well as areas that process visual images.[31] That is, the left brain and the right brain have to cooperate to process the sentence.

We can compare the different sections of a large symphonic orchestra, brass, woodwind, strings, and percussion, to the larger areas in our brain, each of them with its own specialty and a fixed location. Within each section of the orchestra there are different instruments. For example, the brass section contains the French horns, the trumpets, the trombones, and the tuba. Similarly, the areas of the brain consist of subsections, such as all the Vs (the extrastriate visual cortical areas) within the visual area. Finally, within each subsection of the orchestra, there are a number of musicians. In our brain analogy, the individual musicians are represented by cells or specialized cell types.

The comparison with an orchestra is not totally accurate, however. There are far more subdivisions in your brain than in the orchestra. Additionally, if there was a musician for every brain cell, no opera house in the world could contain the performing brain orchestra. Our brain contains around 100 billion neurons!

And what about the conductor? Who is the conductor in our brain? In the brain, there is no unique cell or area that orchestrates and controls the rest, but there are areas that perform an orchestrating or controlling function. For example, the frontal lobes at the very front of the brain are responsible for what neuroscientists call the executive functions.[32] Additionally, the amygdala is a small area of the brain "with a baton" that plays an important role in coordinating the processing of emotions. So one could say that the brain orchestra also has a conductors' section, rather than a single conductor.

For an orchestra to be successful, it is not sufficient that every musician does his or her work properly, correctly reading the music and properly handling the instrument. Five talented violinists are not a guarantee of an excellent performance of a Mozart violin concerto. The violinists in an orchestra must cooperate well, beginning at the same moment and playing at the same tempo and volume. Neurons or groups of neurons within the brain also must cooperate. This is accomplished by horizontal or lateral connections. Further, when it is their turn to play, the sections of the orchestra have to be aware of and responsive to each other. Similarly, for the brain to function well, there must be efficient working connections between and among the different areas. Finally, there must be a good director to help the different sections work well together in order to create a symphony. In the brain, we do not speak of directing but of top-down control.

In summary, the specialized functions in different parts of the brain are more or less useless unless they are able to work together in a coordinated or orchestrated fashion.[33] That is why neuroscientists now are primarily interested in neural networks, interactions and connections within regions and cooperation between regions. Brain activity is a matter of cooperation, a bit like a symphonic orchestra. It is in that cooperation that the role of context in processing information is located. Sensitivity to context is not located in only one part of the brain. Context sensitivity is related to the amount of cooperation between brain cells, groups of cells, and areas of the brain.

It follows that when these connections are not functioning in a coordinated manner, the brain is less sensitive to context. So far, there is no research evidence for this; however, as illustrated in the following, three areas of research provide clues regarding the relationship between a lack of connectivity within the brain and a lack of sensitivity to context:

- Research into context sensitivity in young children
- Research in the field of schizophrenia
- Research in the field of autism spectrum disorders

## Context Sensitivity and Networking in the Brain

The first evidence of the relationship between context sensitivity and networking in the brain comes from studies involving young children. In young children, the connections in the brain are not yet fully developed, and guess what? They are less sensitive to context. Kaldy and Kovacs,[34] two researchers at Rutgers University, demonstrated the relationship between context sensitivity and development. They conducted a study in which both young children and adults looked at visual illusions, such as the Ebbinghaus illusion (named after the German psychologist Hermann Ebbinghaus).

*Context sensitivity is not located in a specific area in the brain. Context sensitivity is the result of cooperation between different brain cells and brain areas.*

The Ebbinghaus illusion is also known as the same-size phenomenon (demonstrated on the following page). With this type of illusion, the external context plays a role: A circle surrounded by smaller circles looks larger than when the same circle is surrounded by bigger circles. The influence of the external context is even greater than that of the internal context. Even when you know that the circles are equal in size, you get the impression that they are different in size.

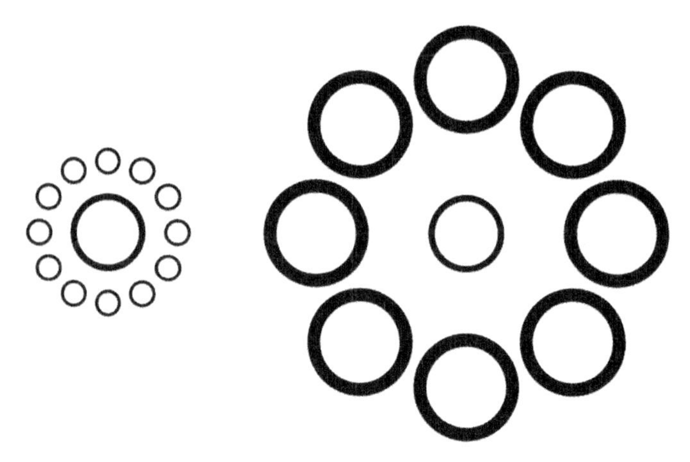

Children do not fall for this illusion; adults do.

Children are less sensitive to this illusion than adults. This finding suggests that context sensitivity is a skill that develops and is not present from birth. According to Kovacs, the reduced contextual sensitivity of young children may be caused by connections in the brain that are not fully developed. It is suspected that the brain circuits that process distinct details develop earlier than the long-distance circuits that integrate information.

A second indication of the relationship between context sensitivity and connectivity in the brain arises from scientific research about people with schizophrenia, a mental disorder characterized by delusions, hallucinations, and confused speech and thinking. In the beginning of the 1990s, the notion grew among a number of brain researchers[35] that a distortion of context could be central to understanding the symptoms of schizophrenia. Since that time, dozens of studies have shown that people who suffer from schizophrenia are indeed less context sensitive in their perceptions and interpretations. It is strongly suspected that this reduced context sensitivity is caused by a disruption in the connection between different areas of the brain,[36] a theory known as disconnection hypothesis.[37]

The third lead to the link between context and neural connectivity comes from research in the area of autism itself. (In an effort not to make things more complex than they already are, we will for now ignore the differences and similarities between schizophrenia and autism. These will be discussed later in the book.) Brain scientists have found differences and deficits in many areas of the brain in people with autism: the amygdala, the corpus callosum, and the cerebellum, just to name a few. In fact, they found differences almost everywhere in the brain, but not every time and not in all persons with autism. That brought researchers to the idea that autism might be more related to a disturbance in the cooperation between different regions of the brain than to a disturbance in one or more specific areas. An article entitled "Autistic Brains: Out of Synch?"[38] published in the scholarly magazine *Science* explored this idea.

Uta Frith was one of the first to show the "lack of cooperation" inside the brains of people with autism. Frith and her coworkers[39] showed videos of moving triangles to people with and without autism. In some videos, the triangles moved randomly, in others the movements seemed to be goal-directed or intentional (e.g., to joke with another triangle). When questioned about what happened in the video, the participants with autism, as expected, gave fewer and less accurate descriptions of these intentions than did the subjects without autism.

Frith and her colleagues also scanned the brains of the test subjects while they were watching the videos. As the non-autism group watched the videos of triangles moving in a way that implied intentions, there was an intensive cooperation between different areas of the brain, primarily between a visual area and a group of regions known as the mentalizing network (a network related to processing social-emotional information). In contrast, in the brains of the persons with autism, there was hardly any cooperation between these areas. This explains why their descriptions of intentions were less accurate. Additionally, reduced networking in the brains of people with autism has been detected in visual-spatial attention tasks.[40]

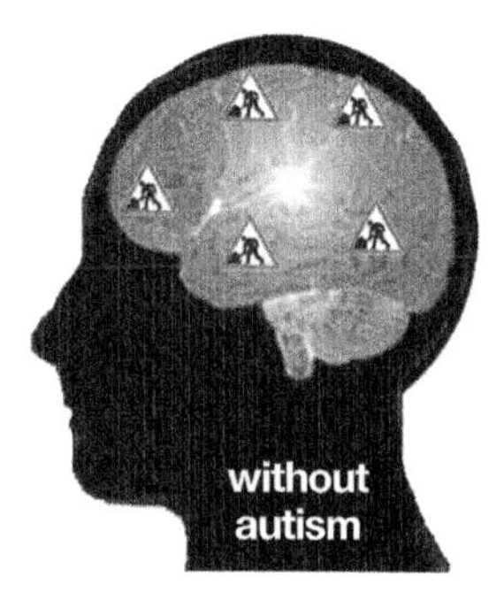


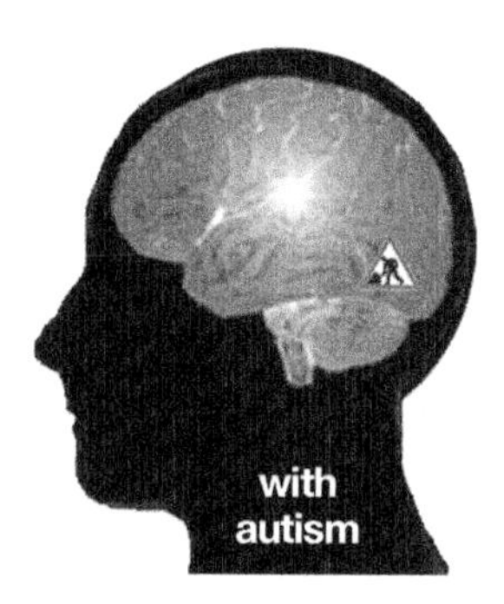


In a visual-spatial attention task, people without autism (left) show activity in different areas of the brain; in people with autism (right) only the visual areas are active.

One of the things that researchers have recently more or less agreed upon is that autism is related to an overgrowth of the brain at the earliest ages.[41] Brain volume and weight in young children with autism is significantly bigger than in children without autism. (Please note: Research findings are based on averages. This does not say anything about the individual head size of people with autism. Do not check head size to determine who has autism, because as of now the diameter of the skull is not of diagnostic value.)

The increased brain volume is related to a disruption in the development of connections in the brain in the first years after birth. At birth, the brain is not yet fully grown. Following birth, it grows and develops in response to our experiences. New connections are formed, especially long-distance connections between areas of the brain that are far away from each other. But that is only half of the story. While new connections are made, others that are inefficient or unnecessary are pruned. This can be compared to tending a garden: When you do not prune the branches, you will get overgrowth. In autism there is an overgrowth of local connections and a shortage of long-distance connections, especially connections with the frontal areas in the brain.[42] As a result, the hypothesis of "poor cortical connectivity" has been advanced, which states that in autism there is local over-connectivity but long-distance under-connectivity.[43]

Again, the image of the orchestra and the musicians is useful. It seems that the "orchestra" of the autistic brain has no conductor; in addition, the musicians cannot cooperate well with each other. Still there are some talented players who, when they play solo, play extraordinarily well. Similarly, we often see "islets of ability"[44] or splinter skills in people with autism.

To take this metaphor a step further, when musicians must play with other sections of the orchestra, this does not go well. To translate into brain language: During the development of the autistic brain, specialized areas are created, but they stay relatively isolated from each other. The brain of the individual with autism, and indeed the individual himself, has difficulties with context and communication.

The human brain looks a lot like a symphonic orchestra. In people with autism, the orchestra does not seem to have a conductor, and the musicians do not always play well together; however, some musicians in the orchestra are often very talented.

Tasks in which the regions of the brain are supposed to work together are, therefore, difficult for people with autism, but skills that are based on specific, local brain activity develop normally, sometimes even very well.[45] Psychologist Marcel Just[46] and his research team conducted a study in which subjects read sentences while their brains were scanned. Just and his coworkers found that, compared to the neurotypical test subjects, the test subjects with autism showed more activity in an area of the brain that is responsible for understanding words (Wernicke's area), but less in the area typically used for the understanding of total sentences and context of the sentence (Broca's area). Thus, rather than connecting words into whole sentences or parts of sentences as they read, individuals with autism may experience reading as reviewing a collection of loose words.

Based on other studies,[47] it appears that people with autism have difficulty integrating emotional information expressed by the face with auditory information gathered from speech. They are more accurate in interpreting the information when it is presented separately. Combining auditory and visual information seems to be difficult for people with autism.[48]

## The Autistic Brain: Little Top-Down Control Based on Context

The hypothesis of weak cooperation in the brain usually refers to poor top-down influence (from higher areas of information processing to lower areas). An important form of top-down influence is, as already described, the influence of the internal context of our knowledge and experiences on how we give meaning to what we perceive. Although scant, there is some evidence to suggest that the knowledge held by those with autism has less influence on their perceptions. For example, in one study subjects were shown ellipses that had been categorized as thin or thick and were asked to judge their width. Knowledge of the categories appeared to have no influence on subjects' task performance.[49] The researchers concluded that there is a form of reduced top-down influence in the brain of people with autism.

In another study,[50] people with autism were assigned the task of drawing a plate or a CD lying on a table. When neurotypical people have to do this, they tend to draw these objects too round (rather than elliptical), because of their knowledge that CDs and plates are round. However, the people with autism drew a form that was closer to an ellipse than to a circle, which was in fact what their eyes saw.

It is not only knowledge that influences our perception but also another part of our internal context, our emotions. The Flemish behavioral biologist Mark Nelissen, in his book *The Brain Machine,* calls emotion the conductor of our actions. The amygdala, part of the limbic system that is responsible for processing emotional information, scans our surroundings for emotionally and socially important matters, and when it discovers something, the amygdala takes the conducting wand for other areas of the brain. British researchers have found recently that the influence of emotions on perception is reduced in adults with autism.[51]

## Context and Mirror Neurons

Because we are talking about emotions, we have to talk a little about mirror neurons. Mirror neurons are nerve cells that react the same way when you perform an act as when you see another person perform the act. Mirror neurons were discovered incidentally by scientists at the Italian University of Parma.[52] They researched the brain activity of apes as they picked up small and large objects – raisins and apples. To their astonishment, they found that the brains of the apes also reacted when they saw one of the researchers pick up a raisin.

Mirror neurons can be directly researched in apes by inserting an electrode into their brain. In human beings, the existence of mirror neurons has not been proven directly, because one cannot, for ethical reasons, open someone's brain and pop in an electrode. However, brain scans in human beings show brain activity similar to that of apes, so the phenomenon of mirror neurons is likely to be the same in humans. Scientists are enthusiastic about the discovery of mirror neurons,[53] seeing in them the basis for understanding actions in other people.

Mirror neurons are essential for social skills such as empathy and imitation, skills that we know are difficult for many people with autism to master. Not surprisingly, at some point, a connection between autism and mirror neurons was made. In a variety of newspapers and magazines, you could read again and again that scientists had found the cause of autism. This time it was the failure of mirror neurons! A restricted number of studies have supported the hypothesis of reduced activity of mirror neurons in autism.[54] In light of the importance of neural networks and cooperation in the brain, it is doubtful that the activity of the mirror neurons in autism is the most important issue, or even the most interesting. Certainly, it is important to determine in which network they belong and how they are activated.

One international study[55] suggests that context also plays a role in this connection. The researchers determined that when we see someone grasp something in a context (in this research, the context was a tea party, where grasping a cup shows an intention to either drink or clean up), there is greater activity in the mirror neurons than when we see the same activity without a context. Additionally, in the two contexts (drinking and cleaning up) the mirror neurons react differently.

So, mirror neurons are context sensitive, and functioning may be influenced by top-down control and interactions with other areas of the brain. By the way, the existence of mirror neurons does not sufficiently explain the difficulties with empathy in autism. Indeed, some research has found no difference in activity in the mirror neurons between persons with and without autism.[56]

While there is clearly a reduced top-down influence in autism, that does not mean that the information processing within the lower areas is always intact. We tend to assume that individuals with autism function adequately or even well on perceptual tasks at a lower level, such as detecting individual letters within a group of letters, detecting changes in patterns and positions, or distinguishing tones;[57] however, there seems to be a problem in relation to the connections inside the base stations of information processing.

Recently, different teams of researchers[58] have discovered atypicalities in the horizontal connections inside the lower visual areas of the brain. These atypicalities have an impact on very basic levels of visual information processing, such as the perception of contrast, contours, orientation, and movement. For instance, people with autism could not detect movements when cooperation between brain areas was required; however, they did detect movements when neural cooperation was not required. Thus, what they are capable of doing depends on the complexity of the neural network that is required to process the information, even on the basic levels of visual information processing.

## Context and Sensory Differences

One characteristic of autism, sensory differences, has long been underexposed. The sensory issues of people with autism have received little attention until recently due, in large part, to the fact that sensory problems often are not apparent and may not impact others. However, sensory differences are of great significance to the people with autism who experience them. Lacking context sensitivity leads to sensory problems: Sensations are processed more absolutely than relatively

Sensory differences can be explained by a lack of context sensitivity and reduced cooperation in the brain. In the previous chapter, we learned how context helps us to pick out the important stimuli among the huge number of stimuli that confront us. Context works like a filter that makes certain the brain does not notice too much but also not too little. That filter is known in the world of psychologists and neurologists as *selective attention.* Each time you pay attention, you make a selection. Context helps to ensure that sensations are processed relatively and not absolutely. Although in any given situation several sounds may be loud, the brain will – based on context – weaken certain sounds and send them to the background while making other sounds stronger and bringing them to the forefront.

*Lacking context sensitivity leads to sensory problems: Sensations are processed more absolutely than relatively*

To illustrate, during an interesting speech or movie, you do not hear extraneous noises, like passing cars. Of course, you hear them in the sense that the sounds reach your eardrum and touch it, but your brain does not pay attention to them. In another context – like when you are waiting inside the house for a taxi – the sound of a car is important. This is similar to the conductor silencing a certain section of an orchestra because its music at that moment does not contribute to or is even disturbing to the concerto.

We are repeating ourselves, but it is an important message of this book: **Nothing has a fixed meaning and nothing is of absolute importance**. What our brain selects from its environment depends on the context. Sensory differences, such as hypersensitivity to light or sound, can be caused by a noncontext-sensitive processing of stimuli in which the stimuli are processed absolutely rather than relatively. When the context is not doing its work well, the processing of stimuli follows an absolute, all-or-nothing principle: A stimulus enters or not and is not "adjusted" by the context and its relation to other sensations.

Different authors have connected the sensory challenges of people with autism to context on a neurological level, especially in connection to reduced top-down modulation of incoming stimuli.[59] With top-down control, not all stimuli are equal in strength, and stimuli that are of importance within the context are given selective attention. The filtering of the attention is, however, only one of many functions of context in human perception. These functions are the topic of the next chapter.

## Summary

To process stimuli efficiently and quickly, the human brain has become context sensitive: It first sees the forest; only afterwards does it see the trees. It uses the forest to recognize the trees as trees. The processing of context happens super fast at the subconscious level. Context sensitivity is not exclusive to a specific location in the brain. It is related to cooperation between the higher levels of information processing and the lower levels, the so-called top-down control in the brain. Also, within areas of the brain, even in those that are there for primary, basic processing of stimuli, there are connections with contextual influence. The context sensitivity of the human brain causes stimuli not to be processed absolutely but relatively; that is, some stimuli get more attention, others less. That is why we are sometimes blind to details or changes. In people with autism, some connections in the brain do not work well. The "brain concerto" consists of fine musicians who do not play well together. The result is that stimuli are processed much more absolutely than relatively. This leads to problems, including sensory challenges.

# Endnotes – Context in the Brain

1. There is also scientific evidence for the influence of context in other areas of perception (e.g., the contextual influence on the tactical-kinetic perception) (Gentaz, Moroni, & Luyat, 2005).
2. You do not see a real car, but only a drawing of a car. For the sake of simplicity, we make an abstraction.
3. The process is much more complex than described here. Opticians, neurologists, and neuropsychologists know this. But we limit ourselves to the essence, to a rough summary, that is useful for this book. We refer those who wish to know more details to the professional literature, for instance: Snowden, R., Thompson, P., & Troscianko, T. (2006). *Basic vision: An Introduction to visual perception*. Oxford, UK: Oxford University Press.
4. More precisely, the corpus geniculatum laterale (the lateral geniculate nucleus; LGN). Again, we simplify things here. We do not look into different sorts of cells in the retina, the different layers in the primary visual cortex, or the magnocellular and parvocellular path in the retina and LGN.
5. In English, also referred to as data-driven.
6. The terms *top-down* and *bottom-up* describe the direction of the stream of information (respectively, from top to bottom and from bottom to top), whereas the terms *stimulus-driven* and *concept-driven* refer to where the stream of information is coming from (from sensations in the outside world or ideas in our brain).
7. *Honey, I Shrunk the Kids*. (1989). Los Angeles, CA: Walt Disney Productions.
8. Neisser (1976).
9. Neisser refers to schemas. On the role of schemas in perception, I wrote extensively in *Dialogica* (Vermeulen, 2003).
10. The picture was published for the first time in an article in the *American Journal for Psychology* (Porter, 1954), but you can find it on dozens of sites on the Internet.
11. In the collection of spots, you can see a man with a beard, some people even call him Jesus.
12. See, e.g., Barcelo and Knight (2007).
13. Hochstein and Ahissar (2002).
14. Biederman (1981).

15. Navon (1977), p. 371: "Moreover, whereas people can voluntarily attend to the global pattern without being affected by local features, they are not able to process the local features without being aware of the whole."
16. Specialists speak of a quick and subconscious "feedforward sweep." For more information about which brain areas are involved in the recognition of scenes, see Epstein and Higgins (2007); Goh et al. (2004).
17. Watt and Phillips (2000).
18. Potter (1975).
19. One speaks of a "coarse representation" that is based on lower spatial frequencies. Lower spatial frequencies give general, vague information such as proportions and orientation, while high spatial frequencies reflect sharp changes in the image, such as edges, and they give far more information about details.
20. We have to see this as a process rather than as a product: The quick and subconscious evaluation of the context is more of a sort of heuristic, a set of "quick fixes," than a complete picture.
21. Dijksterhuis (2008).
22. The connection of the rope to the wood makes it impossible to sit on it. There have to be two adjustment points on both sides of the wood.
23. Simons and Levin (1998).
24. Simons and Chabris (1999).
25. Lord et al. (1989).
26. Dekeukeleire and Steelandt (2003).
27. Lee (2002).
28. Contextual input does not activate the neurons but modulates their response. For a more detailed description of contextual fields and how neural signal detection is influenced contextually, see Phillips and Singer (1997).
29. Marks and Arieh (2006).
30. Rankin and Marks (1992).
31. Just et al. (2004).
32. See Alvarez and Emory (2006).
33. It becomes clearer and clearer that certain functions are spread over various areas. For example, although the left hemisphere of the brain is specialized in language, the right hemisphere also plays an essential role in speech and language understanding. Those who are still thinking only in terms of brain hemispheres and areas have clearly missed the Copernical revolution in thinking about brains.

34. Kaldy and Kovacs (2003).
35. Cohen and Servan-Schreiber (1992); Frith (1991); Hemsley (1993).
36. See Phillips and Silverstein (2003). They connected limited connectivity to the reduced functioning of glutamate receptors; more precisely the NMDA-receptor (N-methyl-D-aspartate).
37. E.g., Dolan et al. (1999); Friston (1998).
38. Wickelgren (2005).
39. Castelli, Frith, Happé, and Frith (2002).
40. Belmonte et al. (2004).
41. For a recent overview article, see (2010).
42. Courchesne and Pierce (2005); Courchesne et al. (2007).
43. Cortical underconnectivity hypothesis: Just et al. (2007), Courchesne and Pierce (2005).
44. Already noticed by Leo Kanner (1943).
45. Brock, Brown, Boucher, and Rippon (2002).
46. Just, Cherkassky, Keller, and Minshew (2004).
47. E.g., Loveland, Tunali-Kotoski, Chen, and Brelsford (1995). Several years earlier, Peter Hobson also found this (Hobson, Ouston, & Lee, 1988b, 1989).
48. Mongillo et al. (2008).
49. Soulieres, Mottron, Saumier, and Larochelle (2007).
50. Ropar and Mitchell (2002).
51. E.g., Corden, Chilvers, and Skuse (2008).
52. Rizzolatti, Fadiga, Fogassi, and Gallese (1996).
53. However not all of them. Some scientists, such as the well-known American psychology professor Alison Gopnik, are very critical. Gopnik speaks about a myth of mirror neurons and calls the theory of mirror neurons the left-right brain hype of the 21st century (see http://www.slate.com/id/2165123/). In the last century, people were very enthusiastic about the difference between the left and the right brain and tried to explain various cognitive and pathological functions based on the difference between the two cerebral hemispheres (including autism). Currently, it appears that although the right and left hemispheres are different, most things cannot be easily categorized based on that difference.
54. E.g., Dapretto et al. (2006); Oberman et al. (2005).

55. Iacoboni et al. (2006).
56. Hamilton, Brindley, and Frith (2007). According to Frith and Frith (2006a), the possibility of mirroring the actions and intentions of others is unimportant for the development of empathy. Empathy requires more than mirroring. It also involves understanding the causes of what the other thinks, feels, and intends. I wrote extensively about that difference in *The Closed Book: Autism and Emotions* (Vermeulen, 2005).
57. Bonnel et al. (2003); O'Riordan, Plaisted, Driver, and Baron-Cohen (2001); Plaisted, O'Riordan, and Baron-Cohen (1998).
58. Bertone, Mottron, Jelenic, and Faubert (2005); Vandenbroucke et al. (2008).
59. E.g., Belmonte et al. (2004); Blakemore et al. (2006); Frith (2003); Iarocci and McDonald (2006).

# Chapter 3
# Context in Perception

Why does the moon look larger at dawn than at night when it is higher in the sky?

Why are you surprised when you see a chicken, a bowling ball, or a kitchen robot in the waiting room of a dentist, but not surprised when the routine in a fast-food restaurant changes?

When would our eyes react more slowly: when seeing a cow in a sauna or a cow in a field?

How are we able to recognize objects in a matter of seconds without even thinking about it?

Why do we remember the books but not the bottle of wine in the office of a professor?

How does our brain know what is important and what is unimportant?

Why are we often not confused by double meanings and vague information?

How is it that a young person with autism calls a counter a sink and an adult person with autism calls an actor Yasser Arafat?

The answers to these and similar questions are the topic of this chapter, which will focus on visual perception and context. In the chapter about communication (Chapter 5), it will become clear that what is valid for perception is also valid for hearing noises and for speech.

## Context Guides Perception

The description in the previous chapter about context sensitivity in the brain makes clear that context influences the most basic levels of perception. These are levels of which we are not conscious and to which there has not yet been assigned meaning from higher levels (like book, car, friendliness, or government crisis). Context influences our perception of clarity, color, shape, and size (to name only a few). For example, the observed clarity of a stimulus not only depends on its own light intensity but also on the light intensity of its surroundings. A grey spot in a dark context looks brighter than the same gray spot in a lighter environment.

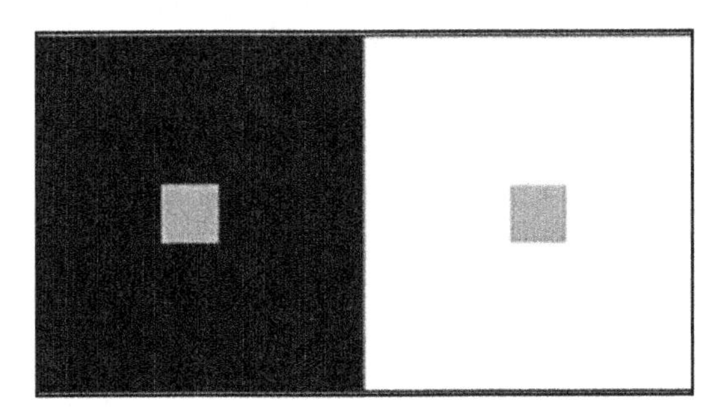

Clarity, color combinations, and intensity of colors are not seen in absolute terms, but in combination with context.

The influence of context on early stages of perception is the source of many illusions. An illusion is an incorrect perception of reality. In the area of visual perception, we use the word optical illusion. Sometimes all it takes is a small detail in the context to cause and mislead our perception, as becomes clear in the following illustration.

This image is known as the Cornsweet illusion.[1] Because of a small fold in the middle, the two halves seem different. Put a pencil or similar object in the middle of the figure, and you will see that both halves are the same shade of gray.

Context also influences our perception of size. This is evidenced in the well-known moon illusion. When the moon is just ascending on the horizon, it looks much bigger than when it is high in the sky.

There are several explanations for this illusion, but without a doubt context plays a role. We do not perceive the size of objects absolutely, but relatively. In other words, we see the size of something in relation to other objects within the context. An example of this was shown (on page 66) in the Ebbinghaus illusion with the circles. A man of average height (5'

10") in a group of basketball players looks short, but within a group of Japanese he will look almost like a giant. When the moon is close to the horizon, it is situated in the vicinity of many small things such as houses and trees that are far from us. We know that these things are not small, but they look small because they are far from us. The moon is rather large in comparison to the trees and houses. Therefore, it looks bigger on the horizon than when we see it up in the sky, where it is alone against a large dark surface.

Context plays a role in a lot of illusions, such as this moon illusion.

But not all (optical) illusions are related to context. Even in illusions where context plays a part, it is often only one of the variables of influence. Perhaps this explains why people with autism, even with their reduced context sensitivity, are also apparently misled by these illusions.[2]

Maybe you now think that it is better to be context blind, since context leads to (optical) illusions. Not a big help, this context, if it can be deceiving. Illusions are no more than funny side effects of our imperfect perceptions. Throughout evolution, our brain has chosen speed and parsimony over perfection. In daily life, illusions do not bother us much. On the contrary, the fact that we observe color and light intensity more relatively than absolutely is useful. For example, if we did not take context into account, we would think that the friend who is biking away from us is shrinking, that the houses on the horizon are inhabited by dwarves, or that clouds passing in front of the sun actually make everything a darker shade. Context sensitivity is rather useful!

The most important function of context is this: **Context guides our perception.** The quickly detected external context (in less than 200 milliseconds!) in combination with our internal context (the concepts in our memory) in a short amount of time provides us with a perception guide.[3]

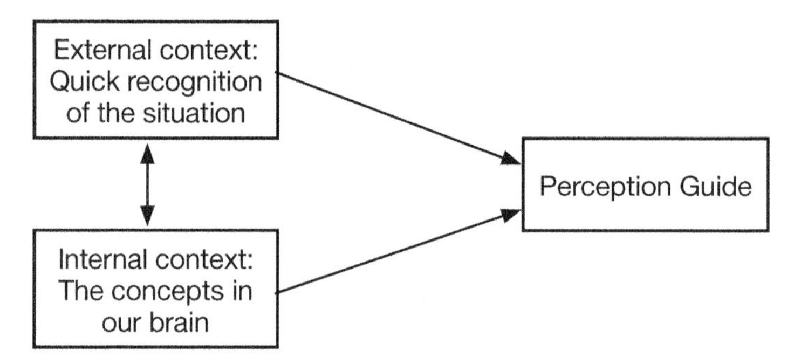


The combination of external and internal context forms a fine guide for our perception.

You can make the analogy that context is a guide of perception much like a guide in a museum, but context guides us in the enormous museum that is called "reality." Context does the job of a museum guide:

- Context tells us what to expect.
- Context helps us to recognize and find things quickly.
- Context tells us where to best focus our attention and where not to focus our attention.
- Context explains things that are not directly clear or understandable.

In the following, we look at these functions and examine the consequences for someone who is context blind.

## Context Creates Expectations

In the blink of an eye, we recognize situations, not in great detail, but in a sort of quick sketch. That rough recognition is enough to activate something in our brain that psychologists call a **cognitive scheme or concept**. Such a scheme or concept is a packet of knowledge that is stored inside our brains, built by experience and learning. Our brains collect all types of concepts: objects (like books), people (like your mother), and situations (the bakery, the school, the zoo, etc.). We also have concepts of events.

Psychologists call these concepts of events **scripts** or **scenarios**, because they are quite similar to what movie directors use. Scripts or scenarios describe who, what, and when. We have scripts of a family visit, a talk show, a city trip, or a bank robbery. A script can be very extended or rather concise, depending on what you learned, but it contains essential information for understanding the world. For instance, your concept of a book consists of facts, such as books contain pages, letters, and often pictures; books can be read; books are objects and not animals; they are most often harmless; they can be exciting or boring; they do not grow on bushes; but rather are the result of the hard work of an author (by the way, we also have a concept of an author), and so on. Your script of a family visit contains the knowledge of what you do and say when you enter the house of the host family, and that this entry is different from the one that is contained in your concept of a bank robbery.

Based on experience, we know that certain things are typical in a certain context, and others are not. For example, it is in your concept of zoo that there are animals, cages, guards, and animal caretakers. When you enter a zoo or see a picture of a zoo, you do not expect to see a luggage conveyor belt, check-in counters, passport controls, duty-free shops, and flight attendants. These belong instead in the context of an airport. By a quick estimation of the context, you do not expect just about anything, but only what fits in the context according to your concept.

The influence of context on our expectations not only works with situations like zoos and airports. Context can be much smaller. Seeing a human head is enough to limit the different possible meanings you can give to the object you see on that head: The context of the head leads you to the category of hats. Indeed, the chance is slight that the object is a bird's nest or a fruit basket.

**Context activates our concepts subconsciously.** When you enter a zoo, you do not have to think first about what you know about zoos. Context does its work in the background. In every situation, without thinking, you more or less know what to expect.

Because context clarifies what we can expect, it makes the world more predictable. For those who have some degree of context blindness, such as people with autism, life is full of unpleasant surprises and unpredictability. As soon as a person without autism steps inside a restaurant, she typically knows more or less what to expect. The brain activates immediately the restaurant scenario. That scenario tells us, among others, which people to expect to be in a restaurant (waiters, other customers, but no nurses or flight attendants – at least not in uniform), which objects (plates, glasses, bottles of wine but no lawn mowers, bicycle pumps, or concrete mixers), but mostly which social events to expect (who is doing what, when, with whom, and why). You know that you usually sit at a table, that someone comes to ask you what you want to order, that at the end you have to pay, and so on.

*Context makes the world predictable. A person who is context blind is more likely to be confused, because events and situations are less predictable.*

Assume now that you do not recognize or do not sufficiently recognize the context, or that your cognitive scheme of a restaurant differs from that of most people (which in autism is often the case[4]). Then it is possible that a number of things are unclear or confusing.

In familiar situations, most people with autism do not have difficulty with context; they manage based on learned routines. However, they can get confused when something changes in the context causing the routine to be canceled or changed. Then, most of the time, the predictability is gone, and they may feel lost and confused.

In Chapter 1, we saw that there is not only one context. Staying with the example of a restaurant, within the context of a restaurant there are other contexts that also have an influence on what you can expect, like how busy it is or how many customers there are. A restaurant that is full of customers is different from a restaurant in which you are the only customer. The expectation of how long you will be inside the restaurant and how long it will take before you get your food depends on the crowdedness of the restaurant. And the context of crowdedness can change the known, ordinary restaurant scenario.

*Peter, a young man with autism, is completely lost in a fast-food restaurant when a person comes to get his order while he is still standing in line. Peter recognizes the place as a fast-food restaurant and has a cognitive scenario for that kind of restaurant. In that scenario, you stay in the line until you get served at the counter where you place your order. But because it is crowded this day, the staff are taking orders while people are still in line. Peter's friends without autism are not surprised by this. The action is easily understandable from the context (it is very crowded). They are even happy with the adjustment, because they won't have to wait so long for their food. But Peter is totally confused, even angry, and no longer wants to order his burger. He is going to send a complaint letter to the hamburger chain.*

People with autism recognize known and learned contexts and situations, like a meeting, birthday party, or restaurant, but they have difficulty accounting for contextual changes in those situations. When you fail to recognize certain elements in the context that change the typical scenario, then situations can become incomprehensible and confusing. It is well known that people with autism need a lot of extra clarification and predictability. One of the reasons for this is that they do not get enough predictability from the situation itself, because they do not pick up the contextual elements sufficiently.[5]

## Context Contributes to Quick Recognition

The fact that context creates expectations is beneficial. That is, on the basis of those expectations, we quickly recognize the objects that are present in a situation. The brain does not have to analyze extensively in order to recognize objects. From the context, certain meanings are matters of fact.

To which object does the arrow point?

In the above photograph, you may immediately recognize a television because you immediately recognized a living room. Your cognitive scheme of a living room contains the knowledge that televisions are often found in living rooms. Therefore, you directly recognized the box with the black square as being a television set. But it is not a television set. It is a microwave that I cut from another picture and "photoshopped" into this picture. The idea of a microwave did not occur to you, because microwaves are rarely placed in living rooms. They are more suited to another context – the kitchen. Although you were misled, the example shows that context allows us to recognize objects quickly and without too much effort.[6]

The psychologist Stephen Palmer discovered this in 1975.[7] He showed people a picture of a kitchen as a context; then they were shown, in very quick succession, objects that they were asked to identify.

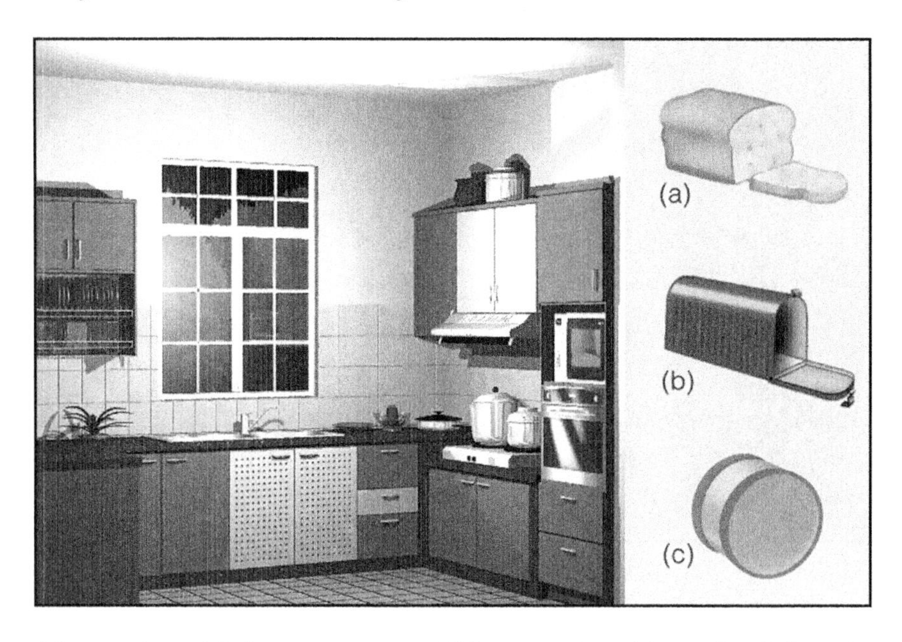


After seeing a kitchen, we more quickly recognize objects that belong in a kitchen than objects that do not belong in a kitchen.

Objects that belonged to the context, like a loaf of bread to a kitchen, were recognized in 8 out of 10 cases. Objects that did not belong in the context of a kitchen, but were similar, like an American mailbox (b) or a storage box (c), were correctly identified only 4 out of 10 times. The degree to which we recognize objects quickly is influenced by the context. We recognize objects faster in their normal context than when we see them in a strange context or detached from any context.[8]

This is contrary to what people believe, which is that unexpected things attract our attention more quickly and are more obvious than expected things. In reality, just the opposite is true. Or, as Peter De Graef, a psychologist who did research on perceptual effects of scene context on object identification, concluded: Our eyes react more slowly to a cow in a sauna than to a cow in a meadow.[9]

The influence of a familiar context is not only present in the recognition of objects but also in the recognition of people. You may have experienced this. In a certain situation, you think you recognize someone, but you do not know who it is; you cannot attach a name to the face that looks so familiar to you. This is known as "the-butcher-on-the-bus" phenomenon, named after the example given by psychologist George Mandler.[10] Although you recognize your butcher immediately in the familiar context of a butcher shop, you have more trouble remembering who he is when you see him in a totally different context, like on the bus, even though he may look familiar. The influence of context on the recognition of people and their faces has been demonstrated in various situations.[11] In the chapter about context and social interaction (Chapter 4), I will return to facial recognition. For now, we will limit ourselves to the recognition of objects.

Previously, we saw that our quick recognition of context is not a detailed image, but a very vague impression. We do not need a clear image of a context in order to identify the objects; a vague idea is enough.[12] In the pictures on the following page, the circled object is the same in both.[13] Still, most people say the object on the left is a drill and the object on the right is a hairdryer.

Even a vague display of a context helps us to recognize objects.

Two British psychologists, Beatriz Lopez and Susan Leekam,[14] gave the test developed by Stephen Palmer to children with autism and their typically developing peers. The researchers expected the children with autism to make more mistakes and to take longer to identify objects than children without autism. But this was not the case. Based on these findings, we could be tempted to conclude that people with autism do not have a problem with context, but that conclusion would be too easily drawn. First, the test contained fairly familiar situations, like a kitchen and an office. Second, as stated above, the recognition of familiar and typical contexts for people with autism is not a big problem. But there is a more fundamental limitation. Although Palmer's test examines the influence of context on the recognition of objects, it does not measure the recognition of objects *in* a certain context, but *after*[15] a context.

In Palmer's test, the context is first shown or determined, and only afterward are people asked to identify the objects. In other words, the context is activated. People with autism have less difficulty with the use of context when we activate the context and clarify it. They have more difficulty when they have to activate the context themselves, when they have to recognize it spontaneously and use it to give things a meaning.

This was the assignment in the master thesis of Therese Jollife.[16] She showed children with autism drawings of situations and asked them to show what did not fit in a given situation (e.g., a squirrel on the beach or a kitchen knife in a child's room). The difference between this test and Palmer's used by Leekam and Lopez is that the children had to give meaning to objects *within* a context. What happened? In this activity, children with autism had more problems and made more errors identifying the object than did the children without autism.

Lopez and Leekam performed another test, the homographs test. In that test, children were asked to read a sentence that contained a word with two different meanings and pronunciations (like the word *read*). It is the context of the sentence that determines which of the two definitions and pronunciations is correct. The same group of children with autism who performed well on Palmer's test made more mistakes on the homographs test than did the children without autism. The children with autism did not have a problem recognizing something *after* the context was activated (as in Palmer's test), but it appeared that the identification *in* a context was much more difficult (as shown in the homograph test).

Palmer's test does not seem to be a good test of context sensitivity in people with autism. To begin with, it uses a static stimulus. Reality is not accurately represented through static drawings or pictures but is more similar to a film in which scenes change constantly. Research shows that people with autism who successfully identify emotions on pictures or drawings still make mistakes recognizing emotions in real life.[17] Another shortcoming of Palmer's test is that objects are shown separately after the context has been shown. This is also not realistic. In real life, we do not see objects isolated from context, but usually *within* a context. The identification of objects isolated from the context probably requires different skills than the identification of the same objects within a context.[18]

Real-world images of objects that enter the retina are not as neat as the images in the drawings of Palmer's test. Most of the time, you do not see an object completely but only partially – a cup hidden behind a coffee can, a significant part of a chair hidden by the person sitting on it, and so on. We see objects from various angles, in different settings, in varying intensities of light; in short, we seldomly see objects in the prototypical and clear form in which the objects were depicted in Palmer's test. As we will see in a moment, context becomes especially useful when we have to identify less clear images.

Finally, Palmer's test measures only one aspect of the influence of context on the recognition of objects. The test simply explores if objects that are part of a context are recognized more quickly and more accurately than objects that do not belong in that context. Irving Biederman[19] demonstrated that belonging to a context is only one of the many contextual variables that influence the speed and accuracy of the recognition of objects within a context. The location and the size of the objects also play a part. Objects that belong in a context but are in the wrong location, for example, are not recognized as quickly.

## Context Focuses Our Attention

In this chapter, we analyze primarily the immediate effect of context on perception. How exactly does context operate while we see a situation? This question has been researched extensively in laboratories throughout the world. All studies show that when we watch a scene, our eyes far from randomly go over the scene.[20] Context influences our eye movements. We fixate primarily on the regions in a scene that are contextually interesting and, more importantly, informative. Context informs us not only about *what* we can expect but also *where* we can expect it.

This becomes clear when we search for something within a scene. Our search is led by both the external (the scene) and the internal context (our cognitive schemes). A quick recognition of a context connected to what we know about where objects are often located in that context ensures that our attention is focused and efficient.[21] Context reduces the number of locations in the image that we have to consider with our detail-focused attention mechanism. In other words, context steers our eyes in the direction of the relevant regions of the visual image.

*Context helps us to focus our attention on the right locations.*

If you were assigned to find an airplane in a picture of a city, you would not start looking somewhere in the lower part of the picture, but in the part of the picture that shows the sky. But in a picture of an airport, you would scan the lower and upper parts of the picture, because you would expect planes to be on the ground.

Psychologists at Durham University[22] recently researched whether people with autism also use context in a visual search task. Against expectations, people with autism were found to perform just as well as people without autism, if not better. In a later publication, the same researchers note that, although there seems to be implicit learning of context in autism, the subjects with autism showed inefficient visual search when required to respond to novel stimuli, which means they had difficulties generalizing what they have learned. [23] In this case, we must also note that the test material, as in Palmer's test, was rather artificial and not representational of what we encounter in real life. That is, it was a combination of abstract forms and a grey background – not a picture of a scene from real life.[24] Contextual guidance of attention is especially useful in complex natural scenes.[25]

A bit less artificial were the scenes in a study conducted at the University of Alabama.[26] In this test, subjects were asked to find Jiminy Cricket, the talking cricket in Walt Disney's *Pinocchio*, in pictures that also showed other Disney figures. In some pictures, test subjects could more or less predict where Jiminy was located based upon the context. In others, Jiminy Cricket was randomly placed. As opposed to the group of young adults without autism, those with autism did not use the context of the picture to quickly find the character.

*I am sitting with a highly gifted man with autism in front of his computer. I just showed him how he can transfer pictures from his digital camera to his computer. The screen shows the thumbnails of his pictures. Primarily, the pictures are of incorrectly parked cars. The man dislikes when cars are not parked correctly, and for that reason he photographs them often.*

*He asks me if I want to see the pictures of a jaybird that he took in the morning in his garden. With the computer mouse, I scroll quickly through the pictures. He calls me to a halt. "Do not go so fast! I cannot see if there is a jaybird in the picture!" I was surprised, because people with autism are supposed to be visually very strong, and quicker to notice details than people without autism. From experi-*

*ence, I know that this man has a good eye for detail. When I asked him how he was doing the search, he appeared to scan every picture for the presence of a jaybird – although more quickly than I would have been able to. My search strategy, however, was completely different. I screened the pictures based on context: a picture of a bird in a garden would contain a lot of green. The pictures of the parked cars, however, were mostly grey (the color of the road, the side of the road, the front windows, the grill, and the front lights). I ignored grey pictures in my visual search and focused on pictures in which there was green. My search criterion was not the bird, but the context of the bird. I could quickly see which pictures would be fitting for the jaybird to appear in. My companion's search process was slower and far less efficient than mine, because his visual scanning was not directed by context.*

Registration of eye movements to determine where attention is focused is an interesting procedure. Researchers are almost able to look through the eyes of test subjects. This type of research is often technically complex and expensive. But there is another way to check where our attention is directed, namely, through our memory. When you focus your attention on something, this results in the storage of this information in your memory. If context directs your attention toward certain parts of the total picture and not toward others, you will primarily remember what fits within the context. You will not as easily remember what did not fit within the context.

In an experiment in the 1980s,[27] test subjects were seated in a university office and asked to wait while the researchers got ready. After a short while, the researchers returned, took the test subjects into another room, and asked them to remember everything they could about the office in which they had been waiting. Everyone remembered things that were typical for an office, such as a chair and a desk. However, the office also had racks with some less typical things, like a picnic basket and a bottle of wine. Few remembered these things even though they were not items generally found in a university office (this study was carried out in an era when scientists were generally very staid and austere people, who never came out to have picnic parties and certainly did not consume alcohol). A number of people recalled things that had not been in the office, like books.[28] This shows again that the influence of context on our expectations is strong. We expect to see books in the office of a scientist. As a result, afterwards we think that there were books, even if there were no books.

A recent study[29] showed that children and adults with autism, after having read a story (for instance, about a tea party) and inspected a scene (such as a living room), recalled fewer context-relevant objects than people without autism. They were also less inclined to selectively attend to context-relevant aspects of the situation.

Another way to investigate the influence of context on attention is to look at changes in the elements of the context. If we primarily remember context-related things, you might expect that we would notice changes in contextually important elements within a situation better than changes in contextually less important elements.[30]

We already mentioned change blindness in the previous chapter. It's not that we never notice changes. Some changes we do observe.

Turn the page and look at the picture there for just a few seconds. Then return to the picture below. What has been changed?

Most people will have no problem noticing that the pen in the right hand of the teacher is gone, although the pen is only a detail of the picture. Fewer will notice that the cup on the right-hand side of the picture has also disappeared. What is the difference between the two? The pen is necessary in the context, while the cup is much less important. When context plays a part in our attention, we are especially blind to changes in things that are irrelevant to that context.

Although change blindness has been extensively studied, the phenomenon only recently began to evoke interest in autism research. This seems peculiar, because it has been known for years that people with autism have a keen eye for changes in details and notice small changes more easily and more quickly than do people without autism.

Recent research results regarding the change blindness of people with autism are fairly contradictory. In a study at the

University of Durham,[31] for example, it appeared that adults with autism were no different than adults without autism in this respect. Both groups took more time to discover incidental changes, and they saw changes in contextually inappropriate objects more quickly than changes in contextually appropriate objects. This seems odd in light of discovering that people with autism have difficulty detecting contextually inappropriate objects in a drawing (as previously discussed).

But in two other studies,[32] people with autism were less context sensitive in a change blindness task. They were slower and less accurate in determining contextually important changes. Notably, in one of these studies,[33] the subjects with autism correctly determined the context only 7 out of 10 times, whereas the subjects without autism did it 10 out of 10 times.

Perhaps the contradictory results can be explained by differences in the methods and tasks the researchers used. For example, across studies, contextual importance was defined in different ways. Sometimes it referred to whether objects fit within a context, in other cases it referred to whether objects did *not* fit within the context. In some studies contextual importance was defined as things that are essential in a context – as opposed to incidental and randomly picked objects.

Even if people with autism are just as accurate and quick at finding contextually important changes, the results can still point to a different use of context. It is known that people with autism are excellent in visual search tasks.[34] We would expect, therefore, that they would detect changes in details a bit faster than would people without autism. To see changes just as quickly means, in the case of people with autism, that they are slower in performing this task than we would expect and that they perhaps do not gain an advantage from the context.

*People with autism have a keen eye for details, but not for all details. They excel in details for which context does not play a role.*

In these studies, researchers did not examine the spontaneous use of context in directing attention. Test subjects were instructed to search for changes. It is possible that individuals with autism are capable of using context to identify changes, but only do so when prompted. Anyone working long enough in the field of autism will have experienced the following: After receiving hints and instructions, people with autism are capable of doing things that they could not do in real life without explicit instructions.

These studies put into perspective the frequent remark that people with autism have a keen eye for details and changes. The truth is that apparently they do not have a keen eye for all of the details, especially not the contextually important ones.

## Context Clarifies What Is Unclear

We have covered three important functions of context: the creation of expectations, the recognition of elements in a scene, and the focusing of attention on important matters. We have yet to cover the most important function of context, the function mentioned in the introduction of this book – the help that context offers when we deal with unclear, vague, or ambiguous stimuli. The world is not as simple and straightforward as the test material used in most scientific research.

When things are obvious, we do not rely on context as much as we otherwise do. Again, the example of the museum guide is fitting. That guide is unnecessary for things that are obvious. For example, you do not need a guide to tell you that the Edgar Degas' painting *Dancers in the Green* shows dancers in the green. That is obvious from the painting itself.

*As soon as the information that our senses give us becomes less clear, the context becomes more important for understanding its meaning.*

You do not want a guide to tell you that the big flat surface on which you stand is the floor of the museum and that the holes in the wall are windows. You expect a guide to explain the things that are not immediately obvious. The guide really becomes necessary when matters are outright confusing, such as spotting a garbage bag filled with paper that is prominently exhibited in the art museum. Without the guide's explanation, the garbage bag might never be seen as a piece of art.

The same is true for the context. As soon as things become unclear, context becomes more useful. The fact that things are not always clear initially is part of everyday life. We see certain objects partially – the magazine in the box for newspapers, the dish under the cup. Context clarifies those things. Although you see only a small part of an object behind the half-open refrigerator door, we know that it will almost certainly be food and not a tin of shoe polish, a tube of depilatory cream, or a container of motor oil. Context completes the half or partial information that our senses offer to us.

You do not know the meaning of some objects when you see them for the first time, but the context often solves the mystery. When I was in a museum in Athens and saw the object on the left side of the following picture, I did not know immediately what it was. I did know that it was ancient; the context of a museum in the vicinity of the Acropolis was sufficient to inform me of that. Only when I saw the picture behind the object did its meaning became clear to me – a potty chair or a toilet.

Without the context of the pictures on the right, the object on the left is mysterious.

Another source of ambiguity is that some things look very similar but have different functions. A pocket calculator, a mobile phone, and a remote control for the television can look very similar, especially from a certain distance. But when you see someone point the device at the television, you know at once what it is. The opposite is also true: Some objects have the same meaning but look rather different. For example, couches and chairs are produced in different forms, but still we recognize them at once. Some "design" couches look far from couch-like, but we still recognize them because of the context in which they appear.

In everyday life, the information received from the things we see is often scarce and/or incomplete because of similarity with other objects and factors such as poor exposure, distance, shadow, or something being partially or completely hidden behind another object. Much of what we see is not in our direct line of sight. Quite often objects are in the periphery of our visual field, where we see things less sharply and clearly. Additionally, real-life situations are not static but are in constant motion. In short, the brain usually receives incomplete information about the identity of things that we see. In that moment context helps us. The more unclear and incomplete the information, the more important context becomes.[35] What do you see in the following picture?

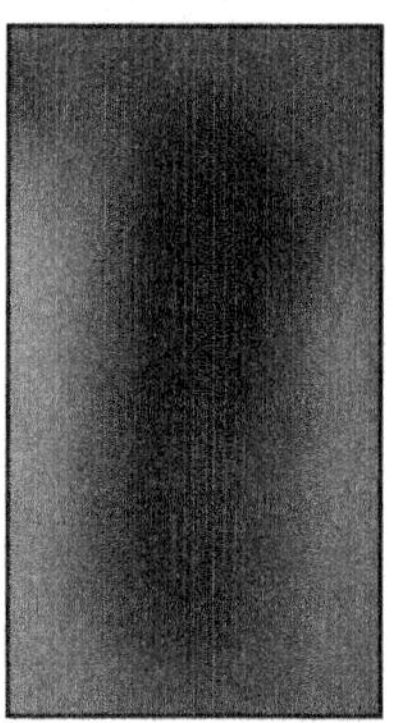

Just a vague spot, right?

In the picture on the next page, you see the same vague spot in a context, although in a very unclear context. However, as we have seen before, when we evaluate context, in a matter of milliseconds, what we get is not a detailed picture but only an unclear sketch. But even that unclear sketch with low resolution is enough for us to recognize what was previously obscured: It's a pedestrian!

Context clarifies not only the unclear information, but also when information has multiple meanings. In the introduction, we acknowledged the ambiguity in our world – nothing seems to have a fixed meaning. A book may be something to read, a step, or a weapon.

The influence of context as a "helpdesk for double meanings" has been extensively researched by psychologists, using so-called ambiguous figures. You are probably familiar with one of the most popular ambiguous drawings in which you can see both an older woman and a younger looking woman. Here is another well-known example.

Apart from any context, this drawing can represent both a rabbit and a duck. It depends on how you look at it. Most of the time, you would spontaneously see either the duck or the rabbit, but as soon as you see the second meaning, you can interpret it both ways. In psychological tests about perception, it is nice that you can see two meanings, and that you can instantly switch from one to the other. However, in real life, it is not very handy to be confronted with all the possible meanings. You would become very tired, or perhaps even crazy, if you were shown all the different options at once. For that reason, without even thinking about it, our brain selects one of the possible meanings as the meaning that is most likely.

On what basis is the brain making this choice? Context! This is illustrated in the picture where you will likely see a duck in the context of a pool of water and a rabbit in the context of eating a carrot. The preferred meaning assigned by our brain remains dominant until we make a conscious effort to look at things differently. You can choose to see a rabbit in the pool of water and duck with the carrot, but that would be unnatural.

Context resolves ambiguity in perception.

The influence of context works not only with drawings that represent something concrete; it also works with more abstract symbols like letters and numbers. The rabbit-duck drawing shows how external context clarifies, but so does internal context or what we know about the world. Ducks, according to the concepts in our brain, are not as fond of carrots as rabbits are. And rabbits that swim in a pool of water perhaps have an identity disorder that will lower their chance of survival.

I encountered a powerful example of how internal context can suddenly show us something in a different way when I coincidentally read on the Internet something about the origin of the logo of the supermarket chain Carrefour:

I had always seen the logo as a somewhat bizarre combination of a stylized red arrow to the left and a right-pointing blue arrow with the tail of a whale, both on a white background. I thought that it was an unclear and pointless logo for a supermarket, even a bit silly – that is, until I found out that it was in fact a white letter C (of Carrefour, indeed) on a red-blue background (blue, white and red are the three colors of the French flag; Carrefour is a French company). Now that I know that, I observe the background and foreground differently.

## Context Blindness: A Different View of the World

People with autism do not cope well with vagueness and ambiguity. In practice, things not being very clear is the number-one challenge for people with autism; they are confused. And that confusion often results in cognitive and emotional breakdowns. Still, scientists have given little attention to the sources of that confusion (the vagueness and ambiguity of information from the senses). A few studies have examined how people with autism cope with ambiguity in language. Those will be discussed in the chapter about communication (Chapter 5).

But the way people with autism cope with ambiguous visual information has received little research attention. Two studies[36] examined whether or not people with autism can look at an ambiguous drawing and think of different interpretations. The researchers showed a maximum of three drawings, too few to be able to make a general conclusion. Nevertheless, the results of the two studies appear to show that children and adolescents with autism are capable of recognizing both meanings in dual-meaning drawings, although they cling more strongly to the first meaning that they assign. The ability to switch between the two meanings appears to be a fairly good predictor of a number of behavioral characteristics of autism.[37]

Whether people with autism use context for one of the possible meanings was not researched in these studies, because no context was involved. However, the preliminary results of a recent study show that when copying ambiguous figures, individuals with autism are less directed by contextual information that suggests one of the two meanings.[38]

At the Yale Child Study Center,[39] people with and without autism were shown simple animated films featuring geometric shapes, such as circles and triangles. The researchers showed two films. One was a story about teasing. The other showed the launching of a rocket and its landing on the moon. The stories were told through the moving geometrical forms. It was up to the subjects to discern the stories from what they saw.

As expected, the participants with autism understood the story about the moon landing but were less likely to follow the story about teasing. The researchers concluded that people with autism are capable of identifying physical relationships in ambiguous material but not social ones. These findings teaches us that a social context for people with autism is far more difficult to understand than a physical context, but it does not tell us anything about their ability to use that context to determine unclear or ambiguous elements in a situation.

In short, scientific research concerning the use of context in giving meaning to things and events, in the case of autism, is very scarce; however, practical experience overwhelmingly supports the view that people with autism have difficulty managing unclear, confusing, or ambiguous information contextually. The following anecdotes are only three of many examples of this.

> *An older version,* WISC-III, *of a well-known intelligence test* (Wechsler Intelligence Scale for Children) *that is no longer in use, contains a subtest that is called Picture Arrangement. The child is shown a number of cartoon pictures in the wrong order and has to sequence the pictures to make a logical story. One of the stories is about a girl who travels by train and is going to the station with her father.*
>
> *I administered this intelligence test to a gifted boy with autism and asked him to arrange the train story. In one of the pictures, the father of the girl is purchasing a train ticket at the counter. Next to the girl and her father are two other passengers. The following drawing shows a part of that picture.*

Used with permission. Swets & Zeitlinger.

*When I asked the boy to tell the story, he began as follows: "The girl is leaving on the train. First they will wash themselves, and then ..." In the drawing, the counter does look a bit like a sink and a mirror. But the whole context would suppress this meaning. To begin with, there is the global context – the story is set in a train station. The boy could see that context because he told me that the girl was travelling by train. There is also the immediate context of the picture itself: The man is holding a suitcase, and there are two other passengers. The boy apparently did not take into account this contextual information when he assigned meaning to the vague illustration of the counter.*

*After an individual conversation with a student, the coach led a pupil with autism back to class.[40] They passed by a room where directors and staff members of the school were having meetings with parents and other visitors. The eye of the student fell on the following object:*

*What could this be?*

*The student with autism thought what you are thinking right now: a saltshaker. He asked his coach, "Why do you give the people salt?" The coach was surprised. Because this was what was standing on the table in the meeting room:*

*Is it still salt?*

Admittedly, the container of sugar resembled a salt shaker, and sugar looks like salt. In the context of a croissant, coffee, and milk, however, one would not typically expect to see salt. The student with autism was apparently blind to that context.

*A group of adults with autism visited Toone Puppet Theatre in the heart of Brussels. The guided tour ends in a room with the walls full of pictures and drawings that represent the many generations of Toones who have managed the theater, often in the company of well-known people who attended their shows. There are a remarkable number of pictures of the previous Toone (Toone the 7th, his real name is Jose Geal), who was the soul of the theater for more than 40 years. That Toone preferred to wear a black-white hat, as did the most famous doll of the theater, Woltje. Among the many pictures of Toone with Woltje is the following painting.*

*The guide concludes his tour with the classical question: "Are there any questions?" One of the adults with autism pointed to the painting, and full of amazement asked, "What is Yasser Arafat doing over there?"*

Just like the sink and the salt shaker, in this case there is a resemblance. The man with the doll does look a bit like Arafat, especially considering the black and white hat, just as the counter looked a bit like a sink and the container of sugar looked like a saltshaker. The interpretations of the people with autism in these anecdotes are not that unusual. You cannot say that they are illogical; however, the "logic" behind the meanings is one that does not involve the context.

The difference between people without autism and people with autism is that the former would say that the counter "looks a bit" like a sink and mirror, that the sugar container "resembled" a shaltshaker, and that Toone "is a bit of look-a-like" of Yasser Arafat. However, the boy with autism really thought he was seeing a sink and mirror, the pupil "saw" a salt shaker, and the adult was surprised to see Yasser Arafat in a puppet theatre. In the case of the puppet theatre, at first glance, others might also have the impression of Yasser Arafat, but they would correct that idea instantly and spontaneously, using the context: "It is very unlikely that there would be a painting of Arafat in a puppet theatre, especially when the painting pictures someone holding a puppet." Similarly, when you saw the picture of the sugar container without the context, you probably also thought of a saltshaker, but you would correct that idea quickly when you would see it in the context of coffee and croissants. That quick and spontaneous correction does not seem to take place in the brain of people with autism.

The lack of context sensitivity in the process of giving meaning to something often becomes clear in the surprising things that people with autism say, as in the anecdote of the boy who asked his coach, "Why do you give salt to the people?" The decontextualized meanings of people with autism only become clear to us when they express them. And that is not always the case. Just as everyone else, people with autism are not constantly expressing their thoughts (many express them even less often, given their difficulty with communication). As a result, there are a lot of decontextualized meanings in the minds of people with autism that we do not know of. A window to the decontextualized meanings of the autistic brain is undoubtedly the literal understanding of language, a well-known characteristic of autism. We will come back to this in Chapter 5 on context and communication. However, the anecdotes above clearly show that the difficulties in taking into account the context extend beyond the understanding of verbal information, but are also present in the understanding of pictorial and other visual, nonverbal information.

## Summary

Context is our guide in processing information coming from our senses. Context facilitates fast recognition and identification of things, and it helps us to focus on what is relevant. Context also gives us predictability in life: A quick grasp of the context tells us what to expect.

We do not use context all the time. When things are clear and predictable, we can manage without context, just as we can manage without a guide in a museum for objects that "speak for themselves." But context is indispensable when our senses present us vague, incomplete, and especially ambiguous information. Then context clarifies, completes, and resolves the ambiguity. This is already happening at the most basic levels of information processing, such as the perception of color and size. So, the context acts pretty much the same way as a guide but with one big difference: Context does its work without us knowing it. Context works behind the scenes, comparable to the hidden activity of many software programs in your computer. The context is a kind of invisible guide – you don't notice him, but he's there and he does his job by stealth.

When there is a less contextual sensitivity, the world can become unintelligible, confusing, and unpredictable. And without context, other meanings pop up, called acontextual meanings (think about the saltshaker, the sink, and Yasser Arafat). These meanings, although not completely unusual or illogical – after all, meanings are always meaningful for the one who gives them – are different from the ones that can be expected from the context. The autistic brain often produces these acontextual meanings, especially in circumstances where sensory information is vague or ambiguous.

Research on the role of context in the information processing of people with autism is scarce, and only recently has the topic received interest. Besides, the findings of the few studies that have been published are quite contradictory. A couple of studies seem to indicate that people with autism can, up to a certain point, use context. However, many of these studies used materials and procedures that are miles away from real-life situations.[41] The often unexpectedly good performance of people with autism on tasks that are supposed to measure context-sensitivity are in contrast to the daily experiences of those who live and work with people with autism. It is comparable to what we see in other areas – many people with high-functioning autism seem to do rather well on tests, but in real life they face a lot of challenges.

If we want to gain a better understanding of what goes on in an autistic mind, we will have to start using more real-life materials in research (this is a big challenge, as research requires an effort to control a lot of confounding elements). In the few studies using more realistic context scenes, people with autism showed less context-sensitivity than non-autistic people.

Research is also needed to distinguish between the various functions of context described in this chapter. For one function, namely, disambiguating ambiguous information, there seems to be preliminary evidence of a diminished context sensitivity in autism. When different meanings are available, such as in the case of homographs, it is difficult for the autistic mind to choose the one that best fits the context. In other words, people with autism do not easily find out what is appropriate and what isn't in a certain context. And the ability to differentiate this is vital in social interaction.

## Endnotes – Context in Perception

1. Cornsweet, T. (1970). The illusion is also known as the Craik-O'Brien-Cornsweet illusion and Craik-Cornsweet illusion.
2. The results of research on the effects of illusions on people with autism are equivocal and sometimes even contradictory. Happé's finding (1996) that people with autism are less sensitive to visual illusions in relation to size has not been confirmed by others (Milne & Scope, 2008; Ropar & Mitchell, 1999, 2001). Why people with autism, against expectations, are affected by illusions is not clear. According to Brosnan, Scott, Fox, and Pye (2004), the specific question that is asked in tests with illusions does play a role. People with autism succumb to the Muller-Lyer illusion (where two identical lines do not look equally long because of the form of the arrows at the ends of each line) when asked, "which line *looks* longer?" but do not succumb when asked, "which line *is* longer?"
3. In technical terms, context strongly influences what psychologists call the perceptual set.

4. I wrote extensively about this in *Dialogica* (Vermeulen, 2003); specifically, about the fact that cognitive schemes of people with autism are more exemplary than prototypical. See further the chapter about context in knowledge (Chapter 6). Trillingsgaard (1999) discovered that the scripts of children with autism for a number of familiar situations (shopping in a supermarket or attending a birthday party) differed from those of children without autism. This was confirmed in a recent study with children and adolescents (Loth et al., 2008b), in which a restaurant scenario was studied. In this study, it appeared that high-functioning adolescents with autism who scored relatively well on a theory-of-mind test did know scripts, but they were less flexible in the use of their scripts.
5. To make it clear: This is not the only explanation for the need for predictability in people with autism. Other elements also play a role; more precisely, challenges with imagination and the tendency to develop detailed and fixed cognitive schemes.
6. Psychologists use the term *contextual priming*: based on the context, one meaning gets priority. Another term for putting forward a certain meaning is *contextual facilitation* (e.g., see Torralba, 2003).
7. Palmer (1975).
8. Murphy and Wisniewski (1989).
9. De Graef (2005).
10. Mandler (1980).
11. See, for instance, Gruppuso et al. (2007) and de Gelder et al. (2006).
12. We identify indoor scenes correctly in 80% of the cases with a resolution of only 32 by 32 pixels. At such a low level of resolution, we even correctly identify 90% of outdoor scenes (Torralba, 2009).
13. Inspired by the photographs from Bar (2004).
14. Lopez and Leekam (2003) offered two versions of the test: a pictorial and a verbal version. In the verbal version, the context was described in words instead of pictures (for instance, the word *kitchen* instead of a picture of a kitchen) and children had to identify words instead of objects. Children with autism performed as well as children without autism on both test versions.
15. There is a clear difference between recognizing objects within a context and identifying and naming them after a context has been shown. In the latter instance, different factors play a role, not only the context but also familiarity with the objects, non-contextual expectations, and characteristics of the cognitive schemas of objects.
16. Jolliffe (1997).
17. Vermeulen (2005).

18. Bar (2004).
19. Biederman (1981) identified five principles of contextual relationships in scenes that are part of our cognitive schemas. For instance, the probability (the chance that an object belongs to a certain context), the position of an object in a scene, and the relative size of an object all influence how we identify the objects. Objects that are in an odd place are, for instance, less quickly identified than objects that are correctly positioned.
20. See, e.g., Henderson and Hollingworth (1999).
21. Psychologists call this effect contextual cueing. The following articles describe the contextual cueing effect: Chun (2000); Chun and Jiang (1998); Brockmole and Henderson (2006); Brockmole et al. (2006); Neider and Zelinsky (2006); Torralba et al. (2006).
22. Kourkoulou et al. (2008).
23. Kourkoulou et al. (2011).
24. A more detailed and technical critique. Firstly, it is not clear in the Kourkoulou et al. (2008) study what caused the quick identification. In the contextual cueing task that Kourkoulou and colleagues used – inspired by Chun et al. (2000) – context can facilitate both the search process and recognition and identification (Kunar et al., 2007). It is not clear whether the good performance of the people with autism is the result of contextually facilitated identification or whether it is the results of the effects of an implicitly learned configuration of the search process.

    According to Ganis and Kutas (2003), the results on these kinds of contextual cueing tasks with geometrical configurations do not reveal a lot about the ability to use more realistic contexts or scenes. The difference is that realistic scenes also involve semantic knowledge (e.g., toasters or cars do not float in the air), knowledge that is not addressed in tasks with geometrical configurations of abstract elements. According to the research by Ganis and Kutas, the contextual influence of scenes on object identification only operates after the associated semantic knowledge has been activated. In short, it is not clear that what Kourkoulou et al. studied really reflects the contextual cueing as it works in real life.
25. Balkenius (2003).
26. Klinger et al. (2008).
27. Brewer and Treyens (1981).
28. As shown a couple of years earlier by Baggett (1975).
29. Loth, Gomez, and Happé (2011).

30. Rensink et al. (1997).
31. Fletcher-Watson et al. (2006).
32. Loth et al. (2008a); Nakahachi et al. (2008).
33. Nakahachi et al. (2008)
34. O'Riordan et al. (2001); O'Riordan (2004). Important note: Many of these search tasks involve rather abstract and meaningless materials.
35. Torralba (2003).
36. Ropar, Mitchell, and Ackroyd (2003); Sobel et al. (2005).
37. Best et al. (2008).
38. Allen and Chambers (2011).
39. Klin and Jones (2006).
40. For this anecdote, I am very grateful to my dear friend Lynette De Wet, who works at Vera Skool in Cape Town, South Africa.
41. We summarize our criticism:
    a. Simple and static materials (drawings and photographs) that not even remotely reflect the complexity and dynamics of real life with its ever changing situations;
    b. A clear instruction to search or identify something, while in real life we use context spontaneously without someone firing the starting pistol;
    c. The things that have to be recognized and identified are usually pretty clear, while in real life, context is usually only used in cases where the brain is faced with vague, unclear, or ambiguous information;
    d. In most cases, a very clear, well-known, or recognizable context is being used, and it is shown for a relatively long time, while in real life we only make use of a quick and vague impression of the context (coarse representation).

# Chapter 4
# Context in Social Interaction

How do you know what it means when someone raises his hand? Is he waving good-bye, does he want to ask a question, or does he want to stop a taxi?

How do we recognize the difference between a genuine and a pretend smile or the difference between tears of sorrow and tears of joy?

Why do we tend to see an angry face in a fearful situation as frightened rather than angry?

We do not usually consciously think about what others feel or think, so what causes us to use our empathic ability when necessary?

Are police officers who confiscate smugglers' loot committing theft?

Why is it that we can think of logical solutions for social situations in which people seem to interact illogically?

How do we know what is a nice present for someone? Why don't we get more inappropriate gifts than we usually receive?

We interact with other people every day, and most of us do it with reasonable success. However, social interaction requires many skills, which – together – make up someone's **social competence.** The following skills are essential to this social competence:

- Reading facial expressions
- Recognizing emotions
- Taking perspective – grasping what others see, think, feel, know, and expect, and knowing why
- Understanding the intentions or purpose of what people say or do
- Knowing which social behavior is appropriate
- Reacting properly to others (social problem solving)

Context plays a role in each of these skills, and context sensitivity is essential in social competence.

## Context and Understanding Human Behavior

*In a railway station shop, a man buys a newspaper, a cup of coffee and some biscuits. He walks to a table where another man, dressed in a neat suit, is already sitting. The man sits down at the table. On his left, the newspaper. On his right, the cup of coffee. In the middle of the table, the package of biscuits. The other man, in the neat suit, picks up the package of biscuits, opens it, takes a biscuit, and eats it.*

Of all the things that have no fixed meaning, and, therefore, are unpredictable and confusing, human behavior stands out. Objects, such as books, can also have different meanings, but they still function in reasonably predictable ways. Throw a book up in the air, and you know that it will come back down. Books, just as all other objects, obey the law of gravity. Put a burning match to a book, and you know that it will become unreadable and soon collapse into a heap of gray ashes. Books, just like other objects, obey the chemical laws of oxidation.

But human beings are more complex. While they must obey the same physical laws as objects (try to float in the air), they also have the ability – within the limits of the laws of physics and chemistry – to initiate their own reactions and behaviors. Unlike objects, people have intentions: They want something. These intentions give human behavior direction. Intentions are literally the reason that people move. They lead us to act by prompting a certain behavior.[1]

Intentions do not emerge spontaneously. Intentions and resulting behaviors are based on the presence or absence of specific knowledge, desires, feelings, and beliefs. Knowledge, desires, feelings, and beliefs are called mental states by psychologists. They are a product of the mind. Mental states are not observable or touchable. You cannot hold them or put them into a box, and you cannot take pictures of them. Still, we often succeed in finding out what is going on in the mind of others – to "see" what others are thinking, feeling, wanting, and so on. This is a miraculous ability, which in psychology is called **theory of mind**.[2]

We have "theories" about the behavior of objects that enable us to understand and predict all types of formulas and laws; we have "theories" about human behavior, too. I have deliberately put the word *theories* in quotation marks. Although they are a form of science (in the sense of knowing something), they are not complex academic conundrums.[3] You do not have to know the formula or all of the technical details in order to understand the law of gravity, for example. Without this knowledge, you still know that a book will fall if you drop it. Similarly, we do not need a degree in psychology to understand the goal of a person's behavior.

*When trying to understand the behavior of others, context helps us to make an educated guess.*

How we recognize mental states in others has been a subject of discussion among scientists.[4] The fact is that we are capable of understanding and predicting others' behavior by reading their mental states, though not always correctly. This ability is present at an early age. For example, a typical toddler understands that someone is going to a restaurant because he *is hungry* and *wants to eat*, and that someone is crying because she is *sad* (italicized words are the mental states).

Numerous books have been written about the miraculous ability to empathize with others, so that does not need to be repeated here.[5] The question that interests us is the following: When mental states are not directly visible, how are we able to trace them? That is, based on what do we derive the intentions of human behavior?

The answer is that we partly use our own experiences. If you whistle when you are happy or have heard others whistle when they are happy, you can predict how someone is feeling when he whistles. Just as we do with physical laws, based on experience we develop a system of rules about human behavior.

To let something loose from your hands ➡ fall
Happy and content ➡ whistle songs.

However, our own experiences and rules are not sufficient to understand others' reactions. In fact, not everybody whistles when they are happy. More information is needed to understand and predict human behavior. We use context.[6] Context gives us information that enables us to make predictions about the intentions of others. We do not guess out of the blue when we interpret others' behaviors; instead, we again switch to context as a guide.

Every behavior can have several meanings. Take, for example, the very simple human action of raising a hand. What does it mean when someone raises his hand? Why is he doing it? There are a number of reasons why someone would raise his hand, but out of the many possible reasons, we normally know immediately and without effort which one applies in a given situation. We are able to do this because we take into account the context of the action. A raised hand during a meeting has a different meaning than a raised hand on the beach.

Human behavior, such as raising a hand, can have different meanings. Context helps us to make the correct choice between the various alternatives.

Without context, much of our human behavior would be unclear, strange, or outright ridiculous – like the previous story of biscuits. Eating someone else's biscuits for no reason is a bit strange. You can think of a variety of reasons why the man would do it, but his behavior becomes even more understandable when you know the context. And for that you have to read the short story about Arthur Dent in Douglas Adams' trilogy *The Hitchhiker's Guide to the Galaxy*.[7]

## Context and Facial Expressions

Facial expressions, the main indicators of emotions, greatly influence human behavior. Although humans have developed the spoken word to express mental states to other members of the species, body language, in general, and facial expressions, in particular, are crucial sources of information about what is going on inside of people. Paul Ekman, pioneer and world authority on facial expressions, calls faces "accessible windows" into the mechanisms which govern our emotional and social lives."[8] The ability to interpret facial expressions is crucial to understanding and predicting human behavior, and is thus a key to success in dealing with other people.

Facial expressions not only tell us about others' feelings, they also tell us if they are lying, if they have a good or a bad hand in a game of poker, if they are concentrating on listening, if they are bored during a lesson, and so on. Facial expressions can even give us information about someone's personality (e.g., whether or not someone is shy). Because people's faces are full of pertinent information, we choose to see people face to face, especially in important situations.

For the same reason, babies choose from birth to focus on the human face above everything else, even though the face is visually very complex. Typically developing babies as young as barely three months are already familiar with the configuration of the human face and make accurate distinctions between familiar and unfamiliar faces. At the age of seven months, they recognize certain emotions on the human face.[9] Apparently, the human face has been so important to survival that our brain developed a area that specializes in facial perception, the fusiform face area.[10]

Facial expressions are like a code we use to decipher the inside of others, especially the emotional inside. For that reason, a lot of research has focused on perception of facial expressions. Researchers like Paul Ekman[11] have mapped all types of facial expressions and have developed them into sets to investigate how and with what accuracy people recognize emotions in facial expressions. This type of research usually uses pictures like the following (with children, drawings are often used instead of pictures).

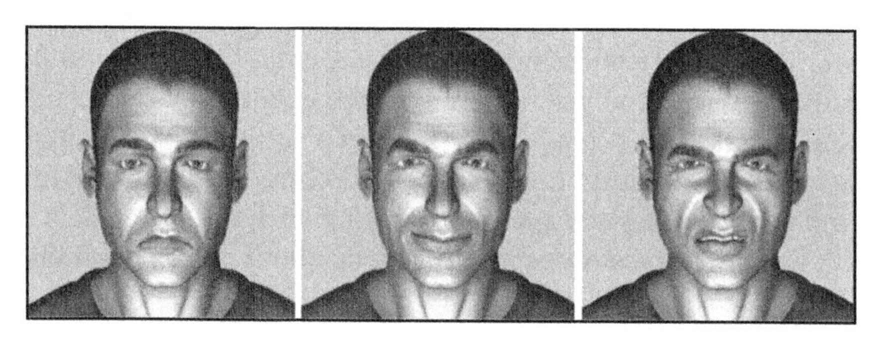

This material not only contributes to research on emotion recognition, it also helps in teaching people to read emotions, often as a part of social skills training. However, this laboratory approach is artificial. To begin with, facial expressions in real life are never like the ones in the pictures. We never see facial expressions that are so neatly isolated. We always see them in a context.[12] Second, this approach assumes a fixed relation between facial expression and emotion. That is, corners of the mouth and the eyes and eyelashes pointing downward means sadness, especially when accompanied by tears. Corners of the mouth pointing upward are associated with happiness.

However, facial expressions are not exempt from the law that nothing has absolute meaning. Tears are not always caused by sadness; there are tears of happiness. A smile can also be a sign of nervousness. Although facial expressions seem to be universal, as we learned from Charles Darwin, there is not an absolute relationship between emotions and facial expressions.[13]

Emotion recognition research, and similarly emotion recognition training, has until now ignored, or at least seriously underestimated, the influence of context on the recognition of facial expressions. That is very peculiar. For some time, we have known that the brain is context sensitive in the identification and recognition of objects (see previous chapter) and that this improves the efficiency of our perception. If context influences the way we give meaning to objects, it also influences the way we give meaning to facial expressions, information that, to most of us, is more important than objects. A variety of studies have confirmed this. We recognize facial expressions faster and more accurately when they match contextual elements that mirror the same emotions. Recognition of emotions is very context sensitive.

To begin with, there is the immediate context of the face. In 1862, during his experiments with electronic stimulation, the French neurologist Guillaume Duchenne discovered by accident the difference between a fake, acted smile lacking happiness and a real, spontaneous smile of pleasure (the real smile was later named the Duchenne smile). The mouth looks identical in both cases; the difference lies in the muscles around the eyes. To differentiate between the two smiles, you have to look at the direct context of the eyes. The mouth alone is not sufficient to see the difference.

The difference between a posed smile (left) and a genuine (right). You do not see the difference by looking at the mouth, but by looking at the eyes.


If one focuses only on a certain part of the human face without incorporating the rest, one often misinterprets the facial expression. That seems to be true for people with schizophrenia[14] but is especially true for people with autism.[15] The results of a number of studies suggest that people with autism look less at the face as a whole, instead focusing on certain details of the face, like the mouth.[16] This has even been observed in a 15-month-old toddler with autism.[17]

Other studies have found that people with autism do process the face as a whole,[18] especially when cued to do so.[19] Thus, in the study of face perception, the difference between global processing of a face (looking at the whole face) and local processing (looking at certain parts or details of the face) is probably less interesting than the ability to combine the information coming from different facial areas when the information from one part (such as the mouth) is insufficient.

A London research group[20] showed the two types of smiles to a group of adults with autism and determined that (a) the test subjects could not see a difference in the smiles and (b) they looked less to the eyes. In addition, the researchers dis-

*Just as with objects, we see faces in a context. The meaning we give to a facial expression is context sensitive.*

covered a correlation between the performance of adults with autism on this test and their social skills. Not being able to use the contextual information of different facial areas apparently leads to a lesser degree of success in social interaction.

Which part of the face contains the most information has not yet been determined. We are spontaneously inclined to assume that the eyes contain the most information. As a result, eye contact is assumed to be very important. But eyes do not always contain the most important information. Eyes are important for decoding the emotion of fear, for example, but to read the emotion of aversion, we look especially to the mouth and nose.[21]

How does the brain know which parts of the face to use to give us quick insight into the emotions of others? You probably guessed it: The context helps us. When people are shown pictures of a facial expression that expresses aversion, their eye-gaze pattern differs according to the context. For example, in a context that is rather disgusting (such as a picture with a lot of trash and debris), people are inclined to look to the mouth and nose. When the same face is shown in a fearful context (such as the picture of a person being threatened by a gun), people focus more on the eyes.

The contextual influence also works the other way around. When people see a frightened face in a context of disgust, they look more and longer to the mouth than when they see the frightened face in a fearful context.[22] In short, the context in which we see someone's facial expression influences the way we scan that person's face.[23]

The fact that people with autism look differently at a face than people without autism has become clear from a number of studies. For instance, they spend more time looking at less important parts of the face (like the ears, the chin, or the hairline).[24] To date, whether or not this scanning behavior is less context sensitive has not been investigated, but it would make sense. One study found that adolescents with autism did not use as much contextual information in a test of face recognition, although they showed the same inversion effect (performing better on tasks of recognizing photographs of upright faces than inverted faces) as people without autism.[25] In another study, it was observed that although, in general, adults with autism looked to the eyes when naming emotions, as often as do people without autism, they looked at the eyes less frequently when naming complex emotions – when the region of the eyes is more important to decoding the emotion than in the case of more basic emotions.[26]

## Context and Recognition of Emotions

It is not only our facial expressions that show emotions. Our entire bodies react and express emotion. We know this as **body language.** In addition, certain sound signals give information about how we feel – what we say and our intonation. A person might scream in fear or say "Oh" when surprised. The expression of emotions is not a static picture of a face alone; it is a dynamic multimedia show involving sound and visual images from the whole body.

Research shows that the way we interpret facial expressions and emotions is influenced not only by the context of body posture and body language,[27] but also by rhythm, intensity, and volume of the voice (prosody).[28] We can read emotions from a face or from the voice separately, but we do it more quickly and more accurately when we combine the two.[29] Obviously, we do not have to consciously focus on combining these two sources of information. When people are instructed to only look at the face and to ignore the voice, their interpretation of the emotions expressed is still a result of combining the two sources of information.[30] Again, this is evidence that contextual influence is automatic and works unconsciously.

In the 1980s, Peter Hobson showed that children with autism have difficulties making a connection between visual and auditory information about emotions. He investigated their skills in connecting sound and vision of social and nonsocial situations.[31] One of the social tasks consisted of connecting a picture of an unhappy-looking face to video images of someone who was causing himself pain and the sound of someone who was crying. A nonsocial task was the connection of a picture of a train with a vague form that moves over rails and the sound of a train.

In the latter case and other nonsocial tasks, there was no difference in the performance of the children with and without autism. The children with autism did, however, make many more mistakes when they had to connect pictures, sounds, and video images of emotionally loaded material. Because there also were a number of modalities in the nonsocial material, the weak performances of the children with autism cannot be explained from the difficulties in integrating and combining sensations of different modalities. Other experiments of Hobson and his colleagues[32] delivered similar results concerning the difficulties of children with autism in connecting facial expressions to the related voices.

Brain research shows that our brain reacts more strongly when emotional information coming from a facial expression coincides with information coming from a voice. For example, a Dutch study found no difference in brain reaction to facial expressions between adults with and without autism. Both groups showed stronger reactions to fearful faces than to happy faces. But when processing face-voice combinations for the emotion of fear, the brain of people with autism reacted differently from the brain of the people in the control group.[33]

That we take into account the rest of the signals sent via body language and voice during emotion recognition is fairly well known and sounds very logical. Less known is the fact that the larger context outside the person also influences how we interpret facial expressions. Normally, we assume that emotional body language is so strong and clear that the context cannot add much to our guess of what another person is feeling. But that is not true. We recognize emotions faster and more accurately when the facial expression emerges in a context that suggests the given emotion than when the same emotion emerges in a neutral context or in a context that suggests another emotion.[34] For instance, people recognize fear more quickly in a frightening context than in a happy context. At a New Year's party, you will have more difficulty seeing if someone is afraid than at a kidnapping (as long as the fireworks are not out of control during the New Year's celebration).

Context and facial expression each makes its own specific contribution. When facial expression is crystal-clear, context does not play a big role. As stated previously, context is especially important when the input is not clear. Therefore, when the information coming from the face is less clear, we use the information coming from the voice; for example, to find out more about the emotion.[35] Additionally, we look at the facial expression of other people in the vicinity of the person on whom we are focused.[36]

But even when the facial expression is clear, context still has a rather strong influence. We think that facial expressions are most important in the decoding of emotions and that they have more influence than other information. If that is the case, we should prefer the message from the face when it expresses something other than the context.

*An angry face in a frightening situation is described as afraid, not as angry. Context has a strong influence on recognizing emotions.*

If we saw an angry-looking face in a frightening context, would we describe that emotion as anger or fear? People who see a frightened face in an angry situation describe the facial expression as angry, not frightened.[37] In some cases, contextual information seems to be stronger than information coming from a facial expression, even with clear facial expressions of basic emotions like aversion, fear, happiness, anger, and sadness. That is, we often judge facial expressions based on the context, much more than on the basis of the emotion that is shown in the facial expression. In early stages of development, children do not often do this, but as they grow up, they use more contextual elements instead of facial expressions to understand others' emotions.[38] This improves their efficiency of reading emotions, and thus increases their social skills.

Research measuring eye movements shows that we look at facial expressions that arise within a context for a shorter length of time than when we see out-of-context pictures of facial expressions.[39] Moreover, sometimes we do not need to see any facial expression to correctly guess someone's emotion. You will not have a lot of difficulty grasping the emotion of the person in the following picture, although his face has been erased.

Sometimes we don't even need a facial expression to know what someone is feeling. The context says it all.

In the perception of facial expressions, contextual sensitivity works just as quickly, unconsciously, and automatically as in the perception of objects. The integration of contextual information occurs at a very early stage of the information processing in the brain, long before we are aware of the emotion of the people we observe.[40] So, even in face perception, context does its work on the most basic, preconscious levels of information processing.

In the book *The Curious Incident of the Dog in the Night-Time,*[41] the main character, Cristopher, who has autism, tells of what he learned about emotions from his psychologist and how difficult it is for him to give meaning to what he sees on someone's face. "If you close your mouth and breathe out loudly through your nose it can mean that you are relaxed, or that you are bored, or that you are angry and it all depends on how much air comes out of your nose and how fast and what shape your mouth is when you do it and how you are sitting and what you just said before and hundreds of other things which are too complicated to work out in a few seconds."

Christopher is right. But he is wrong in the estimation of the time we need to understand those hundreds of things. We do it in far less than a few seconds; normally, we succeed in doing it within a half second. That context has a strong influence on emotion recognition is logical, because there are far fewer fixed connections between facial expression and emotions than earlier assumed. Tears do not always mean sadness; a smile does not always mean happiness. When several feelings are hiding behind a certain expression on the face, context helps us to find the correct feeling. Context does not have to be a complete scene or situation to adjust the standard link between emotions and facial expressions, sometimes a detail in the context suffices.

Without context, the young lady in the picture on the left below looks sad. We default to the emotion of sadness because we connect her facial expression and the presence of tears to sadness. However, in the full picture on the right, her clothes and the decoration change this standard connection to happiness: Her tears are tears of happiness.

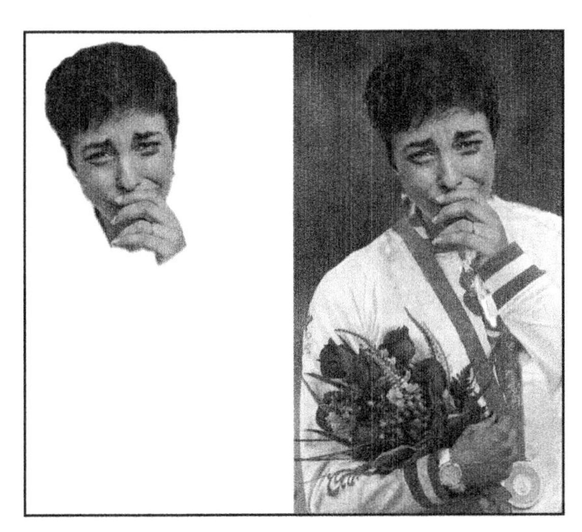

Without context, we think the young lady is sad.
The context changes our interpretation to happiness.

The degree to which we use context is related to the accuracy with which we can attribute mental states.[42] Emotion recognition and context sensitivity go hand in hand. Thus, we can expect that somebody who is less context sensitive will have problems recognizing emotions.

The emotion recognition abilities of people with autism have been extensively studied, and many of the studies support the well-known fact that it is difficult for people with autism to recognize emotions quickly and accurately. Still, there is not a case for a sort of blindness to facial expressions and emotions, as more able youngsters and adults with autism do not perform poorly on tasks in which they have to derive basic emotions (fear, angriness, happiness, aversion) from pictures with facial expressions.[43] When shown some less basic emotions or emotions of less prototypical facial expressions like surprise and shyness,[44] they have significantly more trouble, however. This is not surprising, as in recognizing those types of complex emotions, context plays a far bigger role than with the recognition of basic emotions.

For even the most gifted adults with autism, despite their occasional good performances on laboratory tests of facial expressions, emotional expressions in real life often remain a big mystery.

*In the movie* Autimatically,[45] *Michelle, a high-functioning woman with autism, relates that she sees the changes in the faces of others or that she hears the change in voice intonation, but that she does not know what the change means. She always interprets a loud voice as anger, even when the context would lead to another meaning – especially, when two people are too far from each other to communicate with a normal voice volume. As do other people with autism, Michelle uses a fixed connection between expression and emotions: loud voice = anger. She is not able to adjust the meaning that she gives to expressions based on the context.*

*When a boy with autism saw the medals ceremony of the Olympic Games on television, he was totally amazed by the fact that one of the winners was crying, as in the previous picture. She should have been happy with a medal instead of being sad, he reasoned!*

Most studies about the emotion recognition of people with autism show us very little about how good or how bad they are at reading emotions. This is because the tests, as mentioned before, use "artificial" material. In real life, we see faces within a context, and the information contained in the facial expressions is normally far more varied and ambiguous than in the pictures that are used in scientific research. In real life, expressions of emotions are dynamic, not a static picture. Fortunately, some researchers have recently come to that insight and use more realistic material than before.

An American research team tracked the eye movements of children with and without autism when watching facial expressions in four different conditions: static, pictures of only one face; dynamic, movies of only one face; pictures of facial expressions in a context; and movies of a facial expression in a context. The eye movements of the children with autism differed from those of the children without autism only when they looked at the moving images of facial expressions embedded in a context, the situation that came closest to real-life conditions.[46] With the pictures and the movies with isolated faces, children with and without autism performed equally well. The children with autism performed less well than the control group with respect to the recognition of emotions within scenes.

Research at a Flemish University[47] showed that more able adults who performed well on an advanced task of emotion recognition (the so-called eye test, in which you have to figure out the emotions of a picture by seeing only the eyes of a person), in a more realistic situation (watching a video track of a situation in which the test subjects themselves participated) had trouble figuring out what another person was thinking or feeling, especially in less structured situations.

Research into the use of context in emotion recognition of people with autism is scarce, but the results of the few studies mentioned above seem to indicate a reduced context sensitivity. Contrary to what we know about children without autism, especially when they get older and use more contextual elements, even high-functioning children and adolescents with autism use less contextual elements in emotion recognition. They focus primarily on the face and far less on the other clues in the context.[48] In one of the studies, researchers used pictures of situations in which facial expressions were hidden (comparable to the picture on page 137 with the man by the coffin). The children with autism were not able to use the context to figure out the hidden emotions.[49] But when researchers activated the context, children with autism did much better, which points to the difficulty in autism being primarily the lack of spontaneous use of context.[50]

## Context and Attention to Mental States

The use of "unrealistic" material is not the only shortcoming of many tests for emotion recognition and the ability to empathize. Another important shortcoming of these tests, even those that use more dynamic and contextual material, is that subjects are given the assignment to recognize emotions and to identify them. The researcher or the project leader pushes the start button of the subject's empathic ability: "What do you think this person is feeling?" But in real life, this button is usually not pushed by others. Our brain automatically switches on the ability to empathize; we do it spontaneously. Of course, we are not constantly busy thinking about what other people might think or feel. Our brain has more to do than play psychologist. We also have to think of nonsocial things like the dishes, the fastest lane at the checkout counter, the computer that is failing us again, and which sweater matches the pants we just bought.

Sometimes our ability to empathize is off, and sometimes it is on. But what turns on that ability when there is nobody around to push the start button – such as a researcher asking you to identify an emotion or a spouse reminding you what present to buy ("Honey, you still know what I would like, don't you!")? The answer is that our brain is switching on the empathic machinery based on the context. From the context we derive, most of the time with the speed of lightning and without being conscious of it, that we should decode someone's mental states.

So we expect that whoever is context blind will not move spontaneously into empathic action. With that kind of person, we have to push the button and, thus, activate the ability to empathize. That is the experience that a lot of parents and caregivers have with individuals with autism. "If we ask him explicitly, then he will name the feeling, so he does empathize! He can do it, but usually does not do it, at least not spontaneously." That is also the reason why some people with autism do not perform poorly on theory-of-mind tests. In those tests, their ability to empathize is triggered by a question or an instruction. But when no one is pushing their empathy program button, people with autism pay far less attention to feelings, so discovered the Dutch researcher Sander Begeer.[51]

Begeer[52] asked children with autism and children without autism to sort pictures of male faces. The pictures differed from each other on several variables: Some men wore glasses, others did not; some men had a moustache, others did not; and finally, some men looked happy and friendly, while others looked an-

*The context pushes the button of the empathy program in the brain.*

gry and unfriendly. When sorting, the children with autism less often used the emotional expression as a criterion than did the children without autism; however, when the researchers pushed the button by asking questions that focused attention on emotions ("Who would like to give you a candy?", "Who would shout at you?," "Who would you like to have as a teacher?"), the children with autism began to sort much more based on the facial expression, and the difference from the control group disappeared. Begeer concluded, "Without a clear context, expressions of emotions for children with autism are not more meaningful than moustaches or glasses."

It is generally known that people with autism pay less spontaneous attention to the socially important stimuli that are imbedded in social situations. We cannot exclude the possibility that, in great part, this is due to a reduced sensitivity to context. In the early stages of emotional information processing, there is an automatic, fast, and unconscious estimation of the context that does or does not activate successful empathetic brain processes.[53]

## Context and Ability to Empathize (Theory of Mind)

So far, we have discussed the recognition and identification of feelings based primarily on facial expressions. The ability to empathize, or theory of mind, is more than that. To start with, theory of mind is the ability to attribute a variety of mental states, not just emotions. Some researchers[54] distinguish between different forms of abilities to empathize or take perspective.

- **Visual perspective taking:** finding out what someone is looking at, what someone is seeing or not seeing
- **Affective perspective taking:** deriving what someone is feeling
- **Conceptual perspective taking:** determining what someone knows, thinks, or wants

Persons with autism have the least difficulty with taking a visual perspective. Taking an affective perspective causes a bit more trouble, but some are able to read basic emotions in clear, recognizable situations. The most difficult is taking a conceptual perspective.[55] The well-known Sally Anne Test[56] measures conceptual perspective taking, more specifically, the ability to see false belief (when someone is thinking something that does not match reality).

That conceptual perspective taking is more difficult for children with autism than affective and visual perspective taking can be explained partially by typical development. Children who do not have autism can, at an earlier age, take the visual and affective perspective of someone more easily than the conceptual perspective;[57] however, a part of the explanation lies in the role of context in taking perspective.[58] When taking visual and affective perspectives, we get information from the face. The direction of a gaze and the facial expression tell us what someone is looking at and what someone might feel. On the contrary, to determine what someone is thinking, looking at facial cues does not help. This is when context becomes important. In the following pictures, we can derive from the facial expressions what Lisa is seeing and feeling, but without the context, we do not know what she is thinking about the bee.

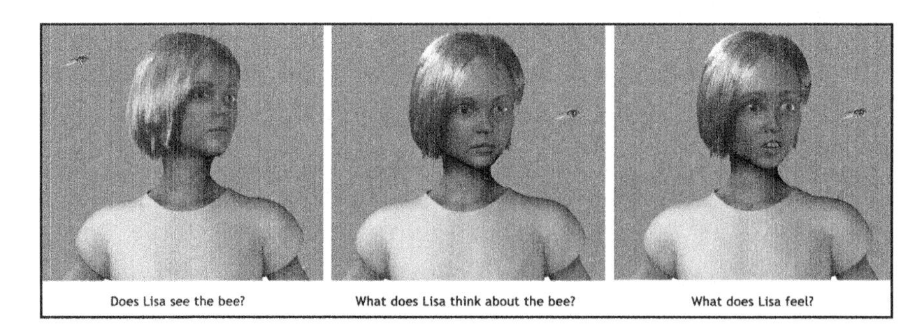
Does Lisa see the bee? What does Lisa think about the bee? What does Lisa feel?

This is not to say that context plays no part in taking a visual or affective perspective. Context appears to play a role in predicting where someone will look.[59]

To recognize and, when necessary, determine the mental state of someone else is an important social skill, but you need more than that to be successful in social situations. Imagine that you are irritated by your coworker's behavior. He consistently has private conversations on the telephone, talking and laughing out loud, making it difficult for you to concentrate on your work. You send him an irritated look. The colleague says, "I see that you are irritated," but then merely continues his behavior. He determines your feelings correctly, but you cannot call his action socially appropriate. Positive interactions require that you not only recognize others' emotions but also know *why* they have those emotions.[60]

It is possible to know that someone is lying but not know why she is lying. It is possible to see that someone is enthusiastic but not know what he is enthusiastic about. It is possible to recognize sadness but not know why someone is sad.

The following pictures all show people who feel sad, but they are sad for totally different reasons. We do not understand the causes of their sadness from their facial expressions but from the context. Context plays a role in identifying emotions, but it plays an even bigger role in identifying what causes these emotions.

Context helps us to retrieve the causes of emotions.

Paul Harris, professor at Oxford University, did extensive research on the development of children's understanding of the behavior, intentions, and emotions of other people; he distinguished three levels in that development.[61] At the age of three or four, children already understand that situations bring out feelings. For example, whoever gets an ice cream cone is happy. They also know that wishes cause feelings. For example, when you wish for an ice cream cone and you get one, you will be happy. Slightly older children, four to six years old, also understand that expectations, independent of what really happens, cause emotions. If you expect an ice cream cone but get a cracker, you are not only unhappy; you are disillusioned.

Research shows that children with autism are capable of predicting someone's feelings when those feelings are connected to a situation.[62] With regard to a clear and known context, for example, something they have experienced themselves, children with autism can make a connection between situations and emotions: Getting an ice cream cone = happy. Sometimes they connect a feeling to someone's desire. But they have difficulty when it comes to predicting a feeling based on what someone is thinking, expecting, or wanting.

John and Mary are playing in the living room. Mother comes back from the store. They expect that they will get a treat. John thinks that he will get a candy bar. Mary

> thinks that she will get a lollipop. Mother enters the room, and both children get a chocolate bar. How does John feel? How does Mary feel?

Eleven-year-old children with autism did not perform as well as five-year-old children without autism in predicting how John and Mary would feel.[63] People with autism are often blind to the context that is connected with what people are thinking, wanting, or expecting. The ability to see that context helps people without autism to consider the connections between situations and emotions or behavior.

The connection between situations and emotions is seldom absolute and direct but is often influenced by what people are thinking, wanting, or expecting. For example, not everyone wants ice cream; perhaps they want something else, they may be dieting, or they may not like ice cream. For those people, receiving an ice cream cone would not be a treat at all. Someone who is using fixed connections between situations and behavior instead of taking into account ever-changing contexts will be continuously surprised, and often will not understand others' reactions.

That was the conclusion drawn by Marike Serra[64] and her colleagues at the Rijksuniversiteit Groningen. They showed children with and without autism a drawing of a girl who was bitten by a rabbit, the class pet. The girl was in pain. The next day, the teacher asked the girl to feed the rabbit. Although feeding the rabbit is a favorite experience (fixed connection: pets are fun), it would not be a nice experience for the girl in light of what happened the day before. She would be afraid of being bitten again.

Compared to the other children, the children with autism were less capable of predicting that fear. They saw less connection between the emotional context of the event and the biting rabbit. Why would the girl be afraid? Rabbits are fun, aren't they? Note: This does not have to do with an inability to recognize a mental state's impact on behavior, as proven by a subsequent study.[65] That study showed that the ability of the children with autism to predict behavior based on convictions and wishes is intact, but they still had difficulties in understanding and predicting emotions based on clues related to the emotional background or context. But as expected, when we activate the context explicitly, they performed much better in decoding what people think and feel.[66]

Context helps us to understand human behavior. Thus, it also helps us to understand a form of behavior that is the cornerstone of human contact: communication. In the next chapter, we describe extensively the influence of context on language and communication, but here we take a small detour because understanding what people mean when they say something also relates to theory of mind. That is, to get a grip on communicative intentions, context is also crucial.

> Katie and Emma are playing at home. Emma takes a banana from the fruit basket and holds it against her ear. She says to Katie, "Look, this banana is a telephone!"

This story is part of the test *Strange Stories*.[67] This test, a collection of stories in which people say things that are not literally true, has been seen as a more advanced test for assessing theory of mind. What people say in the stories makes more sense when you understand their intentions, and those intentions are fairly diverse: to lie, be funny, use irony and sarcasm, and so on. In the example of Katie and Emma, it is about pretending. Not surprisingly, people with autism perform especially poorly on this test.

Francesca Happé, the researcher who designed *Strange Stories,* and first conducted research utilizing it, explained the poor performance of people with autism in the first instance as stemming from a lack of theory of mind. There was something peculiar, however. Adults with autism who performed well on other tests of theory of mind still performed poorly on *Strange Stories*, even though their answers referred to mental states as often as the control group's; therefore, their performance could not be related to the inability to perceive mental states. How was it that people with autism still failed on the *Strange Stories* tasks?

Something became apparent when the researchers began to evaluate the quality of the answers of persons with autism. These subjects explained the behavior of the characters based on mental states, but the mental states they chose did not fit the context of the story. For example, one of the test subjects explained the sarcastic statement of a character as an example of politeness. Happé writes in her conclusions, "It therefore seems that these subjects came to the test situation equipped with one or two explanations for why people say puzzling things. It is possible that these explanations had been told to the subjects in response to questions about particular situations, and that the subjects noted them without understanding the precise nature of the context in which they apply."[68]

When other scientists[69] a few years later repeated the research on *Strange Stories*, they came to the same conclusion: The explanations of the people with autism did not sufficiently, or sometimes not at all, take into account the context.

So, the ability to empathize involves much more than recognizing mental states. You also have to be able to link the mental state to the situation. To understand human behavior, in addition to theory of mind, you need context sensitivity.[70]

*Theory of mind or the ability to empathize requires a lot more than being able to recognize mental states. You also have to be able to connect them to a context.*

From a certain age forward, and given a certain level of ability, individuals with autism are able to perceive mental states, but connecting mental states to the context seems to remain difficult.

This has been confirmed in a few recent studies[71] in which people with autism were asked to explain reactions of people in a story or a movie. For example, children with and without autism were shown a part of a movie in which a young woman hurries to the post office, but when she gets there she finds that it is closed.[72] She knocks on the door, and an older woman, apparently against her wishes, opens it. The younger woman says, "Excuse me, I know that the office is closed."

The test subjects were asked how the older woman would feel and could choose from four alternatives: worried, sorry, unfriendly (the correct answer), and interested. While 8 out of 10 children without autism knew the correct answer, the group with autism gave the correct response just 5 out of 10 times. One out of four children said the woman was sorry. Instead of using the context of the story, these children based their answers on what the young woman was literally saying.[73]

The results of these studies seem to point to the fact that the ability of people with autism to retrieve mental states and use them as an explanation for what people say or how they act is not a significant deficit; they have more difficulty drawing on the context to correctly identify those mental states. When we give them explicit hints or focus their attention on the context, they are more successful.[74]

## Context and Socially Appropriate Behavior

What is, or is not, socially appropriate? Is it socially inappropriate to start eating someone else's biscuits? Is it socially acceptable to take your clothes off in the vicinity of others? The appropriateness of human behavior is not absolute. Terms like *decency, hospitality*, and *well-mannered* are very relative.

Without referring to something else, we cannot possibly determine if a certain behavior is appropriate or not. Of course, there are a number of general guidelines: Touching intimate parts of the body of another person is not appropriate, stealing is not allowed, and murder is totally unacceptable. Long ago, a noble man named Moses returned from a mountain in the Sinai desert with two stone tablets on which a set of Ten Commandments were written. These commandments are still the basic rules of living for three major religions (Islam, Christianity, and Judaism).

But do these commandments apply in all situations? If you were a soldier at war and being attacked by the enemy, what about the commandment not to kill? Touching someone's intimate parts is not allowed, but what if you were a nurse or a gynecologist? And when police seize a smuggler's loot, are they, strictly speaking, committing a theft and sinning against the eighth commandment? In these three cases, we would judge that the behavior is not inappropriate, because the context puts them in a different light. When even the basic rules of human behavior are relative, that is certainly true for descriptions of what is courteous, hospitable, or decent. In short, socially appropriate behavior is behavior that is adapted to the context.

It is not about knowing *if* a certain behavior is appropriate but about knowing *when* a behavior is appropriate or not. Behavior that is totally acceptable in one context can be unacceptable in another context and vice versa. The knowledge of commandments or social rules does not suffice to be able to guess if certain behavior is decent or not.

*It is not about knowing if a certain behavior is appropriate, but about knowing when a behavior is appropriate or not. Context determines what is socially appropriate.*

*Megan, a young female with autism, has learned that nudity is something private. You can only be naked in private spaces, like the bedroom and the bathroom. All other spaces are public spaces, not only outside the house but also inside the house. For example, other people use the living room, so that is a public place. Megan knows perfectly well that it is not socially acceptable to be naked in public situations. She knows the social rule.*

*One day, a plumber was working on the shower drain in the bathroom. Megan entered and – to the plumber's utter amazement – undressed completely. Megan did not spontaneously adjust the social rule to the context. That is, that the presence of a plumber in a private space like the bathroom changed it to a public space did not spontaneously occur to her.*

Because context determines the level of appropriateness of our behavior, people who are blind to context have difficulty guessing if a certain behavior is socially acceptable or not. This is the case for people with autism. Parents and caregivers can give numerous examples of situations in which people with autism totally misinterpret social situations. Indeed, enough of these types of anecdotes would be cause to suspect a diagnosis of autism: "His behavior is always socially unacceptable."

The Texas research group[75] of the psychologist Katherine Loveland showed children with autism 24 short films in which an actor said something or did something, and afterwards asked the children whether or not what the actor did or said was O.K. Some of the films showed socially unacceptable behavior (like suddenly changing the topic of the conversation), others showed acceptable behavior (like saying "thank you" when given an object). In half of the films, the behavior to be judged involved spoken language (the actor *said* something that was inappropriate), in the other half the behavior was nonverbal (like standing in front of a television while someone was watching a program).

Both the children with autism and the children without autism could point out which behaviors were appropriate and which were not. In only one area was there a difference between the two groups of children: The children with autism had more difficulty identifying the inappropriate statements of the actors.[76] According to the researchers, this was because recognition of inappropriate statements and remarks involves the ability to empathize much more than recognition of inappropriate actions. That probably played a role, but when you look closely at the behaviors in the research films, there is another difference between the inappropriate verbal and nonverbal behaviors.

| **Inappropriate Verbal Behavior** | **Inappropriate Nonverbal Behavior** |
|---|---|
| When introduced, asking, "Is your father dead?" | Taking things that don't belong to you |
| Echoing when someone says hello | Hitting someone |
| Laughing in response to a sad announcement | Standing in front of someone who is watching TV |
| Ignoring a speaker and self-stimulating instead of responding | Picking at a neighbor's hair and clothing |
| Making an insulting remark ("That dress makes you look really old and fat") | Destroying property |
| Repetitive questioning | Not waiting your turn; cutting in line |
| A nonsequitur (changing the topic abruptly) | Failing to share cookies |
| Talking loudly in the library when others are quietly reading | Going through someone else's purse |

The inappropriate behavior from the films of the research of Loveland and her colleagues.

In the research films, the inappropriate nonverbal actions in (the right-hand column) are more clear violations of general social rules than the inappropriate verbal actions (left-hand column). Under no circumstances, should you steal, hit, destroy property, or go through someone's purse. And certainly, the children would have learned that you have to wait your turn and that you have to share. In other words, the context does not really count in these examples.

The inappropriate comments in the left-hand column are far less general violations. There are no laws or rules that say that you are not allowed to change a topic of a conversation, that you cannot ask if someone's father has died, or that you cannot smile or talk loudly. What the actors in the films said was inappropriate because of the context.

The results of this research point to the fact that children with autism do not have problems judging behavior based on a general rule or etiquette but have problems judging behavior based on context. That was apparent from the analysis of the answers of the children to the question, "Why is this behavior (in)appropriate?" For the situations in the column to the left, the children with autism tended to give more strange and irrelevant explanations.

I determined in my own research with adults with autism that people with autism are capable of learning a lot of social dos and don'ts.[77] I used *Dewey's Stories*, a test that a mother of a young man with autism designed in the 1970s.[78] The test consists of eight written stories in which certain parts describing the behavior of a character are printed in italics. Test subjects are asked to judge that behavior: Is what the character is doing or saying appropriate, strange, very strange, or shocking? The following is the last story in the sequence from my study.

Story 8. The Afternoon Nap

Frank, age 19, found work at a lawn company. Every day he takes his lunch box. *Around noon time, Frank washes his hands with water from the garden hose and sits in a shady place to eat. Because his lunch break is longer than an hour, he sometimes takes a nap behind a shrub.* One day, it began to rain during his lunch break. Frank knocked on the door and asked permission to eat inside. The owner gave him permission and said that he could enter. Because she was busy with her children, he decided not to bother the lady further. *As a result, he proceeded to look for the bathroom and washed his hands. Then he searched for the dining room and ate his lunch there. He cleaned up his crumbs and, after that, searched for a place to rest.* The carpet in the living room was quite thick, *so he decided to take his nap behind a big chair.*

The adults with autism rated the appropriateness not much differently from the people without autism. Behavior that people without autism find strange, people with autism would also find strange, although sometimes less or more so than the control group. All in all, the adults with autism did not perform poorly. When I asked them to justify their answers ("Why do you find that behavior normal, strange, or shocking?"), the results were remarkable.

In one out of seven cases, adults with more than average intelligence could not give a reason. They simply said, "I don't know." Only one third of them based their answers on the context of the story. Almost half of them referred to a general social rule (e.g., before eating, you need to wash your hands, you do not rest on the carpet but in a chair or a bed, you first ask permission to go to the toilet or the bathroom). One third of the adults found it rather strange to wash your hands with the hose, because washing your hands is something you do in a sink in the restroom, or in a bucket, and always with soap.

Sometimes their judgment was correct, but their explanation suggested behavior that was even more contextually inappropriate than was already the case in the story. For example, one of the adults found it strange that Frank took his afternoon nap behind a shrub. His explanation: "If he would use a chair or a hammock, then I would see it as normal. But taking a nap in the grass would be a little bit strange." Have you ever seen a gardener bring a hammock to rest during a lunch break?

Another example of how little the subjects could adjust social rules to the context involved a story in which a girl in the supermarket was followed by a young man. To get away as quickly as possible, she went to the fast checkout line, where there was a sign indicating a maximum of 10 items (she had 12 items). A number of the adults found this behavior rather strange. Some of those who said it was normal behavior did not see a connection between the annoying behavior of the young man, but instead gave a non-contextual reason for their approval of her actions. "She shouldn't be angry about being followed, but there isn't much difference between 10 and 12 items, so it's O.K."

Contrary to what one would expect, in the story of the gardener, the adults with autism also gave a reason that referred to what another character would think of the behavior. They said that the woman would be shocked to find the gardener behind the chair, and that she would not appreciate it. When I pressed them and asked why the character in the story would not approve of that behavior, they either could not answer the question or gave a strange answer or one that did not take into account the context. For example, one of the men with autism said that Frank's behavior in searching for a bathroom was strange and that the woman would not like it. When I questioned him about that, he answered, "The bathroom is often near the bedroom or on the first floor. The woman does not want him to see the mess." Another man suggested that Frank could ask the woman for a place to rest (instead of lying behind the chair), but that the question could be misunderstood, as in the sense of asking if he could sleep at her place or even "sleep with her."

Funny detail: None of the subjects with autism noticed the characteristics of autism apparent in some of the behaviors in Dewey's stories, although some of them found certain stories rather funny. Dewey based her stories on anecdotes about adolescents with autism. For example, that Frank in the above story lies down behind the armchair is an outcome of his routine of taking a nap behind a shrub.

The answers of the adults with autism confirmed what we already suspected. They know many social rules and conventions and up to a certain level are able to identify the perspectives of others, but they do not often connect rules and mental states to the context. Instead, they evaluate behavior in an isolated way, from an absolute rule, without taking into account anything else, especially social elements in the context. They also give the impression that they are analyzing the evaluated behavior, and they often use very complex explanations, nonetheless, their logic misses the essence of the story.

Recently, *Dewey's Stories* (an adapted version) were used with children.[79] That study confirmed the results of my own research. The children with autism rated socially inappropriate behaviors in the stories no differently from their typically developing peers, but they had a higher tendency to provide inappropriate/bizarre and don't know/no response justifications instead of appropriate/social justifications. In contrast to my research, however, the children referred less to social rules. The fact that the adults did refer to social rules in my research may reflect that people with autism *learn* social rules as they grow older.

The results of my research led us to suspect that the awkward social behavior of people with autism is not caused by a lack of knowledge of social conventions and mental states, as much as it is by an inability to apply that knowledge to a given context. It has come to light in other studies[80] that people with autism have varying degrees of knowledge about social scripts and social situations but have difficulty with variations and situational deviations of the scripts. People with autism who performed well on tests of theory of mind had trouble detecting social blunders (so-called faux pas) in the behavior of others.[81] And when they could do it, they did not take into account the specific context but relied on either general social rules or personal characteristics ("He has a bad character." "She is stupid.").[82]

## Context and Social Problem-Solving Ability

When context is important to understanding what is socially appropriate and what is not, context blindness not only has an influence on the judgment of others' behavior but also on our own social problem-solving ability. No solutions are valid every time and in every situation, just as there are no rules that apply everywhere and always. Social problems cannot be handled in a cookbook fashion.

Assume your name is Tony, and the following happens to you.

*Tony lives in an apartment and is getting new neighbors upstairs. They are nice, but they have dogs that they keep in their kitchen at night; their kitchen is directly above Tony's bedroom. At night the dogs walk around and bark. Tony can barely sleep. He contacted the neighbors about it. Although they reacted with great understanding, they told him that they did not have another place for their dogs.*

How would you handle this situation? How would you solve the problem with your neighbors and their dogs? Think of as many solutions as you possibly can in two minutes.

This problem situation is part of a test for social problem-solving ability. A British research team[83] administered the test to a group of adolescents with autism with average intelligence and a control group. Although the youngsters with autism could think of just as many solutions as the youth without autism, their solutions were less socially acceptable and less effective than the solutions of the control group. Bizarre and extreme solutions arose more often with youngsters with autism. These are only a few of their suggestions for Tony: "Enter the apartment and poison the dogs." "Cut off Tony's ears." Or "Change apartments so that Tony can live in their apartment."

These types of answers suggest not only that the students with autism did not take into account the social context (the effect of the solution on the neighbors) but also that their solutions were less adapted to nonsocial contextual elements (assuming that the neighbors are even willing, the exchange of apartments has little effect on the noise of the barking dogs), and, therefore, were less effective.[84] It became apparent to the researchers that the adolescents with autism had to be reminded much more about certain facts from the story and that they had less understanding of which elements in the stories were of importance. These findings imply that the adolescents with autism were far less sensitive to the context of the problems in the stories.

Another research team[85] studied the social problem-solving ability of able adults and children with autism. The researchers showed participants a few social problem situations, like a couple that argues a lot. The adults with autism performed much better than the adolescents in the above study, showing that the social problem-solving ability matures with age. For example, they took into account the perspective of the characters in the stories. It is unclear how this perspective taking was activated – by the stories or by the instructions. We saw earlier that people with autism are capable of taking perspective when someone "pushes the button." The solutions generated by the adults with autism generally did not differ that much from those of the control group. Yet, their solutions were not what the researchers considered to be ideal problem-solving strategies.[86] Thus, the solutions created by those with autism contained less effective steps and were inherently less adequate than the solutions of the adults without autism. They appeared to be more directed to the present (e.g., giving flowers to make up), taking less into account the time that a process takes (e.g., first cool down, then ask what is wrong).

To solve social problems, you must not only consider the external context but also the internal context. This internal context is what is stored inside your memory about similar experiences, what you know about the effect of certain solutions, and memories of what did and did not work previously. While the adult subjects were thinking about solutions, the researchers asked them to report which images and thoughts came to mind. Just like the participants in the control group, the adults with autism mentioned experiences from their past. But contrary to the control group, there was no link between these experiences and the solutions that they came up with.

This is consistent with what I described in Chapter 2 about context in the brain. People with autism seem to have difficulty with connecting what they observe to the (internal) context of what they learned before.[87] When solving social problems, people with autism make less use of both the external, given context, and the internal context, what they know and what they have learned.

## Context, Systemizing, and Empathizing

One could argue that poorer performance on tests for social problem-solving ability does not have much to do with the social nature of the problems but more with reduced problem-solving ability. Perhaps people with autism are just not as good at thinking of solutions as others. If that were the case, they would have difficulties solving nonsocial problems.

A well-known scientist, Professor Simon Baron-Cohen of the University of Cambridge, would not agree with this hypothesis. For years, Baron-Cohen has been doing research on the social understanding of people with autism. As a student of Uta Frith and Allan Leslie, he was one of the first to apply the well-known Sally Anne Test to children with autism, which prompted the hypothesis that theory of mind in people with autism is not well developed.[88]

Through the years, Baron-Cohen has refined that hypothesis, adjusted it, and placed it within a the framework of typical biological and psychological sex differences.[89] Referring to the writings of Hans Asperger, a pioneer in autism, which state that autism is an extreme form of the male brain, Baron-Cohen now explains autism as a strong disequilibrium between two cognitive styles: the feminine empathizing and the masculine systemizing style.

These two thinking styles pertain to the distinction between objects and people made in the beginning of this chapter.[90] Objects do not have intentions. Changes in their "behavior" can be explained completely by a set of rules, laws, and formulas. To be able to understand the "behavior" of objects, the human brain has to analyze and understand systems. That ability is what Baron-Cohen calls systemizing.

Apart from the physical system, which includes, for example, the law of gravity, there are many other types of systems: technical (machines), abstract (e.g., mathematics), organizational (e.g., alphabetical classification), and even social (e.g., the political system). To understand and predict the behavior of people is not accomplished by systemizing. People have intentions (goals) caused by mental states. To understand human behavior, our brain developed another ability through evolution: empathy, or in the theory of Baron-Cohen, *empathizing*.

Empathizing is almost synonymous with what is usually referred to as social or emotional intelligence. In addition to theory of mind (retrieving what others think, feel, or know), it includes the ability to handle appropriately the mental states of others (the empathic response). Research shows that men are often better than women at systemizing and that women are better at empathizing.[91] By now, everyone knows that stereotype: Men cannot listen and women cannot read a map.

Baron-Cohen developed tests and questionnaires for assessing the ability to systemize and empathize, and determined that people with autism have an extremely masculine style: They excel at systemizing, doing better than the average man, and score very low on empathizing, even lower than the average man.[92] Baron-Cohen's test of systemizing includes some difficult technical exercises that require the respondent to predict the movements of levers based on mechanics diagrams. Results indicate that as a group, people with autism could solve fairly complex problems.

According to Baron-Cohen, the strong performances on these tests show that people with autism are context sensitive, because in many of the exercises they had to use context; for example, to predict the effect of one lever on another. The excellent performance on the tests for systemizing in combination with the weak performance on tests that measure empathizing, according to Baron-Cohen, is proof of a specific cognitive style in autism: less able to understand the world of the mental states and thus solve social problems, but very able in understanding systems.

Baron-Cohen may have overlooked the influence of context; indeed, one of his colleagues, John Lawson, suggested it.[93] Lawson postulated that the difference between empathizing and systemizing relates to the difference between open and closed systems.

Closed systems are fairly predictable because they have a reduced number of variables and are directed by fixed and universal laws and rules. When you execute process B on input A, you always get output C. The world of physics, for example, is a fairly closed system. When you drop (process) an object from your hand (input), it falls down (output). By the law of gravity, this takes place all the time and everywhere. Context does not play a role (unless you are in space where there is no gravity, but predictable laws also apply there). No matter if the object is big or small, if it is of glass or of stone, outdoors or inside, the object will always fall down.

Open systems also have rules, but they are not fixed and straightforward. The outputs of open systems are far less predictable because the system is "open" for all types of influences and variations. The social world is an example of an open system. When it comes to human beings, one plus one does not always equal two. As Baron-Cohen says, "The social world may be only 10% lawful."[94] Social situations have an open outcome because meanings, intentions, and all other contextual factors play a role. Take the next, not even very complex, social situation.

Input = Peter Vermeulen
Process = get a gift
Output = ???

Spontaneously, we are inclined to think that when someone gets a present, he or she will be happy. But that is not always the case. Giving presents is an open system because there are many contextual variables, resulting in an infinite number of possible outputs. In open systems, there is much contextual influence.

Applied to social situations, this means that the output or the outcome, the final reaction of persons, is dependent on an infinite number of elements in the context. As mentioned earlier in this chapter, the outcome is impacted by the mental state of the person who is supposed to receive the gift (if he likes it, what he had expected, etc.). The influence of context goes further than that of mental state, to include who is giving the gift, when the gift is given, which gift is given, what is said by the gift giver ("No thanks! I thought I might give you something that made you smell better from now on."), and so on. All these contextual influences make the social situation of giving a gift an open system, in which the outcome is not rule-abiding but is very open.

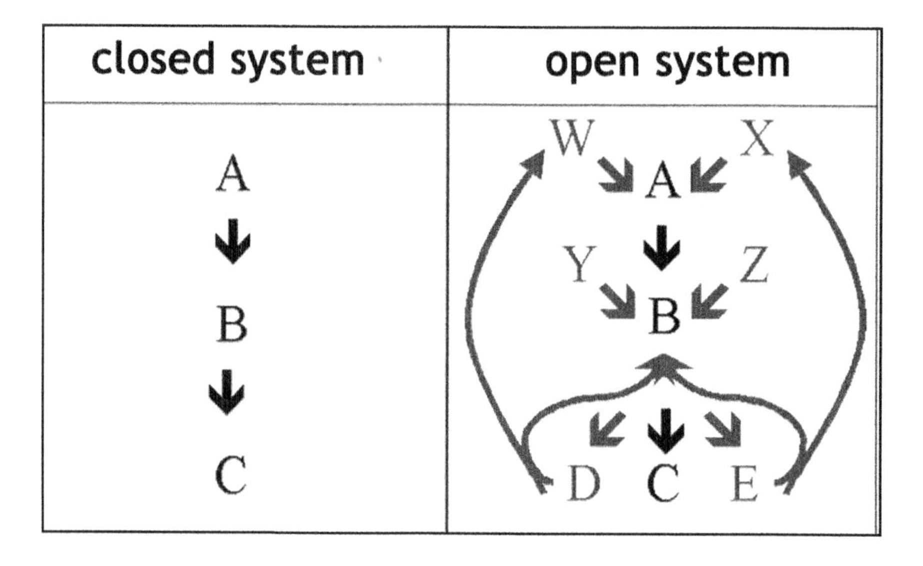


Compared to closed systems, open systems are greatly influenced by elements in the context.

Open systems are more complex and less predictable than closed systems. To understand an open system and to predict its outcome requires much more sensitivity to the context than for closed systems. For straightforward and context-blind thinkers, like people with autism, therefore, open systems are much more difficult to understand. If the distinction between more or less contextual influence is more important than the distinction between social or nonsocial, people with autism would have more problems with nonsocial tasks in which context plays a role.

Based on the previous chapter, this appears to be the case. When context plays a role in the perception of objects, people with autism do not do as well as people without autism, something that cannot be explained from a weakness in empathizing. Similarly, children with autism seem to struggle not only with identifying inappropriate behavior but also with identifying objects that do not fit into a context – a task that does not involve mental states.[95]

Recent evidence for this hypothesis comes from Scandinavian research,[96] in which children with autism were studied using an advanced test for theory of mind. That test, *Stories From Everyday Life,* contains 13 short stories. The test differs from other tests, like *Strange Stories* previously described, because the subjects are not only asked to describe and explain mental states but also to draw conclusions about physical aspects of events in the story (e.g., "What does Jan's room look like?" or "Why does the woman wash her kitchen floor every day?"). The test measures the ability to draw social and nonsocial conclusions from the context of a story.

The researchers found that the children with autism made more mistakes, and also were much slower than children without autism. This was true both for the questions about mental states and those about physical states.[97] In their report, the researchers noted that the children with autism gave many contextually inappropriate answers and their answers included much irrelevant information. That was especially the case with regard to the answers on social issues.

The results of this study confirm that people with autism have difficulty with understanding, explaining, and predicting human behavior; however, given the fact that these children also had problems with the nonsocial questions about the stories, their performances on this type of advanced test for social insight cannot be solely explained by deficits in theory of mind or in the ability to empathize. In the social difficulties of people with autism, the role of context blindness is, *at the very least*, as important as that of mindblindness.

## Summary

*Context sensitivity is the cornerstone of social-emotional intelligence.*

Human behavior becomes more predictable when you understand the reasons for the behavior, the explanations about why someone is behaving in a certain way. These reasons are not directly observable because they are internal: what people think, feel, know, and want.

The degree to which we can empathize with others determines, in large part, how successful we are in interacting with others. Context plays an important role in emotional and social intelligence, because:

- Context activates our ability to empathize.
- Context helps us to focus our attention on socially important information so that we can quickly decode facial expressions and body language.

- Context clarifies unclear body language and ambiguous facial expressions.
- Context gives us clues about the feelings and thoughts of others (why others feel or think something).
- Context gives us tips for how to respond to the feelings and thoughts of others, so that we can react appropriately and find solutions to social problems.

People who are context blind have difficulty predicting the reactions of others and knowing how to deal with these reactions. The result is a rather pervasive social disorder.

## Endnotes – Context in Social Interaction

1. Not all our behavior is conscious and intentional. We also do things subconsciously and without intent. Think of certain reflex reactions or routines that we perform automatically.
2. Premack and Woodruff (1978).
3. That is why the terms *folk physics* and *folk psychology* are also used.
4. See, e.g., the discussion in philosophy and cognitive psychology about the roots of theory of mind or folk psychology. (For a good summary, see Carruthers & Smith, 1996.)
5. I wrote about theory of mind extensively in *The Closed Book* (Vermeulen, 2005).
6. Although the article is not specifically about the role of context, Frith and Frith (2006b) give an outstanding summary of the importance of top-down processes in the ability to understand and predict human behavior. As we saw in Chapter 2, there is a link between context sensitivity and top-down processes.
7. The story is told in the fourth book of the *The Hitchhiker's Guide to the Galaxy*, namely *So Long, and Thanks for All the Fish* (Adams, 1984). The story has become a kind of urban legend. Variants may be found here: http://www.snopes.com/crime/safety/cookies.asp
8. Ekman, Huang, Sejnowski, and Hager (1993, p. 4).
9. Pascalis and Slater (2003).

10. Fusiform face area (FFA). Recently it has become clear that the FFA area is not only active during facial recognition, but also when discerning things (objects and animals) that are important and familiar to us. For example, in car lovers, the FFA appears to be active when they see cars, and in bird lovers the FFA is active when looking at birds (Gauthier, Skudlarski, Gore, & Anderson, 2000).
11. Ekman (2003).
12. We see facial expressions in motion, not static or frozen like in pictures. It appears from research that the processing of static information and dynamic material requires different information-processing processes (Kilts, Egan, Gideon, Ely, & Hoffman, 2003).
13. Fernandez-Dols, Carrera, and Russell (2002) speak about an attribution error. Because we often observe smiling and happiness in the same situation, we have the urge to see a smile as a sign of happiness in all situations and contexts. According to Kappas (2002), we have to stop assuming there is a fixed connection between facial expressions and emotions. This conflicts with the well-known hypothesis, going back to the work of Charles Darwin, that there are universal expressions of emotions. Russell, Bachorowski, and Fernandez-Dols (2003) question this universality and propose a "minimal universality."
14. Shin et al. (2008).
15. For a good overview, see Dawson, Webb, and McParland (2005).
16. E.g., Dalton et al. (2005); Joseph and Tanaka (2003); Klin, Jones, Schultz, Volkmar, and Cohen (2002); Pelphrey, Singerman, Allison, and McCarthy (2003); Teunisse and de Gelder (2001).
17. Klin and Jones (2008).
18. Lahaie et al. (2006); Teunisse and de Gelder (2003); and the review of Jemel, Mottron, and Dawson (2006).
19. Lopez, Donnelly, Hadwin, and Leekam (2004).
20. Boraston, Corden, Miles, Skuse, and Blakemore (2008).
21. Smith, Cottrell, Gosselin, and Schyns (2005).
22. A recent study (Wallace, Coleman, & Bailey, 2008) showed that people with autism have difficulties with the differentiated scanning; that is, they have difficulty reading fear from the eyes and they do not recognize aversion as well from observing the mouth.
23. Aviezer et al. (2008).
24. Pelphrey et al. (2002).
25. Teunisse and de Gelder (2003).

26. Rutherford and Towns (2008).
27. Meeren, van Heijnsbergen, and de Gelder (2005); Van den Stock, Righart, and de Gelder (2007).
28. de Gelder and Vroomen (2000).
29. de Gelder et al. (2006).
30. de Gelder and Vroomen (2000).
31. Hobson (1986a, 1986b).
32. Hobson, Ouston, and Lee (1988a, 1988b).
33. Magneé, de Gelder, van Engeland, and Kemmer (2008).
34. Righart and de Gelder (2008a, 2008b).
35. de Gelder and Vroomen (2000).
36. Russel and Fehr (1987).
37. Righart and de Gelder (2008b). In this research, context and face were shown at the same time. Earlier, Carrol and Russel (1996) found that when subjects heard a story that suggested a certain emotion and were later shown a face expressing a different emotion, in the majority of the cases they identified the emotion from the story rather than the emotion that the face was expressing. This was true for basic emotions like fear, anger, sadness, and aversion as well as for less basic emotions like hope, determination, confusion, and pain. The effect even occurred in ambiguous situations paired with clear facial expressions.
38. Egan, Brown, Goonan, Goonan, and Celano (1998); Hoffner and Badzinski (1989).
39. Green, Waldron, Simpson, and Coltheart (2008).
40. To become a bit "technical," researchers (Bentin, Allison, Puce, Perez, & McCarthy, 1996) found an event-related potential (ERP) that occurs with the perception of faces after only 170 milliseconds (N170). The N170 is not only sensitive for recognizing faces, but also for social and emotional characteristics of the face. Recent studies have shown that context influences the amplitude of the N170 (Righart & de Gelder, 2006, 2008a). The influence of context on the N170 is, just as with the perception of objects, a form of top-down modulation. Just as with objects, this modulation works for low spatial frequencies (LSF) (Galli, Feurra, &Viggiano 2006). Differences in the activation of the N170 have been noticed in people with autism. See Dawson et al. (2005) for an overview of electro-physiological studies of face perception in people with autism. The amygdalae and the fusiform gyrus also play a role in emotion recognition. Context has an

influence on the activation of the amygdala and the fusiform gyrus (Kim et al., 2004).

41. Haddon (2003, p. 28).
42. Green et al. (2008).
43. E.g., Adolphs, Sears, and Piven (2001); Baron-Cohen, Wheelwright, and Jolliffe (1997); Grossman, Klin, Carter, and Volkmar (2000); Volkmar, Sparrow, Rende, and Cohen (1989).
44. Baron-Cohen, Spitz, and Cross (1993); Capps, Yirmiya, and Sigman (1992); Hillier and Allinson (2002).
45. Dekeukeleire and Steelandt (2003).
46. Speer, Cook, McMahon, and Clark (2007).
47. Ponnet, Roeyers, Buysse, De Clercq, and Van der Heyden (2004); Roeyers, Buysse, Ponnet, and Pichal (2001).
48. Koning and Magill-Evans (2001). This is consistent with what Greene et al. (2008) found in people with schizophrenia. People with schizophrenia focused more on faces and less on context. The stronger the focus on the face, the lower the accuracy of their empathic ability. Two other studies also showed that children and youngsters with autism use less context in the recognition of emotions (Da Fonseca et al., 2009; Fein, Lucci, Braverman, & Waterhouse, 1992).
49. Da Fonseca et al. (2009). In contrast with the facial expression, the children with autism could derive the hidden objects from the context. Results of this study also indicated that context sensitivity is not related to intelligence. First, there is no connection between the performance of children with autism and their IQ. Second, children with an intellectual disability performed as well on this test as children the same age without that disability, and even better than high-functioning children with autism.
50. Wright et al. (2008); Balconi, Amenta, and Ferrari (2012).
51. Begeer et al. (2006). Bird, Catmur, Silani, Frith, and Frith (2006) also found a lack of attentional modulation for social stimuli (faces) but not for nonsocial stimuli (houses). Neurological analysis brought to light that this lack is connected to a decreased top-down influence from higher level brain areas on the lower visual areas (V1), which is consistent with what we wrote in Chapter 2 about context in the brain.
52. Begeer, Rieffe, Terwogt, and Stockmann (2006, p. 49).
53. de Vignemont and Singer (2006) showed that even the emotional aspects of empathy, the emotional reaction, in addition to the cognitive aspects (theory of the mind), are activated by a context.

54. E.g., Shantz (1983).
55. Dawson and Fernald (1987).
56. For those unfamiliar with the test, pictures of the test can be easily found on Internet.
57. Shantz (1983).
58. A relationship between reduced context sensitivity and deficits in theory of mind or social cognitions has also been found for people with schizophrenia (Green, Uhlhaas, & Coltheart, 2005; Penn, Ritchie, Francis, Combs, & Martin, 2002).
59. Pelphrey et al. (2003).
60. Baron-Cohen, Wheelwright, Hill, Raste, and Plumb (2001) distinguish between the attribution of a mental state (e.g., recognizing sadness) and the content of this mental state (e.g., to be sad because someone died).
61. Harris (1989).
62. Dennis, Lockyer, and Lazenby (2000).
63. Baron-Cohen (1991).
64. Serra et al. (1995).
65. Serra, Loth, van Geert, Hurkens, and Minderaa (2002).
66. Balconi and Carrera (2007).
67. Happé (1994).
68. Happé (1994, p. 143).
69. Jolliffe and Baron-Cohen (1999b); Kaland, Callesen, Møller-Nielsen, Mortensen, and Smith (2008).
70. This explains why people with autism who performed well on classical tests of emotion recognition, even the most advanced, like the *Reading the Mind in the Eyes* test of Baron-Cohen, Jolliffe, Mortimore, and Roberts (1997), did not perform as well on tests like the *Strange Stories* (Happé, 1994). Tests like the eye test are a-contextual, while tests with stories like the *Strange Stories* are tests in a certain context. Kaland et al. (2008) compared the eye test to two contextualized theory-of-mind tests (*Strange Stories* and *Stories From Everyday Life*) and found that the performance on the eye test did not correlate to the performance on the two contextualized tests for either the subjects with autism or the control group. The findings from the Kaland et al. study were replicated in a Dutch study (Spek, Scholte, & van Berckelaer-Onnes, 2010), which found low or no correlations between the Eyes test and two more context sensitive theory-of-mind tests (*Strange Stories* and *Faux Pas*).

Context sensitivity even appears to play a role in the classical false-belief task of Sally-Anne (Baron-Cohen, Leslie & Frith, 1985). O'Loughin and Thagard (2000) developed a computer model that simulated weak central coherence with a diminished context sensitivity. This computer model also failed on the Sally Anne task. O'Loughlin and Tharad concluded that predictions about someone's false belief are context dependent.

71. Golan, Baron-Cohen, Hill, and Golan (2006); Golan, Baron-Cohen, and Golan (2008); Kaland et al. (2008).
72. This example is from the study of Golan et al. (2008).
73. They do not react to the full context but primarily to language and what someone is saying just before the movie is stopped.
74. Wright et al. (2008).
75. Loveland, Pearson, Tunali-Kotoski, Ortgeon, and Gibbs (2001).
76. For children without autism, this was also more difficult than recognizing inappropriate nonverbal actions.
77. Vermeulen (2002).
78. Dewey (1991); Dewey and Everard (1974).
79. Nah and Poon (2011).
80. Loth, Gómez, and Happé (2008, May); Volden and Johnston (1999).
81. Baron-Cohen, O'Riordan, Stone, Jones, and Plaisted (1999).
82. Zalla, Sav, Ahade, and Leboyer (2009).
83. Channon, Charman, Heap, Crawford, and Rios (2001).
84. The researchers offered the adolescents five solutions and asked them to categorize them from bad to good. The adolescents with autism did not differ from the control group in this assignment. This suggests that the problem related to social problem solving in people with autism lies primarily in generating ideas of what is socially appropriate and producing socially acceptable and effective solutions, a problem that no doubt is caused by the concrete manner of thinking in people with autism. The researchers admit that the five solutions they offered were clearly different from each other, which made categorizing a fairly simple task, even for adolescents with autism.
85. Goddard, Howlin, Dritschel, and Patel (2007).
86. The difference with the control group fell just short of statistical significance, namely (.02).

87. The so-called top-down influence of relevant aspects of knowledge on stimuli, or in the case of (social) problems, the solutions to problems that need to be solved.
88. Baron-Cohen, Leslie, and Frith (1985).
89. Baron-Cohen (2003).
90. It is about the difference between non-agents (phenomena that do not have goals and generate changes themselves, like objects and plants) and agents (phenomena that have goals and come into action, like people and animals).
91. Baron-Cohen (2002).
92. See, e.g., Baron-Cohen, Richler, Bisarya, Gurunathan, and Wheelwright (2003); Baron-Cohen, Wheelwright, Scahill, Lawson, and Spong (2001); Lawson, Baron-Cohen, and Wheelwright (2004).
93. Lawson (2003); Lawson et al. (2004).
94. Baron-Cohen (2006, p. 2).
95. Jolliffe (1997).
96. Kaland, Mortensen, and Smith (2007).
97. Both adolsecents with and without autism needed more time to answer the questions about mental states than the questions about nonsocial aspects of the story, but for the adolescents with autism the difference in time was greater than for the adolescents without autism.

# Chapter 5
# Context in Communication

Why do we recognize words before they are totally pronounced?

Why do we sometimes hear "tata" when someone is saying *papa*?

Why do children effortlessly understand Smurf (group of small blue fictional creatures created and first introduced as a series of comic strips by the Belgian cartoonist Peyo) language when they have never received instruction in Smurf language?

How do you know if "The one that did not dare enter the water" was "cow Ard" or a "coward"?

Why is a dictionary not particularly useful in understanding words?

Why does our language have so many ambiguous and vague words like *light* or *bank*?

How do you know who was angry in the sentence, "Chris didn't give Pete a gift because he was angry"?

Why don't people fully say what they mean? How do you know what they mean?

Why do we understand pictograms or traffic signs we have never seen before?

Mind reading is the ability to read others' mental states; it is crucial in understanding our fellow human beings. However, mind reading alone is not enough. Human beings can express many of their ideas or intentions through facial expressions and other types of body language, but all these signals are too limited to explain to our fellow human beings the billions of meanings contained in our brain. For example, try for a moment to explain with only mime and gestures your opinion about democracy, doping in cycling, or what you know about the origin of molds in wetlands, assuming that your listener is interested in these topics. Rather difficult, right?

Because of restrictions in body language, we developed the spoken language, which at later stages of evolution also was put in written form. Language is a system of symbols. There are auditory symbols (sounds),[1] but also visual ones, like letter signs or symbols (drawings, pictograms, or pictures). The meaning of those symbols does not lie in the symbols themselves. The sound *o*, the letter *p*, or even a drawn arrow, does not mean anything by itself. Even when we combine symbols in words or sentences, they still do not mean much. The sounds of the letters in *chair* are not an actual chair; you cannot sit on it. And the exclamation, "Look, a nice piece of cake!" cannot satisfy your hunger.

Language symbols are referents as they refer to something other than themselves. That "something" is somewhere in the context, close-by or far away, visible or invisible, in the present, in the past, or even in the distant future.

Hence, to understand language is one big exercise in reading the context. From all the possible things in the world, we have to pick out the one to which the symbol used by a fellow human being is referring. Knowing the meaning of words helps, one can get a fair distance with a vocabulary, but vocabulary alone does not suffice, as will become clear in this chapter.

If knowledge of the vocabulary were enough to understand what someone is writing or saying, we would have to memorize at least half of the dictionary in order to understand other people. Fortunately, that is not necessary. We are able to understand words that are not (yet) within our vocabulary. We learn words best in communication with others, not in language lessons. An average 18-year-old knows about 45,000 words. On average, that young man or young woman learned about 2,500 words every year of his or her life, or almost 7 words a day.

If we had to explicitly teach every child all the words that he acquires while growing up by explaining the meaning of each word, showing each word in a dictionary, and giving definitions to each word, a child's entire upbringing would be nothing but language lessons. That is not possible. Children also need to learn other things, like tying their shoes, eating Brussels sprouts, and not peeing on the toilet seat. We learn a lot of words, not because someone is explaining the meaning to us, but because we derive meaning from the context.[2] Think back to the word *convalescent* in the text of Edgar Allan Poe, mentioned in Chapter 1 on what is context. Thanks to the context you could extend your vocabulary without anyone needing to teach you the meaning of the word explicitly.

The same is true when we learn a new language. Once when I was visiting South Africa, my host asked me, "*Haal jij de flits eens? Die ligt naast mijn rekenaar op de stoep.*" (Literally translated: "Can you get me the flash? It is next to my calculator on the sidewalk.") With my weak knowledge of the host's language, I would normally have understood little of the question, but the context clarified everything. Together with my host, I was looking for something in the garden shed as it was getting dark. Just prior to that, he had sent emails from his laptop on the veranda. Thanks to this contextual information, I was able to understand the assignment as "Can you get me my flashlight? It is next to my computer on the veranda." Similarly, context plays a role very early in language development. When an 18-month-old baby hears a new word, she spontaneously looks to what the person speaking to her is looking at to pick up clues.[3]

## Context and Sound Recognition in Speech

In Chapter 3 about visual perception, we saw that context asserts influence on even the most basic levels of perception, particularly the perceptions of size, form, color, and direction. The same influence occurs with regard to hearing, more specifically, the perception of speech.

Just as we do not always observe objects fully within our sight, language sounds do not always arrive neatly and fully organized in our ears. In the middle of a sentence, someone coughs, the telephone rings, or a car passes by. What our brain does with visual information also holds true for auditory information. When incoming information is unclear, incomplete, or ambiguous, we rely on our perceptional guide, the context.

We use context to fill in the correct sound when we do not hear a correct sound in a spoken word. The psychologist Richard Warren[4] was one of the first to discover this. He let people listen to words in which one sound was replaced by a coughing sound. Warren's test subjects filled in the correct sound without problems. Afterwards, they could not even tell which sound had been "coughed away." The repair of missing or deformed sounds is very context sensitive.

Dutch researchers[5] discovered that context plays a role when people pronounce words incompletely or unclearly. For example, Dutch people have a habit in everyday language not to pronounce the end *-lijk* of words like *eigenlijk* (in fact), *moeilijk* (difficult), or *vreselijk* (horrible). What you hear as a result resembles *eigek*, *moeiek*, or *vreesek* (particularly the *l* sound is missing). In the word *natuurlijk* (naturally), they go a bit further in truncating the word's pronunciation: Most of the time, you do not hear more than *tuuek*. Behind these mutilated sounds, you would still recognize the actual word but only when the sounds are part of a context, especially a full sentence. When the words are not part of a sentence, it is difficult to recognize them.

(*) Natuurlijk! (Naturally)
When Dutch people do not speak in full sentences, it is difficult to understand some of their words. The context of the sentence makes them understandable.

In recognizing and, in certain cases, correcting sounds, the super-fast top-down influence of the internal context, particularly the vocabulary in our memory, plays an especially important role. When sounds are unclear, we tend to fill them in with sounds that form a word we already know.

Assume you hear **us*, for which the star refers to a left-out sound like a *b* or an *h*. It could be *bus* or h*us*. Because *hus* is not a word in the English language, our brain is urged to hear *bus,* not *hus*. This has become known as the Ganong effect, named after the individual who first described it.[6] This effect takes place very quickly in the perceptional process. We do not have to recall a word consciously and wonder if it exists or not. The Ganong effect is mostly subconscious.[7]

We saw previously (in the section about illusions, Chapter 3) that if people are less sensitive to contextual influences in visual perception, they encounter less influence from knowledge stored in memory. This holds true for auditory perceptions as well. People with autistic traits are less able to fill in unclear sounds; they do not exhibit the Ganong effect as much as people who do not have autism. Instead, they tend to fill in sounds with non-existing words. The reduced Ganong effect is not related to intelligence and vocabulary, which proves that context contributes to recognition of speech.[8]

However, vocabulary is not sufficient for meaningful speech recognition. When hearing **us*, our vocabulary contains more possible alternatives. **Us* can be *bus* but also *thus*, *fuss,* or *pus*. Even if you knew the entire dictionary, knowledge of words alone would not ensure you could understand unclear or ambiguous sounds. Therefore, you also use the external context: The other words in the sentence that you hear help to repair the unclear or ambiguous sounds in speech. Assume you hear a word where the first sound has been left out or is not clearly audible, like *eel*. Depending on the rest of what someone is saying, this left-out sound could be filled in with a *p*, a *wh*, or an *m*.[9]

The *eel is on the orange
The *eel is on the axle
The *eel is on the table

Another effect of context on the basic level of speech recognition has to do with the influence of what you are seeing while processing sounds and speech. In Chapter 4, we saw that the context of what we hear influences what we see in someone's face. It also works the other way around, because what we see influences what we hear. It sounds unbelievable, but when you hear the word *papa* but see (based on mouth movements) someone saying *kaka*, your brain will interpret it as *tata*.[10] This phenomenon is the McGurk effect, named after the Scottish psychologist Harry McGurk,[11] who discovered it by accident during his experiments with speech perception in young children. The McGurk effect starts at a very young age and has been observed in babies as young as four months.[12] As already noted, the influence of context is subconscious and strong. Thus, the McGurk effect manifests itself even when people know that what they see is different from what they hear.[13]

*Context helps us recognize meaningful speech in unclear, distorted, or vague sounds.*

People with autism are less sensitive to the McGurk effect than the rest of the population.[14] They repeat what they hear regardless of what they see (from the movements of the mouth). A possible explanation for the reduced McGurk effect would be that people with autism look less at the face. We commonly say that individuals with autism are less focused on social stimuli like facial expressions, but that explanation does not explain the response to the McGurk effect.

Julia Irwin,[15] an American psychologist, recorded the eye movements of children observing a film that employed the McGurk effect. Contrary to the children without autism, the effect did not occur in the children with autism, although they looked equally as long at the face. So reduced McGurk effect in individuals with autism is not due to the fact that they look less at the face, but due to the reduced contextual influence of facial perception on speech recognition.

## Context and Word Recognition

Context helps us to recognize not only meaningful sounds but also words.[16] When we hear the first sounds of a word or read the first letters of a word, a sort of competition starts between many potential words. When you hear *k,* theoretically all words starting with a *k* or a *c* could complete the sound. And there are a lot of them. Hearing *ka* reduces the number of possibilities significantly, but there are still a lot of potential words.

To choose from all these options is a lot of work for our brain. Because speech as well as reading goes quite quickly, we do not have the time to wait for all the sounds and letters of the word to be recognized. Our brain wants to be more efficient and faster. It has found a way! Our brain recognizes a word before we observe all the sounds or letters of it. To succeed in this difficult task, our brain again relies on context as a guide. That is, based on context, the mind makes a preselection of the possible options.[17] In the line “The sailors always listen to the commands of the cap ...,” the brain thinks of *captain* before you heard the word or read it. In the sentence “Because of the many investments, the company had a shortage of cap ...,” the word *capital* jumps forward as the best candidate.[18] We recognize words in a sentence more quickly than we do isolated words.[19]

Context in the sentence is also helpful in discovering and correcting mispronunciations.[20] The same is true for typographical errors: Context helps us in correcting written language. That correction happens rather quickly and subconsciously so that we do not even notice the misponunciations and the typographical errors. Some people will not even notice the typo in the sentence above (answer: *misponunciations* instead of *mispronunciations*).

By the way, it is peculiar that children of a young age are already capable of recognizing the individual words in fluent speech. Contrary to written language, in spoken language there are no spaces between the words so all sounds come out in one unbroken sequence. Still, we recognize separate words in that one long flow of sounds. Context is important in this process, along with other factors, like accentuating certain sounds.[21] To recognize the beginning and the end of words is easier in a meaningful sentence than in a sequence of random words. Without context, it gets difficult to differentiate between the next cases:

a pullover <–> a pull over
the stuffy nose <–> the stuff he knows
a grey day <–> a grade A
a handout <–> a hand out

For word recognition, we don’t always need the context of an entire sentence. One other word suffices to bring reasonable options to mind and to thus recognize words faster.

When people are shown sequences of letters and asked to determine if they form an existing word or not, there is a contextual influence, as in the following:

BRONG – TABLE – SCHEDULE – SMORK – DOCTOR – NURSE
BRONG – TABLE – SCHEDULE – SMORK – DOCTOR – LIBRARY

From the above list, most people correctly determine that *nurse* is a valid word and they do so more quickly than they determine that *library* is a valid word.[22] This is because the last word (*doctor*) is contextually related to nurse and not to library. Our brain does not randomly store words; it orders them. The order is not alphabetical, because retrieving information alphabetically would not be efficient. Instead, we store words in a sort of network in which we place words that have a relationship to each other close together.[23] This is similar to a thematic ordering of compact discs or books.

The ordering of words in our brain is fairly complex. Our brain puts words together when they are part of the same class. The terms *dog* and *cat* relate to each other, as both are examples of pets. But the ordering often also has to do with context. Doctors and nurses are in the same context of sickness and hospital. And their relationship is even more intense in an average hospital novel. When one word in the network becomes active, other words close to that word are more quickly activated. This is because the distance between the words is small: Neighboring words are often ready to be activated. For example, when you hear *fork*, there is a great chance that other words like *food*, *knife*, and *plate* will also be used. In other words, through the contextual relationship in the above example, *nurse* is "primed" by *doctor*, which is the reason why people can decide more quickly if it is a valid word or not.

Context prepares us for which words to expect so that we can process language quickly and efficiently. For example, based on the sentence context, we know what the last word in the following sentence will be: *The man steps into his car and starts the ....*

In the 1980s, Margaret Snowling and Uta Frith[24] showed children with autism stories and asked them to fill in the missing words in the sentences. The children had trouble doing it. Some children filled in the word *horse* where the context more than clearly referred to a beaver. The words used to fill in for missing words were grammatically correct, but their meaning did not fit in the sentence. Even when they were allowed to choose from some options, the children rarely chose the most contextually fitting word (e.g., "Curious Tom looked in the *drawers/legs/puppets* of the cupboard."). The children also had trouble detecting contextually inappropriate or "silly" words, as in the sentence "The hedgehog could smell the scent of the *electric* flowers."

Neurologic research shows that high-functioning adults with autism have fewer expectations about the last word in a sentence.[25] When a sentence finishes in a contextually senseless word ("Erik repaired the flat tire of his toaster"), a typical brain has a sharp reaction of surprise:[26] We did not expect toaster! The brains of people with autism give the same type of reaction to sentences ending in a contextually matching word ("Erik repaired the flat tire of his bike") as they do to sentences ending in contextually senseless words. It looks as if they make less use of the sentence context in activating potential words. They have to process every word without active preparation. That means that words that look like obvious choices because of the context and, therefore, require little processing energy can be as surprising as unexpected events for people with autism, and thus require a lot of brain work. This is an argument for giving even high-functioning individuals with autism more time to process the information that we convey in our communication with them.

## Context and Understanding of Words

Context not only helps in recognizing, remembering, and learning words; it is especially useful, even crucial, in giving meaning to words. To understand the influence of context on giving meaning to language, we must make a distinction between different types of meanings.[27]

To begin with, words have lingual meaning, the definition or the description of the word as in a dictionary. We could call this the "dictionary meaning" or lexical meaning. For example, "Banana; n: long, yellow fruit."[28] But in addition to the lexical meaning of the dictionary, there is the "world meaning."[29] This is not found in the dictionary, but it is essential for understanding language.[30] Whoever knows a word knows more than its definition. He or she also knows what the word refers to in the real world. That is the real-life meaning, which is far less fixed than the dictionary meaning.

The word *banana* has a fixed dictionary definition, but what the word is referring to in reality is far less fixed. For example, not all bananas are yellow. They are green when unripe and brown when overripe. There are large bananas and small ones. Although we observe apparent differences in the characteristics of bananas, we still call all of them banana.

The world meaning of the word *banana* goes even further. It contains not only the possible concrete appearances of bananas but also all the knowledge that we have collected about bananas. For example, you know that you have to pull off the peel of the banana before you can eat it. When someone tells you to eat a banana, you do not directly sink your teeth into it. You peel it first. You also know that bananas are fruits. Assume you are shopping with your mother in the supermarket. As you enter the checkout lane, she asks, "Can you quickly go get some bananas?" You won't search the aisles with cleaning products or dairy. You also know that banana peels are the cause of many unfortunate tripping accidents. That knowledge is necessary for understanding the next heading from a Flemish newspaper, commenting on the Belgian government formation: "Political banana peels are still lying out there."

Lastly, there is communicative meaning. This meaning often deviates from the literal meaning of words and sentences. Linguistically, the sentence "Can you give me that banana?" means "Are you physically and mentally capable of bringing me that banana?" *Can* means capable of doing something. But in reality, we understand this question as a request to give the banana, not as an intellectual inquiry about our physical and mental ability to move a banana.[31]

Another example is the real-life meaning of the word *minute*, which refers to the time period of 60 seconds or 1/60$^{th}$ of one hour. However, when someone asks if you "have a minute," he probably means more than 60 seconds. The communicative meaning of a minute is, in that case, an undetermined, but short time period.

Obviously, to understand language it is not enough to read a dictionary. The relationship between a word and its meaning is not as straightforward and absolute as dictionaries are inclined to let us believe. While this goes against our intuition, there is no absolute definition of a word. Certain words may have only one definition in the dictionary, but what they refer to in real life (their world meaning and their communicative meaning) is infinite and variable. Therefore, we have to make a distinction between *knowing* words (their lexical, or dictionary meaning) and *understanding* words (their significance in the real world).

*To understand language, it is not enough to read the dictionary.*

To know words, you learn the vocabulary using dictionaries that give isolated meanings to words. But in real life, words appear without warning, like facial expressions, and seldom stand alone. To understand words in real life, you especially need the context, because every word can have multiple meanings. **To get the correct meaning from these multiple meanings, we use context.**

An excellent example of contextual influence on the understanding of words is Smurf language. Smurf language is the imaginary language of the Smurfs, a population of imps made up by the Belgian cartoonist Peyo. You are probably familiar with them: the little blue people with white bonnets. The story[32] is that the Smurf language was invented in the late 1950s one evening when Peyo had dinner with his colleague, the cartoonist Franquin. Peyo wanted to ask Franquin to hand him over the salt. But he couldn't remember the word, so he mumbled "Passe moi le ... uhm ... le schrtoumpf!" (Pass me the ... the Smurf!). Peyo and Franquin liked the word so much that the rest of the evening they added "smurf" to everything they said.

The words *smurf* and *to smurf* can mean almost anything:

> Next week we smurf a new mayor smurf. You will all get a smurf form with on it all of the smurfs that you can smurf to the function of mayor smurf. With a red smurf you smurf a checkmark next to the name of the smurf that you desire as your new mayor smurf. It is strongly forbidden to smurf four-letter words on the smurf form!

Without a lot of difficulty, you can replace any occurrence of the word *smurf* in the text with the correct English word. And many young readers of the Smurf stories can do that as well. Smurf words get their meaning from the context. By themselves, they are reasonably *smurfless*. To understand Smurf language requires a lot of context sensitivity. And that is not only true for Smurf language but for any language.

That is what you will feel when you want to translate something into another language. With knowledge of the vocabulary of isolated words, you will not get very far. Translate the following Dutch words to English (you can use a dictionary):

Kussen = ....
Bos = ....
Hoop = ....

Were you successful? Use your English words now to translate the following Dutch sentence: *Leg die bos bloemen maar bij die grote hoop cadeaus naast het kussen op het bed.*

More than likely, you ended up with a more or less weak sentence like: "Put the forest of flowers next to the big hope of gifts next to the kissing of the bed." You get an equally bad result when you let translation sites on the Internet do the work. Translation computers and translation programs on the Internet contain a large vocabulary, but – until now – they are not excelling in context sensitivity. That is why they often make many translation mistakes. Here is a small selection of the translation talents of some of the most popular translation websites:

"Lay who bunch of flowers soley towards who major pile present next to the kiss worn the bed."
"Put the bunch of flowers but with great hope that the next gifts pillow on the bed."

And this is the human translation, made by a context sensitive brain: "Put the bouquet of flowers together with the big pile of gifts on the bed, next to the pillow."

## Context and the Ambiguity of Words

Like translation sites, someone who is not context sensitive will have no problems with the vocabulary meaning of words that have only one meaning. As soon as you know the vocabulary meaning of banana, it is simple: Banana means banana. But it becomes increasingly challenging for words that have multiple meanings.

Our language consists of numerous *homonyms* – words that are spelled and pronounced the same but have different meanings. Some examples are:

- *Cool*: cold, awesome
- *Bank*: financial institution, sand bank
- *Plant*: factory, a growing green thing
- *Glasses*: optical object, plural of glass

*Homographs* look like homonyms. They have the same written form but a different meaning and different pronunciation. Examples are:

- *Bow*: I bow to the emperor and shoot an arrow with my bow.
- *Do*: What do you think you are doing? I am singing the scale from do.
- *Lead*: He can lead the way by pointing with his lead pipe.

If you want to pronounce homographs correctly, context is crucial. As a stand-alone word, you do not know how to pronounce *bow,* but in the context of a sentence like "During the Olympic Games, the contestant shot an arrow with his bow," it becomes obvious.

*Homophones* are a different form of ambiguous words. These are words that have different meanings but sound the same and are spelled differently:

- *Sail, sale:* The sail is for sale
- *Sole, soul:* I am the sole person in the house while I listen to soul music.
- *Stair, stare:* I stare at the stair.
- *Mail, male:* The male got mail.

To correctly spell a homophone in dictation, you need a context.

Homonyms, homographs, and homophones are examples of what linguists call polysemy. Polysemy occurs when a word or group of words have different meanings. But polysemy can also occur more subtly. Sometimes it is about variations of one and the same meaning. For example, the word *newspaper*, which, according to the dictionary, has only one meaning (periodic publication about news), can refer to what you read as well as to who is producing it:

> The accident with the two journalists was in the newspaper.
> The journalists of the accident both worked at the same newspaper.

According to the cognitive psychologist George Miller, it is a perverse characteristic of language that the words that we use the most often frequently have multiple meanings.[33] An example is the word *head*, which in each of the following sentences has a different, although related, meaning:

He wears a hat on his head.
He is head over heels in love.
You must keep your head.
The head of the surgery department is on vacation.
Write the date on the letterhead.

Context solves the problem of polysemy and makes words *monosemous*.[34] Based on the context, only one meaning remains. Without context, you quickly run into trouble trying to understand words with multiple meanings.

Applying meaning to words is often about canceling out ambiguities. Psychologists and linguists say we *disambiguate* by canceling out ambiguity or clarifying a word by identifying a single meaning.[35] So, in the battle against ambiguity, context is our main weapon.

On a daily basis, we solve countless ambiguities in language without any problem, spontaneously, quickly, and even unconsciously. Study of eye movements and brain activity[36] during the reading of texts with double meaning or multiple-meaning words has shown that we use context within the first hundredths of milliseconds of information processing – so quickly that we are not even aware of it.

Contextual disambiguating is completed before we consciously recognize the words.[37] This is very handy, especially in spoken language. Imagine if, for every word with multiple meanings, we had to think consciously about which meaning is more fitting than another.

Reduced context sensitivity is only a disadvantage when words have multiple meanings. Acquiring vocabulary is not

*In the battle against ambiguity, context is our main weapon.*

by itself particularly difficult for people with autism. Many people on the severe end of the autism spectrum lag behind in language development or have a reduced vocabulary. High-functioning individuals, on the contrary, often have an impressive vocabulary.[38] On tests that measure understanding of words (like naming pictures, connecting pictures to words) children with autism do not score lower than other children of the same age. They can give definitions or synonyms of words just as well, and their reading of single words appears to be intact. According to one study, children with autism are even better at naming pictures than children without autism.[39]

Moreover, children with autism can put words into meaningful categories. Just like children without autism, they memorize words that are semantically related (like the names for different animals or vehicles) better than words that are randomly placed on a list.[40] In that respect, the development of a vocabulary is intact in autism.[41] People with autism are quite capable of making meaningful connections between single words and their meanings.

It becomes more difficult when there is no one-to-one relationship between a word and its meaning, but a one-to-many relationship – when one word can have multiple meanings. Evidence comes especially from research involving homographs. Numerous studies[42] have shown that people with autism, even high-functioning adults, have difficulty with the correct pronunciation of homographs, giving evidence for a reduced use of context, because it is the context that determines how to pronounce the homograph.

In search for empirical proof of a reduced context sensitivity in autism, studies using homographs give us the most robust evidence; however, the results from these studies have been contradicted by other studies indicating that people with autism do make use of context in canceling out ambiguous homographs and other words. For example, Canadian researchers[43] have found that children with autism can pronounce homographs correctly when the homograph is preceded by a prime. A prime is a word that is related to one of the two meanings of the homograph; therefore, it can be said to "prime" the meaning. For example, *arrow* may be used as a prime for the pronunciation of *bow* as bòòw (instead of bóów). With a prime, children with autism were as accurate as children without autism in the pronunciation of homographs.

The researchers saw this as evidence of context sensitivity in autism. But here is what happened when the researchers offered primes for both meanings of the homograph (they offered every homograph twice). Contrary to the children without autism, the children with autism made more mistakes in the second offering of the homograph. It is as if they were stuck on the first meaning that the researchers had primed and did not adjust to the new context that the other prime suggested. This again suggests reduced context sensitivity.

People with autism tend to remain fixed on the first learned or dominant connection. In general, they have few problems with the dominant, most apparent meaning of words. Those connections of meanings can even be very strong. However, what is difficult for them is to spontaneously and flexibly adjust meanings to the context, in other words, letting go of the dominant meaning.

Rhonda Booth and Francesca Happé[44] asked people with and without autism to finish sentences like:

The sea tastes like salt and …
You can hunt with a knife and …
The night was black and …

Contrary to people without autism, the people with autism fell much more into the trap of dominant connections of meanings (instead of taking the context of the sentence into account) and finished the sentences as follows:

The sea tastes like salt and pepper.
You can hunt with a knife and fork.
The night is black and white.

In another recent study,[45] researchers thought they found proof of the use of context by people with autism in the processing of words. They let adolescents with and without autism look at a computer screen while listening to sentences. There were always four things to look at on the computer screen: a target object (e.g., a hamster) and three distracters. One distracter was a phonological competitor and resembled the target object with respect to pronunciation (e.g., a hammer in the case of hamster). The other two were not related to the target (e.g., pills and a medal). The sentences the subjects heard were either contextually related to the target object (e.g., Joe stroked the hamster softly) or not (e.g., Sam chose the hamster reluctantly). When they recognized a word of the sentence, the subjects had to push a button, and their eye movements were recorded as they looked at the screen. The following picture shows the test setting of the experiment.

In a sentence that primes the word *hamster* contextually (Joe stroked the hamster softly), people look less to the similarly sounding distracter (*hammer*) than in a sentence that is not contextually related to *hamster* (Sam chose the hamster).

Contrary to expectations, the adolescents with autism benefited just as much from the sentences associated with the target as did the subjects without autism. They looked less to the similarly sounding distracter (*hammer* in the case of *hamster*) in a sentence that made that meaning quite improbable (Joe wouldn't softly stroke a hammer) than when the sentence did not contextually clarify anything (Sam could choose a hammer).

Although this study provides evidence of context sensitivity in people with autism, it is different from the studies with homographs. In the latter, subjects were required to give meaning, not to recognize meanings. The hammer/hamster study is not proof of the ability to cancel out ambiguity in word meanings. At most, it is proof of some context sensitivity in word recognition. Despite the presence of distracters, there was no ambiguity of meaning in this experiment. The distracters were always related to pronunciation, not to meaning.

In what respect does this research measure context sensitivity as we use it in real life? To study something scientifically, researchers design strict procedures and attempt to keep as much control as possible over the variables. This inevitably makes many experiments far removed from what happens in regular, everyday life. In the quick recognition and understanding of words, we not only use the language context (the sentence around a word) but also the context of the situation: the who, what, when, and where – what do I see and hear around me?[46]

The hamster/hammer study contains a relatively noncontextualized assignment: to give meaning to words connected to drawings on a computer screen and sentences heard on headphones. In real life, we give meaning to what flesh-and-blood people communicate in situations full of contextual elements.

What we learn from both of these recent studies is that people with autism are capable of using context up to a certain level and with reasonable success, but only when their attention is being directed to the context (either by a primer or by the assignment to recognize a word in a sentence). That pushing the "context button" helps people with autism became clear already from the first studies with homographs.

Beatriz Lopez and Susan Leekam[47] discovered that children with autism pronounced more homographs correctly when the homograph was shown after the context of the sentence ("Molly was very happy, but on Lily's cheek there was a big tear") than when they were put before the context ("There was a big tear on her cheek"). Surprisingly, this did not make a difference to children without autism. Earlier, Margaret Snowling and Uta Frith[48] had noticed that children with autism made far fewer mistakes in the pronunciation of homographs when they were informed about the ambiguity of the homographs and when they were cued to be attentive to the correct meaning. In short, people with autism seem to be context sensitive when we "push the button."

Along with these scientific studies, everyday experience provides evidence of the difficulties that people with autism have with canceling out the ambiguous meanings of words with multiple meanings.

> *The students in a class for students with autism read together a story about Christmas. They arrived at the part where the shepherds and kings were searching for the manger, led by the star above the stable. The teacher asked, "And how did the three kings find the stable?" To which one of the children answered, "Very beautiful!"*

Perhaps the best proof is the anecdote that professor Ina van Berckelaer-Onnes shared in her retirement speech.[49]

> "Henk is a highly gifted man with autism who has difficulties with homonyms and synonyms. In his dictionary he always marks out one of the possible meanings of homonyms. He is confused that a 'school' can refer to an institution where you gain an education as well as a group of fish. Synonyms are also difficult for him. Why do we have next to crying the word 'whining,' which in Dutch can also refer to the capital of Austria?"

## Context and the Vagueness of Words

As if it was not difficult enough for Henk above, language contains far more confusion than what stems from polysemy.

In addition to double or multiple meanings, word meanings, in general, are vague. When we deal with ambiguity, the difference between possible meanings is somewhat reduced, but when we deal with vagueness, the difference between meanings is great, with innumerable possibilities. Ambiguity can be reduced to differences in dictionary meanings; vagueness, on the other hand, has to do with differences in world meaning and, therefore, is not as easily resolved.

Here are some examples of vague words with numerous meanings:

- *Of:* The banana of John (possession), the peel of the banana (part), the rotting of a banana (aspect), the eating of a banana (usage)
- *Take:* I take a bite of my banana, I take the banana of my neighbor, I take a banana to my neighbor

When someone says that he has something "on his computer," it can refer to:

- Something to see on the screen
- Something that is positioned on the screen, like a webcam
- Something that is in the memory of the computer

It is the context that helps us understand the world meanings of these words. For example, when someone says that he will take the plane from Brussels to Paris, you know that "to take" does not mean holding it in one's hand and that the plane referred to is not a super-big Boeing that is normally used for transatlantic flights, nor a single-engine sports aircraft.

Reduced context sensitivity also leads to incorrect interpretation of vague words, as illustrated in the following.

*Robbie is cycling on a tandem bicycle with his father. Robbie is sitting in the back. After a while, he does not pedal any more, so his father says, "Come on, Robbie, push it!" Robbie promptly pushes the back of his father with his hands.*

Every parent or teacher of children with autism can give numerous examples of a similar nature. People with autism seem to connect only one meaning to a word, and they do not spontaneously adapt it to the context. For Robbie, *pushing* meant pushing with his hands. It did not occur to him that his father meant for him to pedal.

The fixed connection of meanings to words and the weak flexibility in revising these connections was already noted by Leo Kanner.[50] He described how one of his patients, John, corrected his father when he told about the pictures hanging on the wall in their house. "We have them *near* the wall," John said. For John, *on* meant somewhere on top. When Kanner asked Donald, another boy from his practice, to lay something down, Donald promptly put it on the floor. To Donald, to *lay something down* meant *lay it on the floor*.

Here is another example of the immense diversity in world meanings: What does the word *work* mean? When a psychologist proposes that you work on your problems, you understand that she means you and she will talk about the problems during the therapy sessions. In this context, *work* means to think and to talk, not to do manual labor. Ben, an adult with autism, could not switch spontaneously to that context, and, therefore, asked his psychologist when she told him they would work on his problems: "And which clothes do I have to wear?" Ben connects *work* to a physical job, such as he does in the factory where he works. At the factory, he must wear overalls and a helmet.

It must be confusing for people who are context blind that words in the real world can refer to so many different things. Vague words rely even more on context than do ambiguous words. In the case of ambiguous words, the linguistic context often suffices for disambiguation, but this is insufficient with vague words. For vague words, we also have to take into account the nonlinguistic context. For instance, what do you do when someone says, "It is time!" Time for what? Time to sleep, to work, to eat a banana, to leave? Again, from the context, you would not have a problem discerning the purpose of the statement.

When you finish your food and the person who says "It is time!" puts on his jacket, you know that it is time to go. When the school bell rings after the end of a lesson, you know it is time to play outside. In my book *Brain Deceived,*[51] I wrote that what is difficult in communication for people with autism is not so much what we say, but what we do *not* say, as in the example "It is time [... to go to school, go to bed, etc.]. More than once, I have been asked, especially by people with autism, why we "leave out" so much in human communication. The answer is simple: because we get so much information from the context. So, returning to the example above, it is obvious to us what it is time for.

*To understand language is more than understanding the language. It is understanding language + involving the context.*

And because that information is obvious, we do not have to say it out loud. To understand is more than understanding what has been said or what has been written. To understand language = understanding what someone is saying or writing + using context. For the one who is context blind, certain statements are very absurd and confusing.

*After Christmas vacation, there is a change in the schedule of gym lessons at the school. Gym lessons in the gymnasium at the school are replaced by swimming in the municipal swimming pool. The teacher reminds the children that they have to bring their swimsuits. "Children, tomorrow we will go to the swimming pool!"*

*Hannah, a girl with autism, arrives home after school in a panic saying that she does not want to go to school the next day. Even though she likes swimming, she wails, "I will not go to the swimming pool!" After a long conversation, it becomes clear that she did not know that the children would return to school from swimming after an hour, because the teacher did not mention that. Every other child in the class understood from the context, "We will go to the swimming pool" [and after an hour of swimming, we will return to the school].*

*During math, Peter receives his worksheet with math assignments. On top of the page, the assignment is written, "Solve the problems of the clown." Peter protests, "I cannot do that!" even though he is capable of doing the assignment. He is the best of the class in math. When the teacher urges him, "Of course, you can do it," Peter gets angry and shouts, "No, because I am not a shrink!" For Peter, solving someone's problems is the work of a psychiatrist. Did his mother not say that to him when he had to go to the psychiatrist the first time? "That man will help you solve your problems." Peter does not spontaneously take into account the context of the math sheet and is not able to change the fixed connection in his brain between the word* problem *and the meaning* psychiatry *contextually into: problem = calculation exercise.*

**Solve the clown's problems**

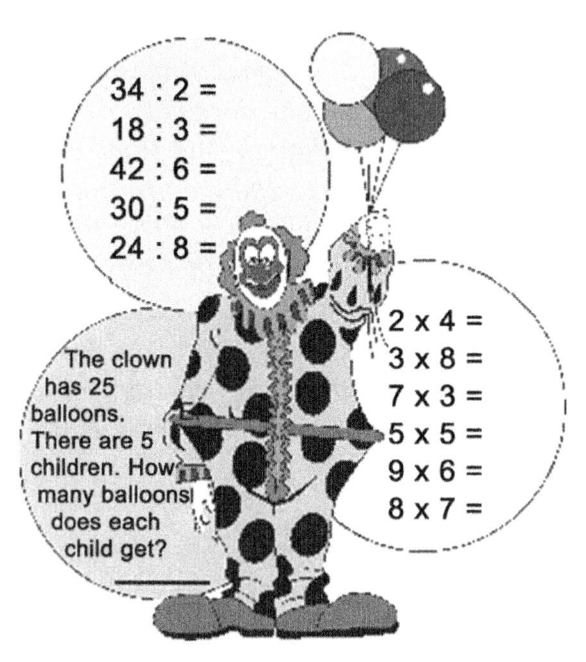


What problems? Depression? Marriage problems?
A bit of a difficult exercise if you are not a psychiatrist!

As if vague words and words with more than one meaning were not confusing enough, there is a class of words that by themselves do not mean much; they only derive their meaning from the context. This is the case in words like *he*, *later*, *earlier*, *big*, *there*, and *good*. The meaning of these words is not absolute, but relative. In absolute terms, a big mouse is still smaller than a small elephant. The location to which we refer using *there* is actually *here* for the person located over there. These types of words are called referential or *deictic* words. To understand them correctly, context is crucial. Referential words are the biggest source of confusion for people who are context blind, as illustrated in the following.

> "Not now. I will tell it to him later." When is *later*? What is *it*? Who is *him*? Without context, these questions remain unanswered.

> "John did not give Pete a present because he was angry." Who was angry, John or Pete? Dictionary knowledge will not help in the case of referential words. According to the dictionary, *he* is: third person, masculine, single. But who is he?

Pronoun reversal is a well-known language phenomenon in the speech of younger children with autism and language delay: They refer to themselves as *you* or *he* and refer to other people, such as their mother, using *I* or *me*. We can connect this to context blindness and making fixed, unchanging relationships between word and meaning. That is, because children with autism are often spoken to using the word *you*, they begin to make a fixed connection between *you* and themselves. They sort of hang their own picture on *you*. That is why they call themselves *you* and the other person *me*. The fact that the picture of *me* can change with every person who talks about himself is too difficult for certain people with autism to fully grasp.

## Context and Concrete vs. Abstract Words

We often hear and read that people with autism have more difficulty with abstract than with concrete words. The traditional explanation is that concrete words are more visual than abstract words. Concrete words like *chair*, *book*, or *banana* are more easily pictured than words like *quantity*, *honest*, *later*, or *big*. For people with autism, the advice, therefore, is to visualize abstract meanings.

The assumption that concrete words are easier to process than abstract ones because they are more visual is not supported by recent research, however. Neurological research shows that we also visualize in the processing of abstract words, and that in processing concrete words we also use nonvisual language processing areas of the brain.[52]

Along with availability of visual images, context contributes to the difference between abstract and concrete words,[53] because abstract words are only more difficult than concrete words when there is no context.[54] Abstract words without context require more processing time because it is more difficult to call the related knowledge into memory. As stated earlier, the external context (e.g., the sentence context) helps us to activate the internal context, our knowledge. In other words, the challenge we face in processing abstract words is to make them concrete in the given context. For example, what do you visualize for the words *drink* and *bird*? A lot of concrete images are possible. With the context added, it becomes easier:

> At breakfast, the truck driver took a sip of his drink.
> Robert put the canary in the birdcage next to the other bird.

The context helps us to reduce a number of alternatives for *drink* and *bird* and to understand what the words mean in this situation. With concrete words, we need less context. When the words *coffee*, *tea*, or *fruit juice* are used, the context of *breakfast* is less necessary. Giving meaning to concrete words is less context dependent than giving meaning to abstract words.

*Abstract words are more difficult than concrete words only when there is no context.*

Someone who is context blind will, therefore, have more trouble with abstract words than with concrete words. And that is what we notice with people with autism. Here again, the distinction between knowing words and understanding words is of interest. In practice, we notice that high-functioning people with autism know a lot of abstract words and even use them. And while they do not have as much trouble with abstract words, they do have difficulty understanding them in concrete situations. For example, what does the word mean here and now? That is because concretization is contextually driven.[55] Think back to the examples of working on problems and solving the problems of the clown.

## Context and the Understanding of Sentences

Until now, we have discussed only the understanding of individual words and how context helps us understand ambiguous, vague, and abstract words. What is true at the word level is also true at the higher levels of sentences and full texts. Sentences may also be ambiguous or vague. Many sentences are syntactically or structurally ambiguous because the same word can have multiple grammatical functions in the sentence and, therefore, the sentence can have different meanings.

Depending on how you group words in a sentence, a sentence can have quite different meanings, as illustrated in the following:

- He bought the statue on the market (he bought the-statue-on-the-market vs. he bought the statue, on the market).
- White men and women go to different shops (do white men and women go to different shops than colored men and women, or do white men go to different shops than women?).

What do you think of this variant of Groucho Marx's well-known one-liner, "One morning, I shot an elephant in my pajamas. How he got into my pajamas I'll never know."

"The man saw his wife with his glasses."

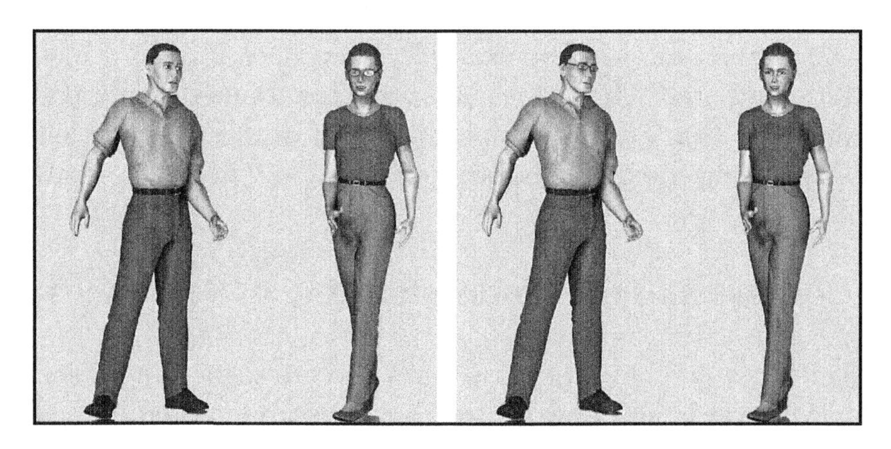

The man saw his wife with his glasses. Who is wearing the glasses?

Next to structural ambiguity, there is often vagueness in sentences:[56]

- I made her a duck. Did I prepare a meal of duck for a woman? Or did I create a toy duck for a girl? Or am I a character in a bizarre fairy tale that changes a girl into a duck?

- The girls are playing with the puppets. (Together or separately?)
- At each game, a player leaves the field. (Is that the same player each time?)
- Every hour someone in Europe has an accident at work. (Poor guy!)
- We have a French impressionist hanging in our house. (How cruel!)

All trousers at 19.99 euros.

A young man with autism goes with his dad to buy new pants. He wants to be independent and does not want the dad to go into the shop with him. "I can do this alone," he says. After a minute he is back out, without new pants. Surprised, his dad asks why he did not buy the pants, especially considering they were on sale. The young man answers, "I do not need so many!" The dad did not understand until he entered the shop and saw the sign, "All pants on sale at 19.99 euros."

Without context giving meaning to structural ambiguity and vagueness, we would have to make endless sentences to fully explain what we mean. Yet in everyday communication, most of us do not have a problem with ambiguities and vagueness, because we can understand the messages quickly and correctly based on the information from the context (both the internal and the external). A statement about the French impressionist hanging in the house does not create any problem. You know that people usually do not hang people in their house, and you know that French impressionists are painters. And even if you did not know French impressionists were painters, undoubtedly the sentence will belong in a conversation about paintings or art, and then you can derive from that external context that a French impressionist must be a painter (a sculptor would be less probable, because you usually do not hang sculptures).

Different studies have shown the effect of context on solving ambiguities in sentences. In one study,[57] people were given the assignment to "put the apple on the towel in the box." The most apparent meaning would be to put the apple on the towel that is located in the box. But the statement can also mean that you have to put the apple, which is on the towel, in the box. The researchers varied the context. In a certain situation there was an apple on a towel, in another there was an apple on a towel and one on a napkin, and in still another situation, in addition to the apple on the towel, there were three apples that were not on the towel.

Using eye tracking, the researchers found that the subjects used the context to know which apple was referred to. In the situation with an apple on a napkin and an apple on a towel, subjects reacted as quickly to the ambiguous instruction as to the unambiguous instruction (put the apple that lies on the towel in the box). This demonstrates that the visual context helped immediately to cancel out the ambiguity.

Based on the difficulties that people with autism have in understanding ambiguous and vague words, we can expect that they would also have trouble with dual-meaning and vague sentences, despite reasonable grammatical skills. In fact, they may struggle even more with meaning, because sentences are more complex than words.

American researchers[58] gave adolescents with autism and average intelligence ambiguous instructions like "Put the apple on the towel in the box." In this study, the researchers did not use a visual, but an auditory context; specifically, the way the instructions were pronounced. Pronouncing the instruction "Put the apple on the towel" – short break – "in the box" (emphasis on *in*) gives the sentence a different meaning than "Put the apple" – break – "on the towel in the box." The adolescents with autism did not take advantage of these contextual hints and made as many mistakes as when there was no contextual help.

Therese Jolliffe and Simon Baron-Cohen[59] researched the ability of a group of high-functioning adults with autism to decipher ambiguous sentences. The adults saw cards with two sentences on each, one of which had a double meaning. The first sentence served as a context for the second. For example:

> The woman liked to keep her house tidy.
> She said that visiting relatives can be a nuisance.

Here the first sentence was in line with the most common interpretation of the second, ambiguous sentence – that to get a visit from family members annoyed her. Sometimes the context of the first sentence steered the meaning of the second sentence in the direction of a less common meaning:

The woman hated traveling.
She said that visiting relatives can be a nuisance.

The researchers asked the subjects what the woman meant and gave three possible meanings:

- Having relatives was a nuisance
- Having relatives visit was a nuisance
- Having to visit relatives was a nuisance

Compared to a control group, the adults with autism gave more wrong answers, especially when the context pointed to less probable meanings. Further, they needed more time to answer than the test subjects without autism. They made more mistakes with the less probable meaning than with the more dominant meaning, a difference that was not present in the control group. Finally, they appeared to stick to the dominant, most probable meanings, having difficulty letting the meanings relate to the context.[60]

## Context and Understanding the World Behind the Words

To understand what we hear and read, we cannot rely solely on dictionary definitions. We have to get the "world meanings" behind the words, and those are much broader than the formal definitions. To construct these world meanings, we use the knowledge that is stored in our memory. We involve the internal context of our knowledge of the world to make practical decisions about what others are saying to us and to react accordingly. We usually do that subconsciously and quickly. Read, for example, the following two sentences:

> Lily opened the door and saw that Jumper was no longer in his cage. Crying, she walked over to her mother, who told her, "He will not fly far away and will come back."

Although not stated explicitly, you understand that Lily is a child (not a grownup), a girl (not a boy), that Jumper is a bird (not a hippo), that Lily is sad (not happy), and that *come back* means coming back to the cage. You know these things because you added information to what you literally read. You used your imagination to create a context for these sentences that was not given. That internal context is dependent on the external one, the words and the sentences. If the words *crawl* or *walk* had been used in place of *fly*, for example, you would not think of a bird but of another pet that is usually kept in a cage, like a hamster.

When we do not switch on our acquired knowledge, for example, the knowledge that door-to-door salespeople do not sell body hair, misconceptions are bound to occur:

> She: Honey, there is a man at the door with a moustache!
> He: Tell him that I already have one.

The internal context of our knowledge plays an important role in understanding language. We often involve our knowledge of the world without being conscious of it. That is why sentences that look absurd on the level of dictionary meanings can be quite familiar. For instance, you don't panic when someone tells you that "the office called," because you know that offices cannot make phone calls. You understand from the message that someone from the office called. Similarly, if ordered to "eat that banana," you will not eat the whole banana, but will peel it first. With the words *train strike,* it is clear that the trains themselves are not striking, but the train personnel.

World knowledge is an important context from which to retrieve the difference between what people say and what they mean. Someone who is less spontaneous at switching on this context, including the context of stored knowledge, sometimes interprets what is said differently from the intended meaning.

> *When a mother gave her child with autism, Sarah, the order to wipe her feet before entering, Sarah removed her shoes and socks and wiped her feet on the doormat.*

Every human being has a mass of knowledge stored in their brain. How do you know which knowledge to use? Here again, we have context as our guide. Context helps obtain the right information behind the words and sentences we hear. This is known in linguistics as *inferences*. Inferences are conclusions that you derive based on the external context (the linguistic and nonlinguistic context around a word or sentence) as well as the internal context (your world knowledge). Here is an example:

> With a big plop, Michael uncorked the bottle and poured Bert and himself a glass full of bubbles.

What did they drink? Using both the sentence context (bottle with a cork – plopping sound when uncorking – bubbles) and your knowledge of drinks, you easily understand that we are talking about champagne or sparkling wine.

Jolliffe and Baron-Cohen[61] researched whether adults with autism were capable of making bridging inferences between short phrases like the following:

Albert said that he wouldn't return to the restaurant. He left without giving a tip.

The adults were given three sentences, one of them being a coherent inference, explaining why Albert did not give a tip.

Albert didn't leave a tip because ...

- He only had enough money for the meal.
- He was dissatisfied with the service.
- When he arrived the restaurant was closed.

The subjects with autism made more mistakes on this task than the control group, and they also required more time.

In a followup study, Jolliffe and Baron-Cohen[62] increased the level of difficulty of the test, making it a little more realistic. Now no alternatives were offered; the subjects had to spontaneously draw their own conclusions. This time they were told short stories, about five sentences in length (e.g., about a woman who wants to buy a painting but does not find anything to her liking and then decides to buy a clock instead). After the story, subjects were asked why the woman bought a clock. The adults with autism made a lot of mistakes and often gave an explanation that was unrelated to the context of the story.

The findings from the research of Jolliffe and Baron-Cohen have been confirmed by other studies with higher functioning children and adolescents with autism.[63] Can these poor performances be caused by a lack of context sensitivity or are other explanations possible?

Difficulties in making inference from a story, even a short story, may be caused by reduced language skills; however, that was not the case in the above studies. Subjects' understanding of language was carefully evaluated, and it appeared to be comparable to that of the test subjects without autism. No relation to verbal intelligence was found. In most studies, the subjects with autism had average to above-average verbal intelligence. Moreover, in one of the studies,[64] the subjects with autism made even more mistakes when making inferences than did the subjects with language impairments (this last group also made more mistakes than the typically developing control group).

Could memory be an issue? When you have difficulty remembering the information in a story, you are likely to draw wrong conclusions; however, the subjects with autism performed just as well as the control groups on giving answers to memory questions. Further, in one study, the subjects' memory was explicitly tested using memory tests,[65] and no connection was found between memory and inferential processing abilities. If there is a connection between memory and understanding, it would follow that a better understanding of the stories would result in remembering them better (and not the other way around).

In making inferences, both the acquired world knowledge and the linguistic context (of the text) are important. Another possible explanation for the inferencing deficits of people with autism might be found in a reduced or distorted world knowledge. But that does not seem to be the case in the studies mentioned above. All of these studies involved people with autism with IQ scores comparable to those of the control groups. Most stories were about everyday recognizable situations that the subjects would be expected to know or at least to recognize. Finally, when assessing the ability to retrieve information from texts, even for people without autism, general acquired knowledge plays only a modest role.[66]

Fans of theory-of-mind explanations of autism could say that the ability to empathize would play a role in making inferences. In the example of Albert, who did not give a tip, the conclusion requires a certain level of ability to empathize. But this explanation is not satisfactory either. For example, Jolliffe and Baron-Cohen only used subjects who were successful on theory-of-mind tests. In addition, only a small minority of the stories in these studies involved an inference that referred to a mental state of the characters in the stories.[67] The greatest counterargument comes from a Scandinavian study[68] that used stories from which subjects had to infer both physical and mental states. Here the subjects with autism performed lower than the control group on both types of tasks.

One final counterargument: Perhaps people with autism are just not good at inferring information and drawing conclusions. But this explanation also does not work. From each of the above studies, it is apparent that the subjects were indeed capable of drawing conclusions, but their conclusions often did not apply to the context of the story. The mistakes they made in their inferences confirmed what we already described with regard to the relationship between context and ability to empathize: People with autism often fall back on previously learned, fixed scripts and associations instead of taking the present context into account.

In a story in which a boy gets a drink out of his bag and shares it with a friend, a child with autism gave the following answer to the question where the boy got his drink: "from the waiter."[69] The performance of people with autism on tests of inferencing abilities correlates with their performance on other tests of context sensitivity in understanding language, like the homographs test and tests with ambiguous sentences.[70]

There is further proof. The more explicit the context, the more easily people with autism could draw the right conclusions. For less explicit contexts, they made more mistakes and also needed more time.[71] This all points to the fact that people with autism have more trouble than people without autism in using context to activate those aspects of their world knowledge that are necessary to understand what they read or hear. It is not that people with autism do not have world knowledge, nor that they have more difficulties accessing that knowledge. Instead, they have a hard time using the context to access the appropriate knowledge and using it.

## Context Blindness and Literal Understanding of Language

What people say and what they mean is not always the same. Even with knowledge of both the lexical and the world meaning of a word, there can still be confusion. Even if both meanings are clear and known, it can be difficult to understand what another person says, because what the other person means with the word can be different from the most obvious meaning. For example:

> The apple does not fall far from the tree.
> You have a good heart.
> He has only hay for one cow.

To understand these sentences, the skill to retrieve things contextually is essential. What is written and what it means can be the same.

> Wendy does not like standing under a tree because she fears an apple will fall on her head. Father lets her stand away from the tree and calms her down by telling her that an apple will not fall on her head because "The apple does not fall far from the tree."

After a stress test, the cardiologist calms the patient with the words, "You have a good heart."

A news reporter talks about the poverty of Senegalese farmers. He stands in front of the stable of a farmer and says about the farmer, "He only has hay for one cow."

But these sentences can also mean something completely different. In the case of the Senegalese farmer, the sentence could also mean that he cannot financially afford a second wife (a Senegalese expression). In that case, the sentence is meant figuratively, and you do not have to think about cows but about women. A person who thinks in terms of cows understands the sentence literally.

Literal understanding is a well-known phenomenon in autism. In fact, according to Leo Kanner, taking things literally is one of the basic characteristics of autism. In almost every text about autism, taking things literally is mentioned as part of the difficulties that people with autism have in communication. But literal understanding is not just a language problem; it is primarily a problem with context. Speaking figuratively is a form of double meaning or polysemia, but on the level of communicative meaning. The words in idioms and sayings may have only one vocabulary meaning or world meaning, but the communicative meaning can be different.

*To understand literally is not just a language problem. It is a problem with context.*

The key is to decide if you need the classical, close-at-hand (another idiom) meaning or the less dominant, figurative, meaning. To make that decision, we use context, the internal as well as the external. An example of how the external context helps follows.

> Ron, who had been ill the previous week, had to work hard to survive his fight with boxing legend Marco. In the last round he got in serious trouble, but just when he was about to be knocked out, he was saved by the bell.

In this case you know that the phrase "saved by the bell" is not to be taken in a figurative sense because the first sentence already makes it clear that we are talking about a boxing match. In another context "saved by the bell" should be interpreted in a figurative way.

> Just as the teacher was about to call on Allen to answer a difficult question in class, the principal came into the classroom and asked Allen to come with him. Allen stood up and said: "Oh, saved by the bell!"

To understand figurative language, we have to first understand that it is not meant literally. To reach that understanding, we use context, quite quickly and – most of the time – unconsciously. This is true for idioms we have learned and know, and also for figurative expressions we have never heard. A number of studies have shown that when sufficient context is available, we understand figurative meanings immediately without first having to analyze and check the literal meaning.[72] But without context, or with reduced context sensitivity, we have to consciously analyze. That is what we see in high-functioning people with autism.

For example, Frank explains that when interpreting figurative language, he always first "sees" the literal meaning. If, after consciously processing, he realizes that this meaning cannot be correct, he searches for a figurative meaning. The problem of figurative language for people with autism is not that they do not know the figurative meanings, but that they have difficulty *recognizing* figurative speaking. That recognition is based on the context.

The tendency of people with autism to interpret language literally is often explained by a deficit in theory of mind – because of their reduced ability to empathize, they have difficulty retrieving what someone means and, thus, have difficulty making a distinction between what is said and what is meant.[73] It is true that theory of mind plays a role in retrieving what someone means, but it does not play a role in determining if someone means something other than what he is saying. The discovery that something is meant to be figurative activates our ability to empathize, not the other way around.

We learned in Chapter 4 that the ability to empathize is contextually activated. From the context, we understand that someone means something different from what she says, and only then do we turn on our ability to empathize in order to interpret the meaning. A study[74] about children's (with and without autism) understanding of idioms and sayings found no correlation between theory of mind and understanding figurative use of language. From the same study, it appeared that when we focus the attention of children with autism on the possible figurative use of language and also activate the context, they are fairly capable of understanding figurative statements.[75]

Figurative speech can also be perfectly understood without the ability to empathize. You don't need a lot of theory of mind to find out what the idiom "to kill two birds with one stone" means. And when theory of mind does play a role, we additionally use context (see Chapter 4 on context and social interaction). Children with autism can retrieve mental states from stories, but they cannot adjust them to the context.[76]

The tendency of people with autism to interpret things literally goes beyond a failure to understand figurative speech, idioms, and sayings (e.g., the example of "wipe your feet"). Here is an example from Rory Hoy, a young man with autism who made a film about his autism.[77] When his teacher gave the instruction to write the days of the week on a piece of paper, his classmates wrote "Monday, Tuesday, Wednesday," and so on. But Rory wrote, "The days of the week." There is no figurative speech involved here, but Rory calls this an example of his literal understanding of language.

Literal language understanding is a form of acontextual language understanding. One remains fixed on the immediate, dominant meaning of words and sentences and does not change it for other meanings that are contextually more appropriate. The core problem with autism in the case of literal understanding is not the tendency to take things literally, but the difficulty in leaving the dominant meaning behind and replacing it with a less dominant one when dictated by the context.

A recent Japanese study[78] showed that when offered sentences that are usually understood in a figurative way but presented in a context that encouraged a literal interpretation instead, children with autism selected the nonliteral, more conventional meaning. The researchers concluded: "This conformity of children with high-functioning autism spectrum disorders to conventional interpretation of ambiguous language seems to account for over-literalness and over-nonliteralness."

In another, French, study[79] researchers found the same: Once they know an expression as idiomatic, adolescents with Asperger Syndrome seemed to have difficulties considering an alternative, less conventional or more literal meaning. The adolescents were less likely to use the context to interpret sentences, instead automatically activating the well-known meaning of idiomatic expressions.

Because literal meanings are often more dominant and conventional than figurative ones,[80] we see over-literalness in people with autism more often than over-nonliteralness. Literal understanding is by itself not a problem, nor does it signify a lack of something. To understand something literally is not necessarily a fault. In the example of Ron the boxer, the literal meaning of "saved by the bell" was the correct one. To understand a word or expression figuratively when it should be understood literally is just as contextually inappropriate as the other way around. Understanding a word figuratively when it should be understood literally is also seen in people with autism. It just happens a lot less than literal interpretation of language because figurative meanings are seldom the dominant, or first learned, meanings.

*While a mother and her son with autism get the groceries from the car, they have a dispute. Mother wants her son to help unload the car. She takes a bottle of milk and says to her son, "Now you take this from me." He reacts as follows, "No, I do not agree with you." He does not understand that she is asking him to take the milk and not accepting her opinion in the discussion.*

*After the statement by a classmate that she "learned her lesson," a student with autism asked, "And what did you do wrong?" But, in fact, the girl meant literally that she had learned her lesson.*

In these anecdotes, people with autism react the opposite of what is said about them: They do *not* take things literally although the context requires it. These types of anecdotes are proof that literal understanding is not the difficulty, but rather failure to let go of the dominant, or first learned, meaning when the context requires it. In this connection, the cognitive psychologist George Miller introduced the term *contextual representation.*[81]

Contextual representation is the ability to understand different context-dependent meanings of a word. You do not make a fixed connection between a word and its meaning, but you connect the different meanings to a word depending on the context and the amount of possible meanings. For example, you know that in a conversation about trains the word *miss* means something different than in a conversation about the shooting range. The person who is less context sensitive, however, will likely be confused by this supposedly funny bumper sticker: "I miss my wife, but my aim is getting better."

To know whether you have to take something literally or not is the question. The answer requires context sensitivity. For that reason, I prefer the term *acontextual understanding* above *literal understanding*. Ironically, the word *literal* has been used more and more figuratively in recent years and, as such, means the opposite of what it is supposed to mean. Hence, strange sentences such as "I was literally struck by amazement" occur.

## Context and Pragmatics in Communication

Pragmatics refers to the use of language within a certain context; it is about the communicative meanings and what people mean by what they say (or write). From the previous discussion, it should be clear that lingual information is not enough to give meaning to what someone is saying to us. *Pragmatically understanding communication* is a synonym for the ability to use the context in determining the meanings of language (in any possible form – spoken, written, body language, or with other symbols, like pictures and objects).[82]

One aspect of pragmatics involves the skill to understand the *function* of a statement. In everyday human communication, we typically do not specify the function of our communication. For example, when a man in a café says. "Waiter, a glass of water!" it can have different functions and, hence, different meanings[83]:

"Waiter, (look there) a glass of water!" (a remark)

"(But) waiter, (that is) a glass of water!" (I had ordered a beer! Also a remark but different from the previous one)

"Waiter, (have) a glass of water!" (an offer)

"Waiter, (give me) a glass of water (please)?!" (a request)

What the man in the café means becomes clear only when we connect his statement with the context:

The facial expression of the person (asking, angry, ...)
The gestures (pointing, both hands in the air, one hand in the air, ...)
The situation (who serves who, is there already an empty glass, ...)

So, here again, the ability to incorporate context plays a role, especially when the purpose of the statement is different from what the statement in isolation might seem to indicate.

He: Will you come to the movies with me this evening?

She: I have to work.

Her reaction sounds like a simple, informative statement, but it actually means, "No, I cannot go." Especially in this type of vague or ambiguous statements, the context is informative. Suppose someone asks you, "Where do you come from?" Are they asking about your birthplace, where you live, or where you just came from? We say that you have to see this question in context to be able to understand it correctly. That context is double – the situation in which the question is asked and the purpose of the speaker (of course, they are related to each other).

In Chapter 4 about context and social interaction, we discussed the research with *Strange Stories,* in which the characters said something that did not correspond with reality, and thus meant something different than what they said. The subjects with autism understood that the characters said things that were not true, but they could not come up with a contextually adjusted explanation.

To understand what others mean, we retrieve from the context things that are relevant to understanding the intention behind what people say.[84] Understanding intentions in communication is also a form of making inferences. To find out what someone is talking about and what he or she means,[85] children at a young age use context, although the distinction between what is relevant and what is not takes many years to develop.

Pragmatic skills in communication, especially reading the intentions behind words, is often ascribed to the ability to empathize. The pragmatic difficulties of people with autism have traditionally been linked to their deficits in theory of mind.[86] But maybe it is the other way around: Rather than being the consequence of theory of mind, understanding intentions activates our empathizing abilities. That is, from the ability to retrieve communicative purposes and meanings from the context, we develop theory of mind.

Researchers at the University of Torino[87] researched the role of context in the understanding of communicative intentions. They found that different categories of context have an influence:

**The physical context**:

- The presence or absence of a physical object to which an expression is referring
- The spatial position of the objects to which an expression is referring
- The time span of events to which the expression is referring

**The social context**:

- The course of the conversation and what was said earlier
- The posture and movements of the speaker
- The status of speaker and listener

One change in one of these contextual elements is enough to completely change the meaning of a sentence.

The question "Do you like bananas?" means "Do you find bananas tasty?" when you have in your hand, at that moment, a banana. But when you do not have a banana in your hand, the question can mean "Do you want a banana?"

The following is an example of how the spatial position of the objects about which communication is taking place changes the meaning of a sentence:

> "You want the glass of wine?" is a request to get the glass of wine when the glass of wine is with the listener, but an offer when the glass is in the vicinity of the one who is asking the question.

The following is an example of how the speakers' posture and movements influence the meaning of a sentence.

> "Interested in playing with the cars?"

When the person who says this looks invitingly toward the listener, it is an invitation to play with the cars *together*; however, when the speaker is doing the dishes and does not look to the listener, it may mean, "Maybe you want to play *on your own* with the cars while I do the dishes?"

The researchers found that even young children between three and three and a half years old are capable of using these types of subtle contextual elements to retrieve the intentions in communication.[88]

The fact that one detail in the total context can change the meaning of what has been said makes it necessary to identify what is relevant in the context in order to understand communication. According to our definition earlier in this book, that is the core of context sensitivity. ***Context sensitivity* and *relevance* are synonyms.** At a young age, children can pick out of the context relevant information in order to understand communication. As they move past the age of five, they begin to express themselves more parsimoniously. They know that the listener, just like them, also considers the context and, therefore, do not tell him everything, but only what is essential.[89]

It seems a bit strange that human communication, meant to clarify something for another person, is full of obscurities. We leave a lot of things unsaid, we often say something different from what we mean, and we use words and other symbols that have no fixed or absolute meaning, which means those words and symbols have inherent double meanings (and often multiple meanings). Should human communication not have become a bit clearer? Did evolution fail? No. Evolution means survival of the fittest, thus our unclear communication must have an evolutionary advantage.

*Communication is full of ambiguity and vagueness. But that is not a big deal, because context helps us to overcome it.*

That advantage is efficiency. It is faster and less cumbersome. What we say may be unclear, ambiguous, vague, or incomplete, but if we develop context sensitivity, we can retrieve as much, or even more, information from the context than from what has been said or written. Because estimating context is super-fast (in fractions of seconds), everything can be shorter and more succinct. It saves time, saliva, and mental energy, and, therefore, it is more efficient, just as it is more efficient to connect one word or symbol to multiple meanings. Vocabularies are already big enough. Imagine if you had a separate word for all possible meanings.

The pragmatic difficulties of people with autism are well known, and even characteristic for the group of people with a diagnosis of high-functioning autism or Asperger Syndrome, about whom it is assumed that they do not have a delay in language development and have average or above-average (verbal) intelligence.[90] These difficulties can be seen both in their understanding of communication and in their use of communication, when they express themselves or tell you something.[91] For instance, high-functioning people with autism may tell you things that you already know, or that given the context are so obvious that they need not be mentioned.

Here is an example: One time, a young Dutch man introduced himself to me with a clear Dutch accent and ended with the totally superfluous question, "Did you know I came from the Netherlands?" The opposite can also happen. Someone with autism may tell a whole story about a guy named Mark that you do not know without explaining who that Mark in the story is. People with autism often find it hard to make their story understandable by describing relationships or clarifying connections between different aspects of their story.[92] When asked to narrate a clip of a film they saw, adults with autism were less likely than controls to provide information about the characters, setting, or central theme of the scene as a whole. For example, while control participants described stories as taking place in a hospital or in an office building, participants with autism were less likely to do so. They did not clarify the context of their story as much as the control group.[93]

In research concerning the ability to make inferences based on the context of short stories,[94] some high-functioning children with autism sometimes gave the right answer, but they offered totally irrelevant explanations about how they arrived at the answer. This did not occur in any of the children without autism.

In our own research, we found such elaboration on contextually irrelevant details even in high-functioning adults with autism. We asked adults to judge the social appropriateness of behavior in stories.[95] One of the stories was about a man, Roger, who was on a diet and received an invitation to dinner. Because the dinner was not ready when he arrived at his friend's house, Roger got out an apple and some nuts from his bag and ate them while waiting. When the hostess served the dinner, Roger thanked her, saying that he just ate and that he wanted to wait another hour to eat. One of the subjects thought this was strange behavior and gave the following explanation:

> Test subject: *That is a bit strange about Roger. He is on a diet, but he should not overdo his diet. If he ate only apples, vegetables, and fruit, this would not be enough. He has to learn to put a bit of variety in his food. You should not always restrict yourself to vegetables and fruit. But, of course, when you get cancer, and you want a cure from the cancer, then it would be normal to only eat vegetables and fruit. That's what we call the "Moerman therapy."' (Moerman is a doctor who prescribes vegetables and fruit for people who have cancer.)*
>
> Project leader: *You think that he should not overdo it?*
>
> Subject: *I think that he should not overdo it, especially because he did not eat for an hour; yes an apple, but an apple is not enough. He could end up becoming anorexic.*

Irony, jokes, sarcasm, and lies, in short, all the expressions in which the truth is slightly altered, demand extra context sensitivity. When on a cold, drizzly, windy day, someone says,"Nice weather today, isn't it?" we know immediately that this is a sarcastic remark.

Research on children with autism shows less use of contextual clues to determine if a remark is meant ironically.[96] In processing these kind of expressions, their brains are much more active than the brains of children without autism. They have to think consciously about the purpose of the speaker, while children without autism derive it spontaneously and implicitly.

While typically developing children of barely three years old already understand that someone is making a joke when he says something that does not match the truth, this remains difficult for children, teens, and grownups with autism.[97] The fact that people with autism make jokes, even language jokes, means that their problems are not caused by an inability to understand humor and language games.

Again, one could explain it from a lack of theory of mind; however, based on her research of the ability of adults with autism to understand irony and similar types of communication, psychologist Francesca Happé[98] concluded that the problems primarily have to do with reduced context sensitivity. Her subjects understood that what had been said was not factually true, but they could not explain this based on the context.

## Context and Nonlinguistic Communication

So far, we have only described linguistic communication – communication using spoken and written language. But context is just as essential for understanding nonlinguistic forms of communication. In Chapter 4, we looked extensively at the role of context for understanding nonverbal communication such as facial expressions. We also use context to understand other nonlinguistic forms of communication, like the interpretation of pictures, symbols, and pictograms.[99] The following pictures will likely not tell you much and even may seem bizarre or confusing.

Imagine that the first sign was put on a high-voltage station, together with an exclamation mark and the word ATTENTION! The second sign stands at the entrance to a steep and uneven bridge paved with stones (making it difficult to enter) that leads to a tourist attraction in China. The third sign is located at the entrance of a museum next to the following signs:

With the context added, the signs are suddenly a lot less enigmatic. Chapter 3 about visual perception explained that context plays a role in recognition and understanding, even recognition and understanding of objects.

With people with autism and serious cognitive delays, we often use objects as a means of communication. Because of their developmental delay, they have a reduced understanding of spoken language and even pictures. For example, we might use toilet paper to show them that they need to go to the bathroom, a plate to say, "It's time to eat," and a cup to signify a break. But even on this concrete level of communication, context sensitivity plays a role.[100]

Imagine that you live in a place for adults with severe learning difficulties and a staff member gives you a cup as a means of communication. You would know that it is time for a break, and you would understand that you will be getting a drink. But what will you drink? How much? How long? Where? Depending on the context, the drink you will be getting could take a variety of forms. For example, on a hot day, it is more likely to be a soda than a cup of coffee or hot tea. In other words, as a symbol of communication, the cup does not say that much: It can refer to cola as well as coffee, be used outside or inside, and so on.

In practice, this does not create significant difficulties for people with autism and cognitive delays when they have an established routine. Each break looks a bit the same. They may only get confused when the routine changes, and they get an unexpected drink instead of the expected cup of coffee. They may not adjust the meaning of the cup to the context but have a fixed connection between the communication object and the meaning. In this way, they are not different from the high-functioning adult who refused to take part in the tea break at work, until the day he learned that the tea break did not necessarily mean that he had to drink tea and that coffee or sodas were also allowed.

## Summary

We often talk about *the meaning of a word*, but there really is no such thing as the unique meaning of a word. This is true for every symbol we use in communication. The meaning of words, sentences, pictures – whatever we use to communicate – is not absolute, but depends on the context. That is especially true at the level of world meanings of symbols, what they refer to in the real world. A word can have only one vocabulary meaning, but it can have thousands of world meanings.

There is a big difference between knowing words and understanding words. To know words, it is enough to learn their definitions. That is no problem for people with autism, as far as their intellectual capabilities allow. To learn the rules of grammar is also something they are able to do. What is challenging for them is using context to understand the particular meaning of communicative expressions in a certain situation. In spite of their sometimes excellent and impressive vocabulary, people with autism may have a difficult time understanding communication.

The fact that communicative competence requires more than semantic knowledge (knowing the meaning of words) – it also involves context sensitivity – implies that in assessing the communicative skills of someone with autism, classical language tests are not sufficient. We often overestimate the level of understanding of people with autism because we base our estimate on their semantic and grammar abilities (their language knowledge) instead of their ability to apply that knowledge flexibly within the context.

People with autism can connect meanings to symbols (again from a certain level of development), but they often remain fixed on learned connections between symbol and meaning and have difficulty letting go of the conventional meaning when context urges to. Flexibility in terms of connecting meanings to symbols is a core feature of the human ability of sense making.[101]

## Endnotes – Context in Communication

1. The more technical term is *phonemes*; for script signs, one can also use the term *graphemes*.
2. Sternberg (1987). The principle of learning vocabulary based on contextual elements is known as contextual vocabulary acquisition.
3. Baldwin (1993).
4. The phenomenon is known as phoneme restoration (Warren, 1970). Similar evidence of the influence of context on the basic levels of perception of sound was found by a Dutch-Finnish research group (Bonte, Parviainen, Hytönen, & Salmelin, 2006). Senseless syllables

activated a reaction by the brain consistent with the reaction to existing words in the early stages of processing (around 200 to 300 milliseconds) in a context where meaningful speech was expected. Linguistic context activates the areas in the brain that are in charge of the meaningful analysis of speech.

5. Ernestus, Baayen, and Schreuder (2002); Kemps, Ernestus, Schreuder, and Baayen (2004).
6. Ganong (1980). This concerns a top-down lexical influence on phoneme categorization. The Ganong effect occurs not only in spoken language. It is also present in written language, where recognition of letters is dependent on word images (McClelland & Rumelhart, 1981; Reichler, 1969).
7. According to recent neuroimaging research (fMRI-study), the fast top-down influence from higher levels of word processing to the lower level of the processing of phonemes is partially perceptual by nature and partially a form of executive top-down control (Myers & Blumstein, 2008).
8. In two studies involving university students without autism (Huang, 2007; Stewart & Ota, 2008), a relationship between the students' autism quotients and the Ganong effect was found: Students with high autism quotients were less vulnerable to the Ganong context effect in the recognition of sounds.
9. Warren and Warren (1970).
10. On YouTube there are different videos that let you experience the McGurk effect.
11. McGurk and MacDonald (1976).
12. Rosenblum, Schmuckler, and Johnson (1997).
13. Massaro (1987).
14. deGelder, Vroomen, and Van der Heide (1991); Massaro and Boesseler (2003); Mongillo et al. (2008).
15. Irwin (2007).
16. Context is not the only factor to influence the speed and accuracy of word recognition; other factors also play a role. For instance, frequent words are more quickly recognized than words that are used less frequently.
17. In technical terms, there is lexical priming of word candidates in a cohort. According to the cohort model of William Marslen-Wilson (1990), speech input activates a great number of word candidates, called a cohort. This cohort originates bottom-up and contains also a

number of word candidates that are incompatible with the context. However, based on the context we eliminate these candidates (top-down selection).

18. Example of Zwitserlood (1989).
19. Simpson, Peterson, Casteel, and Burgess (1989).
20. Cole and Jakimik (1978); Marslen-Wilson and Welsh (1978).
21. Goldwater, Griffiths, and Johnson (2007). One could argue that to understand language (and thus to understand the meaning of words) is a condition for recognizing individual words from the "noise" of words around us, but that is not the case. From the age of five months, children are capable of recognizing words in continuing speech, although they do not understand any of it. Purely based on sounds, children learn to distinguish words and word borders and thus discover what a word is and what it is not (Kooijman, Hagoort, & Cutler, 2005).
22. Meyer and Schvaneveldt (1971). The authors discuss semantic priming based on the semantic network in the brain. In addition, there is a phonologic and orthographic network, and that can lead to priming effects, such as phonologic priming – harp/harf, short/shirt or school/scope.
23. We will go into more detail later, when we discuss the contextualized representation of concepts in our brain.
24. Frith and Snowling (1983); Snowling and Frith (1986).
25. Braeuttigam, Swithenby, and Bailey (2008); Ring, Sharma, Wheelwright, and Barrett (2007).
26. Visible on the N400 potential.
27. We do not discuss here the levels of meanings as described by Roger Verpoorten (1996). Verpoorten distinguishes four levels of meaning: sensation, presentation, representation, and meta-presentation. The different forms of meaning that we describe are located on the levels of representation and meta-representation in Verpoorten's model, the levels on which there is conceptual understanding of symbols or referents.
28. Semantics is the study of the relations between words or sentences (form given in sounds or letters) and their meanings.
29. The difference between a dictionary meaning and the world meaning is related to the distinction between denotation (the concrete meaning of a word) and connotation (the emotional meaning of a word) but is much broader, because it goes further than the emotional value of words.

30. According to one of the founders of cognitive psychology, George A. Miller (1999), we know the meaning of a lot of words in real life (the world meaning) but not the dictionary meaning. "Without special training, most people have trouble defining words whose meanings they know perfectly well" (p. 5).
31. Where semantics involves lexical meanings, the domain of pragmatics is communicative meaning.
32. See www.smurf.com
33. "It is a perverse feature of natural languages that the more frequently a word is used, the more polysemous it tends to be" (Miller, 1999, p. 12). See also Jastrezembski (1981).
34. "Durch den Kontext wird ein Wort eindeutig gemacht oder monosemiert." Hönig and Kussmaul (1982, p. 96). *(Through context a word acquires a single meaning or monosemous.)*
35. In computer linguistics, the technical term *word sense disambiguation* is used.
36. See, e.g., Kambe, Rayner, and Duffy (2001); Rayner, Cook, Juhasz, and Frazier (2006); Van Berkum, Brown, and Hagoort (1999).
37. Moss, McCormick, and Tyler (1997).
38. Frith and Snowling (1983).
39. Walenski, Mostofsky, Larson, and Ullman (2008).
40. This seems to contradict what we described before: that children with autism perform less well than a control group on a test involving reproducing lists of related words. But differences in the research design, especially the age of the subjects, may explain the inconsistent results. See Lopez and Leekam (2003). In studies like that of Tager-Flusberg (1991), performance was compared with, on the one hand, a list of unrelated words and, on the other, a list with related words. However, when different lists of related words were used (resulting in more semantic categories), the children with autism appeared to use the semantic categories as well as the children without autism.
41. For an overview, see Walenski, Tager-Flusberg, and Ullman (2006).
42. Frith and Snowling (1983); Happé (1997); Jolliffe and Baron-Cohen (1999a); Lopez and Leekam (2003); Snowling and Frith (1986).
43. Hala, Pexman, and Glenwright (2007).
44. Booth and Happé (2010).
45. Brock, Norbury, Einav, and Nation (2008). Norbury (2005) did similar research with children with autism, children with language disorders, and typically developing children. In that study, it was also con-

cluded that children with autism use context in processing ambiguous words. However, decreased use of context was present in children with language problems. Context sensitivity in language would, thus, be related to the level of language development. Our criticism of the Brock et al. study also holds true for Norbury.

46. Clark and Carlson (1982) criticized the way context is defined in many psycholinguistic studies. According to them, researchers often use de-contextualized materials. Performance on this type of materials can hardly be generalized to everyday use of language and language understanding. Context is much more than just the linguistic context of sentences and words around a "target stimulus". The extralinguistic context (the world around us) also plays an important role in the understanding of language, perhaps an even more important role than the linguistic context.
47. Lopez and Leekam (2003).
48. Snowling and Frith (1986).
49. "Also on June 29th Santa Claus exists." Speech by Dr. I. A. van Berckelaer-Onnes at her retirement as professor at the University of Leiden (June, 29. 2007, p. 10).
50. Kanner (1943).
51. Vermeulen (1998).
52. Fiebach and Friederici (2004).
53. This is known as the context availability model (CAM). Alongside the availability of visual images, context plays a role in the difference between abstract and concrete words. According to the CAM model, our language understanding is highly dependent on contextual information, including both the external and the internal context. See, among others, Jessen et al. (2000) and Liebscher and Groppe (2003).
54. Schwanenflugel and Stowe (1989).
55. See Hampton (2003). Hampton speaks of "instantiation." Instantiation is influenced by context. Instantiation of an abstract concept means estimating the probability of a concrete interpretation of the concept within a certain context. Contextually induced instantiation involves the replacement of a general, overarching, abstract concept by a more concrete understanding (e.g., "drink" replaced with "coffee").
56. There are different forms of vagueness in sentences, like metonyms, ellipsis, and anaphors.
57. Spivey, Tanenhaus, Eberhard, and Sedivy (2002). See also Spivey-Knowlton, Trueswell, and Tanenhaus (1993) and Tanenhaus, Spivey-Knowlton, Eberhard, and Sedivy (1995).

58. Diehl, Bennetto, Watson, Gunlogson, and McDonough (2008).
59. Jolliffe and Baron-Cohen (1999a).
60. In this study, the researchers also gave the subjects a homograph test. The scores on the test with ambiguous sentences were highly correlated with the scores on the homographs test, which is additional proof of reduced context sensitivity in the subjects with autism.
61. Jolliffe and Baron-Cohen (1999a).
62. Jolliffe and Baron-Cohen (2000).
63. Dennis, Lazenby, and Lockyer (2001); Kaland, Callesen, Møller-Nielsen, Mortensen, and Smith (2008); Kaland, Mortensen, and Smith (2007); Loukusa and others (2007a); Norbury and Bishop (2002).
64. Norbury and Bishop (2002).
65. Norbury and Bishop (2002).
66. Cain, Oakhill, Barnes, and Bryant (2001).
67. E.g., in the study by Norbury and Bishop (2002), only 15%.
68. Kaland, Smith, and Mortensen (2007). For the subjects, discerning mental states was still more difficult and took much longer than did discerning physical states. Additionally, subjects without autism also required more time to determine mental states, but the difference in reaction time with determining physical states was smaller.
69. From the study of Norbury and Bishop (2002).
70. Jolliffe and Baron-Cohen (1999a).
71. Saldaña and Frith (2007).
72. This is known as the direct access model (DAM). For an overview, see Gibbs (2002). There is discussion about the role of context in canceling out ambiguities of literal and figurative language, especially about how instant and direct the effect of context is. See for instance Dascal (1989). However, researchers have generally agreed that context gives at least some direction in distinguishing between figurative and literal language use.
73. Happé (1993).
74. Norbury (2004).
75. This corresponds to what we described earlier in the case of understanding homographs.
76. Dennis et al. (2001).
77. Hoy (2007).

78. Oi and Tanaka (2011).
79. Le Sourn-Bissaoui, Caillies, Gierski, and Motte (2011).
80. But not always. Gibbs (1984) and Giora (1999), although disagreeing in other areas, agree that the distinction between literal and figurative understanding is less important than the distinction between dominant and less dominant meanings. It appears that people need more time to give the literal meaning of a well-known idiom than to retrieve the figurative, more dominant meaning (Laurent, Denhières, Passerieux, Iakimova, & Hardy-Baylé, 2006). In the case of frequently used and well-known idioms, figurative meanings are more dominant and conventional than literal meanings.
81. Miller and Charles (1991). According to these authors, contextual representations consist of three types of contexts: the situation in which the communication occurs (and in that, the roles of the speaker and the listener), how a certain word is used, and the local context (the context of the other words and sentences around the word, the so-called co-text).
82. See especially the seminal work of Paul Grice (1989).
83. I used this example before in *Autistic Thinking* (Vermeulen, 1996a).
84. Sperber and Wilson (1995).
85. Bezuidenhout and Sroda (1998).
86. Tager-Flusberg (2000).
87. Bosco, Bucciarelli, and Bara (2004).
88. Especially the presence and the absence of objects that the conversation is focused on and what has been said previously in the conversation. They still have trouble with other contextual elements, like the posture and the movements of the speaker, but from the age of 6 onwards, children also take that into account.
89. Karmiloff-Smith (1986).
90. American Psychiatric Association (1994).
91. We refer here to the earlier studies about inferential understanding (e.g., Dennis et al., 2001; Kaland et al., 2007, 2008; Loukusa et al., 2007a, 2007b; Norbury & Bishop, 2002). For a brief overview, see Martin and McDonald (2003) and Noens and van Berckelaer-Onnes (2005).
92. Fine, Barolucci, Szatmari, and Ginsberg (1994); Losh and Capps (2003).
93. Barnes and Baron-Cohen (2011)
94. Loukusa et al. (2007a).

95. The *Dewey Stories* (Vermeulen, 2002).
96. Wang, Lee, Sigman, and Dapretto (2006).
97. Jolliffe and Baron-Cohen (1999a).
98. Happé (1994).
99. Many visual representations in manuals, pictures, signs, etc., are easy to understand in an "autistic," literal way. Darren Barefoot, a Canadian writer, collects on his website in a "hall of technical documentation weirdness" visual representations that he interprets in a funny way, often literally the "autistic" way: http://www.darrenbarefoot.com/hall/.
100. Noens and van Berckelaer-Onnes (2007).
101. Boser, Higgins, Fetherston, Preissler, and Gordon (2002, p. 564): "Flexibility of reference is a powerful central feature of our semantic system."

# Chapter 6
# Context in Knowledge

Why do we think a 3, 7, or 9 are better examples
of an odd number than 97 or 447?

Is the pope a bachelor? And why does it take
us longer to answer that question than if we were
asked if George Clooney is a bachelor?

How do we know if an exotic fruit we have
just seen for the first time is a fruit or a vegetable?

Why is a chimpanzee sometimes more similar
to a wild pig than to a gorilla?

Why does our knowledge about dogs include
things like fire hydrants and sidewalks?

Why do we remember words that we have never heard?

A river eel looks more like a snake than a fish.
Still we recognize a river eel as a fish. How is that?

How do you know which door to open
when someone asks you to "open the door"?

When we think about a morning drink,
why do we more often think of coffee than whiskey?

What is the difference between intelligence
and common sense?

What we know about the world is contained in what psychologists call concepts.[1] Concepts are the units that our brain uses when it thinks. They are stored in our memory and together form our knowledge of the world. Every concept contains our knowledge of a piece of the world, more exactly of a category of phenomena, like a dog, book, refrigerator, news broadcast, football game, or fight.

Our brain contains thousands of concepts. Some relate to natural phenomena, like plants, animals, clouds, or sand. Other concepts relate to things that are made by human beings, like a toaster, a car, underwear, and a pyramid. Some concepts are very concrete and easy to visualize, like pyramid, Christmas tree, and toaster. Others are more abstract and more difficult to visualize: truth, democracy, lies, and freedom. Still other concepts are somewhere in between. You may visualize concrete examples of the concept, but these examples of the same concept can look very different. Examples include meal, mother-in-law, fight, hooligan, bachelor, and pet. The concept pet has far more variations than the images you might have of concrete concepts like toaster or Christmas tree, even though there are different kinds of toasters and Christmas trees.

How do you develop these concepts? By a complicated process involving summarizing your experiences in this world.[2] When you see a book for the first time, you see similarities to and differences from earlier perceptions of other objects. "Ah, this is the same color as that thing I saw before. It looks a bit longer than what I saw before, but it is also a little smaller and a bit thicker," and so on. You still do not know what you see, so you do not recognize it as a book, but there are certain features you recognize from earlier experiences on which you can rely to form an idea about it. The next time you see a book, you will adjust the knowledge that you gained at the first perception with the knowledge from the current perception. That way you may determine that the exact thickness of the object is not the most important characteristic, nor is the color. It looks like the last time, only a bit thicker; and this time it is green and not blue as the last time. This is the way we continuously adjust our concepts and correct them (that appears to go reasonably fast after only a few experiences), and in your brain something like the term *book* will form: You have a concept of book.

Concepts are categories. The concept of book stands for all books, regardless of their look or content. Certain categories also belong to a broader category. For example, the concept of a book is embedded in the broader concept of reading material. The concept mother-in-law belongs in the category mother, and that concept, in turn, belongs to the category of parent.

Concepts are crucial to survival. To start with, we need concepts for communication: They help us give meaning to what others are telling us. In Chapter 5, we saw how important world knowledge is for understanding communication. Thanks to your concept of book, you know what someone is referring to when he says that he just got a book. You know that he is not referring to some kind of contagious disease, for example.

Concepts contain information not only about what something is and what it looks like, but also about what you can do with it and what you cannot do with it. Your concept of book contains the knowledge that you can read the book. And your concept of dog contains the knowledge that dogs can bite and that dogs are not pieces of furniture. This explains why, in general, people do not sit on a dog. Therefore, concepts help us to cope with the world and to solve problems.

*By developing categories (concepts), our brain can recognize things and cope with them more efficiently. Without the concept book, you would have to store all the books you ever saw in your memory in order to be able to recognize a book you had never seen before.*

The main function of concepts or categories is to prevent overloading our brain. Imagine that you did not have a category for book in your brain. You would have to memorize all the individual books you ever came across. The concept or the category for book makes us capable of recognizing books, to think about them, and to handle them without having to remember all our concrete experiences with books. Concepts or categories, as a kind of filtered essence of the things and events around us, make it less tiresome to perceive than if we had to collect all the details. The only way of "not becoming a slave to details," as the writer Umberto Eco[3] formulated it, is to develop the ability to form categories, such as book, bank robbery, sweet, dog or mother in law.

Temple Grandin,[4] a well-known woman with autism, explains that she has to make do without these types of categories. She compares her mind to an Internet search engine like Google that collects all types of pictures. Her concept (as far as we can call it that) of dog, for instance, is a collection of pictures of all the dogs that she has ever seen through which she has to browse very fast in order to recognize a dog. To develop the concept of orange, she acquired a collection of images of all types of orange things, like oranges, pumpkins, orange juice, jam, and so on.[5] It seems that Temple does not develop typical concepts, but a huge encyclopedic collection of concrete perceptional experiences. Similar to many other people with autism, this makes perception and recognition for her a very tiresome and nerve-wrecking activity. All that paging through and comparing quickly over-stresses the brain.

Is Temple Grandin an exception? Is what she has said about her brain proof that she does not have any concepts? What is the possible role of context in the way that our brain forms and uses concepts? To be able to offer answers, we have to look at how we develop concepts. It is a bit of a long story, but one that is necessary to tell in order to understand the role of context in the development of concepts.

## Concepts: Criteria, Prototypes, and Examples

We are not born with all the concepts that we possess later as adults. If that were the case, we would not experience objects, things, or situations as new or unknown. Children do not come into this world with knowledge about the world. If they did, toddlers would not put filthy things in their mouths, because they would already know that the things are filthy and, therefore, bad for them. However, as they experience putting something filthy in their mouths, they come to do it less often in the future because bit by bit, their brain develops a concept of filth.

What we are born with is the ability to develop concepts, in other words, to categorize. Babies of only a few hours of age are already able to categorize faces.[6] As a result, after a few weeks, they are capable of distinguishing people from non-people. And that is helpful when you look for something that can give you food or can change your dirty diaper. Yet, people greatly differ in appearance. That is a real *tour de force* for those babies.

Psychologists believe that the ability to see and react appropriately to things that look very different but are members of the same category is fundamental to human intelligence. Categorizing is a very complex skill, yet most of us succeed at mastering it without effort. You recognize a chair without thinking much about it being a chair, although chairs can look very different from each other. You will not categorize as chairs certain objects that look a lot like chairs, like sofas, benches, or bar stools, but chairs that look like something totally different you will recognize. It will never occur to you to try to milk the thing that is portrayed in the following photograph, although it appears to resemble a bunch of cows.

How do we categorize? Scientists have fiercely debated this in recent years.[7] How do you arrive, for example, at the concept of chair? The first answer was: Based on our experiences, we distill certain rules or criteria. A chair has four legs, an area to sit on, something to lean back on, and so on: Aha, a chair!

For a number of concepts, especially concrete concepts like chair, this seems to work. Yet, this cannot be the method for developing concepts. As soon as we try to formulate criteria, we get into trouble. A bench also has four legs, an area to sit, and a back to lean against, but it is not a chair. And not all chairs have four legs. And what about a bar stool? Even with concrete things, in principle, criteria cannot be the sole basis on which to form a concept. That is because concepts are not strictly defined but have vague and fuzzy boundaries.[8] Where does chair end and bar stool or bench begin? It's hard to tell.

Using certain criteria will not help with a more abstract concept, like bachelor.[9] The criterion for the category of bachelor is fairly simple: an unmarried adult man. But is that not also applicable in the case of a Catholic priest? He meets the criterion, but most people do not see a priest as a member of the club of bachelors. And what about an unmarried man who lives with a woman? And is a boy living at home on his 18th birthday suddenly a bachelor?

It is clear that criteria alone are not very helpful in developing concepts. Or, as psychologist and linguist Steven Pinker[10] framed it, whenever you try to determine criteria, the concept falls apart. Criteria do not work well because most categories have vague borders and great variation across the examples that belong to them. Chairs come in many different forms and colors; yet, despite the rich variations, you still have a concept of chair. According to some psychologists, this is because you developed a prototype of a chair,[11] a sort of average, typical chair. A lot of categories are not about yes or no, but about more or less. For example, one chair is more chair-like than another. Prototypes can work well when there is a lot of variation, like in the categories chair, dog, and bird.

There is proof for the existence of prototypes in our brain. For instance, in the category of fruit, people in our culture first think about apples and not about melons. Regarding the category of bird, we think more about a dove or a sparrow than about a penguin or an emu. Apples are a more common fruit than melons, and although a penguin or an emu are undoubtedly birds, we consider them less bird-like. Similarly, people have to think longer about the question of whether the pope is a bachelor than about other men, which points to the fact that we use a sort of prototype of bachelor to make our decision, a prototype to which the pope does not immediately relate.

The curious thing is that we even form prototypes for things that, in principle, can only be categorized based on rules and criteria, like triangles, square, red, woman, or odd number. Contrary to birds and chairs, triangles cannot be "a bit like a triangle" and numbers cannot be "more or less odd." A number is either even or odd. Still, people view the numbers 3, 7, and 9 as better examples of an odd number than 97 or 447,[12] even though they know that a number cannot be "a little bit odd."

Since most concepts or categories do not have sharply outlined boundaries or a set of fixed criteria, prototypes have an advantage. A penguin does not fit the criterion of flying, but we can still categorize it as a bird. We add new members to a category based on their resemblance to the prototype. As soon as a certain piece of furniture bears more resemblance to a chair than to a loveseat, we categorize it as a chair.

What can we say about the concept of game, for example? Philosopher Ludwig Wittgenstein[13] asked himself how we categorize something as a game. The differences among all types of games (social games, ball games, sports, card games) are extensive. If there were prototypes for our concepts, what would be the prototype of a game? Football? Chess? *Monopoly*? It is highly improbable that we have a prototype of a game, and it is equally improbable that we have prototypes for concepts like work, family, furniture, or bachelor (despite competitions for Bachelor of the Year).

It is more probable that we use different examples[14] of those categories. According to this assumption, concepts do not consist of one member, the prototype, but are collections of more or less known examples that belong to that category (e.g., a collection of chairs that are "chair-like," games that are "game-like," and our collection of well-known bachelors). According to this theory, we recognize a chair based on its resemblance to examples that are stored in our brain related to the category of chair. We categorize someone as being a bachelor when he belongs in a collection of bachelors that is stored in our memory.[15] In that view, what Temple Grandin does (sorting through pictures in her brain) is not so strange, although our collections are probably a lot more restrained than hers.

It is a little difficult to choose between the three approaches to how we develop concepts or categories. Presumably, we use all three ways, depending on the type of concept: one or more criteria, the forming of a prototype, the collection of a number of typical examples, or a combination of all three.

## All Dogs and Bikes: Being Unable to Categorize?

Despite the fundamental importance of concepts for coping with the world around us, the way a person with autism forms concepts has been researched very little. The story of Temple Grandin makes us suspect that people with autism have difficulty forming concepts or categories. Temple does not even store typical examples of dogs in her memory; she simply stores *all* the images of dogs that she has ever seen. And she does not form any prototypes!

The idea that people with autism do not form prototypes or other forms of abstract categories has been around for a long time. The pioneers of psychological research in autism Beate Hermelin and Neil O'Connor[16] showed with their ingenious experiments that children with autism do not support their memory by grouping information in categories. On a word recall task with words from a certain category (i.e., banana, prune, apple), children with autism did not perform better than on a task with random words (i.e., motorcycle, milk, chair, newspaper). By comparison, children without autism can repeat more words when there is a relationship between them because they belong to the same category.

Based on their experiments, other scientists from the early days of autism research[17] came to the conclusion that children with autism did not form categories, but remained fixed on the concrete experiences from their senses. That is also what Temple Grandin says. To recognize a specific dog as being a dog, she compares the dog's nose, ears, and so on, with the pictures she already has in her head.

Temple Grandin once asked people she met to search in their memories for church towers and describe what they looked like. She says, "I was shocked to find out that a lot of people see only a vague, general top of a tower, while I see a whole sequence of photo-realistic images of specific towers."[18] If people with autism do form categories, they are based on detail characteristics, not on essential or more abstract characteristics.

For many years, the prevailing thought was that people with autism barely formed prototypes due to a restricted ability to abstract. For example, two American researchers[19] showed children with and without autism drawings of imaginary animals and asked them to categorize them. In one set of drawings, the animals could be classified based on rules, and in the other set, the animals could be classified based on a prototype.

In the rule-based categorizing, children with autism performed as well as children without autism; however, in categorizing based on prototypes, they did not perform as well as their neurotypical peers. Children with Down's syndrome also struggled with categorization by prototype. This seems to indicate that the problem with forming prototypes is not autism-specific; it has to do with the intelligence level of the specific subjects participating in the studies. British researchers[20] replicated the research, but with higher functioning children. They came to the conclusion that children with autism with higher intelligence did not have problems forming prototypes, thus indicating that intelligence is indeed a factor.

The ability to see resemblances is essential in concept formation, whether the concept is a prototype or a collection of typical examples. When you do not see the resemblance between all the books, dogs, or toasters that you come across in your life, it is difficult to develop concepts about them. Being able to recognize a book as a book depends strongly on the resemblance that you find between a given book and your concept of book.

The British psychologist Kate Plaisted[21] found that adults with autism are not good at processing features held in common between stimuli; however, they process differences (features unique to a stimulus) quite well. That would mean that they have difficulty with filling a representative collection with enough typical examples that, in spite of their differences, still belong to the same category.

> In the story about her son Thomas, Hilde De Clercq[22] gives a number of good examples. One is about Thomas' concept of a bike. "Thomas had different names for everything that we just call a bike. He had 'bike,' 'tractor,' 'wheels in the mud,' 'wheels in the grass' and 'foot on the pedals.'"

Thomas saw the differences between different bikes, not the similarities. As a result, he had difficulty developing a concept of bike. Thomas was still relatively young when he had trouble with the concept bike, so perhaps it had more to do with his developmental age at that time than with his autism.

It seems contradictory: On one hand, some research suggests that people with autism have trouble forming concepts, whereas other research states that they do not seem to differ from people without autism in terms of the process of forming concepts. What is going on?

A recent study at the University of Pittsburgh[23] provides some clarification. According to this study, people with autism do not differ from people without autism in the progress they make during the development of the ability to categorize. That is, adults are better at it than adolescents, and adolescents are better at it than children, even when they have autism. This explains the results of the early studies about categorizing people with autism. The subjects were children; furthermore, they were children who had cognitive challenges.

According to the Pittsburgh study, adults with autism do not seem to have problems with categorizing concrete things such as dogs. They also do not have problems with cats, chairs, and seats, all concepts that were researched. Still they did not perform as well on the test as did the persons without autism. This was true especially for recognizing less typical examples in a category. For instance, recognizing a typical chair as a chair was no problem, nor was recognizing a typical bench as a bench. But when faced with a bench-like chair, the subjects with autism had more difficulty than the subjects without autism. As soon as the differences from the prototype or the most typical examples of the category became greater, the subjects with autism, regardless of age, had more problems with categorizing. That is consistent with Kate Plaisted's hypothesis: People with autism see the differences more than the resemblances.

People with autism usually understand typical examples of a concept. This indicates that they do form concepts similarly to people without autism, as is true for Temple Grandin. The fact that she has a collection of dog images demonstrates that her brain knows the category dog. That she pages through her collection of dog pictures when seeing a dog means that she has a suspicion that what she sees is possibly a dog; otherwise, it would be impossible for her to make the correct choice among the many collections of pictures in her memory. Besides, when seeing a dog, she would also have to page through her collections of cats, shag carpets, or end tables because cats, shag carpets, and end tables share at least one characteristic of the dog category: cats have a tail; shag carpets are "furry"; and end tables have four legs.

Thus, people with autism possess concrete and clearly defined concepts like dog, cat, chair, or bench. They also are capable of developing concepts for simple things like schematic line-drawn cartoon animals or the geometric figures and patterns that are frequently used in research, and that can be categorized based on either prototype or a reduced number of recognizable criteria. However, we warn against early optimism, because research materials are often not realistic models of life (as seen in the research on emotion recognition and language understanding). This is not sufficient evidence that people with autism develop concepts in the same way as people without autism. Stories like those of Temple and Thomas are too numerous to be regarded as exceptions.

In real life, most things do not belong to concrete and clearly definable categories. Many concepts are relatively vague, such as bachelor or game. These types of vague concepts are often difficult for people with autism to understand and use. Normally intelligent adults with autism who can categorize dot patterns and schematic, line-drawn bugs and animals without too much difficulty still make mistakes when having to categorize more realistic but less clear-cut definable things, such as a certain type of landscape.[24] They can categorize typical male or female faces as male or female without much difficulty but are less successful at categorizing atypical faces.[25] Thus, with clearly definable concepts and typical examples of concepts, people with autism do not have great difficulty.[26] In contrast, vague concepts and atypical examples are difficult for them. What makes the difference? Context, again! Context plays an important role in the way we form concepts and manipulate concepts, as we will describe in the following paragraphs.

## Context and Atypical Examples

Let us first look to some atypical examples. Even people without autism sometimes find it difficult to determine based on the face alone if someone is a man or a woman. But this happens only in rare cases, for instance, when seeing a transvestite or in cross-dressing for disguise or performance art. In general, people without autism do not have difficulties distinguishing male and female faces. That is because when we categorize, we usually take the context into account, like the shape and the form of the body and the clothes that someone is wearing. And because we also take into account the clothing, we are misled in cases of cross-dressing.

According to Belgian researchers, the categorizing of a face as male or female is very context sensitive, especially in the case of atypical or ambiguous information.[27] When a face was not clearly male or female, subjects made use of contextual information, such as someone's first name, to determine the gender.

Context sensitivity can be used to explain why Temple Grandin goes through so much work when having to recognize a dog. She reports that she has to check numerous characteristics, such as nose, ears, mouth, and so on. That would make it particularly difficult to recognize atypical dog breeds. People without autism not only recognize a dog based on its physical characteristics and the degree to which it matches the prototypes in their memories, but also based on context, such as the fact that the animal is on a leash, which would be unusual for similar pets, like a cat. So, context is more influential in categorizing atypical examples than in categorizing typical examples. That might explain why people with autism have more difficulties with atypical examples than with typical ones.

## How Do You Categorize Things You Have Never Seen?

Context not only plays a part in categorizing atypical examples. Context becomes especially useful when we try to categorize examples that we have never seen before. An example is the categorization of unknown species of vegetables and fruit. The following picture shows a number of examples of the *antroewa*, a delicacy that is used in African, and especially Surinam, cuisine. Unless you are familiar with those types of cuisine, you probably do not know the *antroewa*. But what is the *antroewa*: a vegetable or a fruit?

The *antroewa*: vegetable or fruit?

Based on the picture, it is hard to say, but if you were to walk the market in Paramaribo, the capital of Suriname, you would have far less difficulty. Chances are great that you would find the *antroewa* in the stalls and shops next to carrots, and most probably even next to eggplants, because the *antroewa* is a kind of eggplant (also called the African eggplant). Based on that context, you would immediately decide that the *antroewa* is a vegetable. Thus, context helps us to categorize new and unknown things.

## Changing Categories

So far, we have assumed things belong to only one category. A dog is an animal and not a piece of furniture. A chair is a seat and not a fruit. And the *antroewa* is a vegetable and not sports equipment, although it is round like a ball. A lot of things that we come across in our lives do not belong to one, but to multiple categories. Categories or concepts not only have blurry borders, they also do not have a fixed set of examples. Every example can also belong to other categories.

Your female neighbor, for example, not only belongs to the category neighbor, but perhaps also to the following categories: woman, mother, driver, American, landscape architect, blonde, and curious. Depending on the context, you put the female neighbor in a given category. When you are planning to create your garden, you will more likely put her in the category of landscape architect than in the category of driver. But if you could not drive a car and were in urgent need of transportation, you would likely think of your neighbor as an example of the driver category.

The sparse research on the categorization skills of people with autism shows the same flaws as the research on emotion recognition. One unjustifiably starts from the idea that there will be a direct connection between a stimulus (facial expression) and emotion, or in the case of concepts between examples and category. But things can belong to different categories, depending on the context. Is a tomato a vegetable or a fruit? It depends on the context. Scientifically, tomato is a fruit, but in the context of preparing a dish, the tomato is often viewed as a vegetable.[28]

*Is a tomato a fruit or a vegetable? It depends on the context!*

The strawberry and the melon are just the opposite. In a culinary context, they are fruits, but in professional magazines about vegetables and fruits, they are often found in the category of vegetables to which they belong, strictly speaking. That is nice to know, you probably think, but these are exceptions. Most things belong clearly to one category. Not true! Even everyday objects can be put into multiple categories.

For instance, a television set belongs to the media category (along with a newspaper), but also to the furniture category (along with a seat), and the electrical equipment category (along with a vacuum cleaner). The category in which you put the television set depends on the context. The fact that a lot of things can belong to multiple categories means that most of our concepts, like furniture, are vaguely defined. When people are asked if a television set is a piece of furniture, they are often unsure of how to answer. But such uncertainty vanishes when you put the question into a context, like reorganizing the living room. People will place television sets in a category depending on the context.[29]

Remember our discussion of the concept of book? A book belongs in the category of reading material but is also a member of the categories of insect killer, protection against rain, and even gift.

Here is one last example. Cows and horses belong to the same categories of mammals, farm animals, and milk producers. In the context of a conversation about milk, people see a cow as a more typical example than a horse, but in the context of riding, a horse is often seen as a more typical example than a cow.[30] Context determines the typicality of a certain example for a certain category.

## Context, Concrete and Abstract Categories

When categorizing, we can choose from different levels of categories, from very specific and concrete to very general and abstract. For instance, we can categorize a specific chair as a garden chair, as a seat, and as furniture. Often we spontaneously categorize at the middle level. What do you see in the next picture?

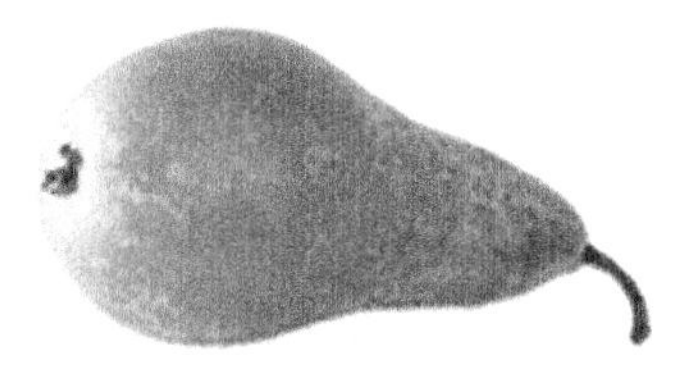

Most likely, you will say *pear*, and not *conference pear* or *fruit*. The level of categorization as *pear* is what psychologists call the basic level of concepts.[31] The basic level is what we use to explain information about the world to children. When a young child points to a car and asks what it is, you will answer with "a car," not "a vehicle" or "a Peugeot."

But we do not always categorize on the basic level. If you witness a traffic violation, you will not tell the police that you saw a "vehicle" pass through the red light. You would categorize on a more specific level, or at least try to – not everyone is capable of distinguishing a Peugeot from a Renault. We are very flexible in choosing the level on which we categorize and let the choice depend on the context. Research has shown that even babies of barely 18 months have that flexibility and that their choices are context dependent.[32] Depending on the context, they will consider fish, birds, and cows as being of different categories or belonging together in the general category of animals.

In one of the first scientific studies concerning categorizing by children with autism,[33] researchers discovered that the children were able to put examples into categories but that they did so based on very concrete perceptional elements and not based on more abstract, functional characteristics. Categorizing based on concrete perceptional characteristics is often called *perceptual categorizing*. When you group by more abstract characteristics, one speaks of *conceptual categorizing.*

Which ones belong together?

According to the study, children with autism would group the pictures above at a perceptual level: They would put the ball and the orange together, and next to that the banana and the boomerang, because they look alike. People without autism would categorize on a more abstract, conceptual level, and would place the orange together with the banana (fruit) and the boomerang together with the ball (toys). But is this a correct conclusion? Will people without autism always choose the more abstract conceptual level to categorize and never the more perceptual level, that of concrete perceptional characteristics? Absolutely not.

Imagine you are in a bowling alley[34] where two teams are competing. In the left lane, the women are playing in green suits, while in the right lane the men are bowling in red suits. A woman enters the bowling alley wearing a red suit. In which lane will she bowl? Did you guess that she would bowl in the right lane? In this context, it is a perceptual characteristic, or the color of the outfit, that is the more important criterion for determining the group than the more abstract, conceptual characteristic of the person's gender.

How do we know on which level to categorize? There are no fixed rules; that much is clear. We are flexible in the way we categorize things. That means we keep context in mind and change levels when necessary. When you pack a suitcase for travel, you usually first group on the conceptual level: shirts together, sweaters together, and pants together. But when your suitcase becomes full, you switch to a perceptual level. You look where there are empty spaces, and you pack things that fit according to their size and form, unrelated to the conceptual category to which they belong.

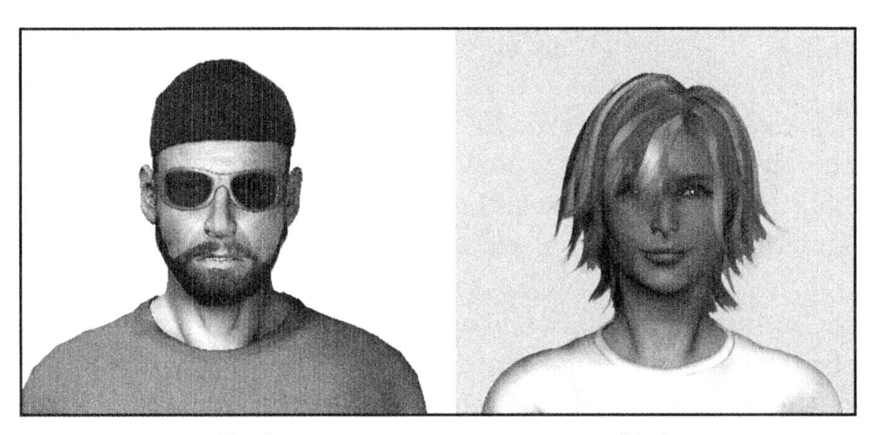

Fred Linda

Suppose you see Fred and Linda on the previous page walking in the street, each carrying a laptop. One of them is a thief. Who is the thief? Without more information, you will think Fred is the thief because he looks a bit like a thief, hiding behind dark glasses. But what if Fred and Linda are the main characters in the story that follows?

> Fred lives on a fixed income. He likes to surf the Internet but cannot afford a computer. When his parents bought a new computer, Fred went to their house to pick up their old laptop.
>
> Linda is jealous of her next-door neighbor, Jenny, who just bought a new laptop. While Linda is visiting Jenny one day, Jenny leaves for a moment. Linda takes this opportunity to pick up the laptop and take it to her own apartment, whereupon she quickly returns to Jenny's apartment, not intending to tell what she has done.

Who is the thief? Because of the context, now you will not categorize Fred as the thief, but you will categorize Linda as the thief, even though she has a nice face that does not look like that of a criminal.

For this type of context-dependent categorizing, we have some scientific evidence. A chocolate Easter egg looks like an egg, but it is not an egg. A scrambled egg does not look perceptually like an egg, but conceptually it does. Depending on context, people may or may not see the chocolate egg and the scrambled egg as an egg.[35] In other words, the weight that people give to superficial, perceptual resemblances or to more abstract, functional resemblances is context-dependent.

One assumes that categorizing based on concrete perceptual characteristics is of a lower level than categorizing based on more abstract conceptual characteristics. In large part, this is true. In typical development, children first place more importance on how something looks and only later on how something functions. For example, going back to the study mentioned earlier, the children who put the ball and the orange together were said to be functioning on a lower level than the children who put the orange with the banana.

The *Comfor*[36] is a well-known test based on this principle. It analyzes the level of understanding of people with autism and/or a cognitive delay. Subjects sort all types of objects, like forks and balls, and pictures of those objects. If they do not match objects or pictures of objects that look different but conceptually belong together (like nonidentical forks or balls), but only put things together that are identical, they are said to understand at a presentational level. In other words, they categorize literally based on perceptional characteristics. However, when subjects put different forks together (and thus see the "forkness" as the common characteristic, despite differences in concrete appearance), they are said to understand on a representational level.

For people with autism and at a young developmental age, matching on a representational level is difficult. That is not only related to their autism, but also to their cognitive development.[37] Research with higher functioning people with autism has shown that they are capable of categorizing concrete objects, like benches and chairs, on a representational level.

Based on this finding, one could incorrectly conclude that higher functioning individuals with autism do not have problems with categorizing concrete things. However, as we have seen, they have difficulty with atypical examples, perhaps because they pay too much attention to differences in details instead of functional resemblance. From that perspective, higher functioning people with autism do not differ much from persons with autism and a cognitive disability who have difficulties seeing the resemblance in the "forkness" of two different-looking forks. So, people with autism tend to focus more on (sometimes detail) differences in concrete and perceptual characteristics of things. But should we consider this as a "lower" level of categorizing?

*Context determines the level on which we categorize things. Flexibility in choosing the level is more important than the actual level on which we categorize.*

In the development of concepts, the human brain evolves from the basic, middle level (pear) to both the more general, abstract level (piece of fruit) and the underlying level (conference pear). Development of concepts leads not only to an increasing ability to abstract but also to an increasing ability to differentiate. Seeing differences on the level of concrete details is, therefore, not necessarily a lower level of understanding, because the different levels of categorizing do not reflect a strict hierarchy in cognitive development.

Human intelligence is not so much reflected in the level of categorization as in the level of flexibility in the choice of the level of categorization. In certain contexts, categorization based on concrete, perceptual characteristics is more appropriate, and you will have little success when you categorize on a more abstract level. For example, in many situations, the physical differences between birds are not very important; it is sufficient to categorize them all as birds. But for someone joining an annual bird counting day, those differences in detail are important. Similarly, the differences between forks are generally not important. But for someone who is working in a restaurant or is organizing an upscale dinner for important guests, the differences in details have to be taken into account, and only appropriate forks will be placed on the table. In short, flexibility in categorizing is more important than the level of categorizing, and that flexibility requires context sensitivity.

## Context and the Criteria We Use to Categorize

Even within one category level, context has an influence on what we fit together and what we put in a separate category. For example, what belongs together in the following?[38]

White hair, grey hair, and black hair
White clouds, grey clouds, and black clouds

In the case of hair, according to most people, white and grey belong together, but in the case of clouds, grey and black fit together. Hair and clouds form a different context, and that has an effect on the categorization of the three colors. In the context of hair, white and grey belong together because they are signs of old age. In the context of clouds, grey and black belong together because they are signs of possible rainfall. Here is another example: Which animals fit together?

Gorilla, chimpanzee, wild boar, and desert warthog

At first sight, in this case, the gorilla goes together with the chimpanzee and the wild boar with the desert warthog. In zoos, you will most often find these animals in each other's neighborhoods. Zoos generally place biological sorts together: hoofed animals together with hoofed animals, birds together with birds, and monkeys together with monkeys. That is easier for the visitors. When they want to see monkeys, they should not have to go to 10 different places. But for the animal caretakers who give food to these animals (in another context) the wild boar fits with the chimpanzee and the gorilla fits with the desert warthog because the first two are omnivores and the last two are herbivores. The animal caretakers thus use a totally different criterion than the designers of zoos, because their contexts differ.

When we categorize, our choices of both the level and the criterion are highly dependent on the context. Studies in which people with autism are asked to categorize various types of drawings or words out of context (this includes all of the studies conducted to this point in time) do not tell much about their ability to categorize. It would be much more interesting to research how flexible they are in categorizing. I have a strong suspicion that they would not perform well, because context sensitivity is involved in flexible categorizing. But this remains a suspicion, until flexibility in categorizing in human beings with autism is better researched.

However, one test has already confirmed my suspicion – the *Wisconsin Card Sorting Test*, often abbreviated as WCST.[39] Psychologists have used the WCST for years to test executive functions, especially cognitive flexibility. The WCST consists of a set of cards with simple geometric figures that are different in their form (triangle, circle, star, or cross), color (blue, yellow, green, or red), and number (1, 2, 3, or 4). The instructions are to sort the cards; thus, it is a categorization assignment. The examiner does not disclose on which basis one is to sort the cards (form, color, or number); however, for every card placed, the examiner tells the test subject whether or not the card is placed correctly.

The WCST measures cognitive flexibility because the sorting rules are changed without warning. The test measures how long it takes the participant to switch to a new criterion and how many mistakes he or she makes during this learning process. These mistakes are called perseverative errors. Various studies have used the WCST with people with autism, and many have found that they committed many more perseverative errors than did people without autism.[40] This points to the fact that people with autism have difficulty with shifting the criteria on which they categorize.

According to the psychologist Lawrence Barsalou,[41] we do not categorize according to predetermined strategies or rules. We do so in full interaction with the world, taking into account what is going on in the moment. (Barsalou uses the term "on the fly.") How we categorize – that is, which dimensions and characteristics we use – is dynamic and strongly dependent on the situation. Without context, we categorize things based on their most apparent characteristics, like the form and the color of a basketball and the characteristic that a basketball is used in sports and games. But a basketball has more characteristics. It can be put in more categories than round, orange, ball, and sports equipment. A basketball also belongs to the categories of floating objects and made of rubber.

Barsalou[42] asked people to judge statements about a basketball (e.g., "A basketball is round: true or false?," "A basketball can float: true or false?"). Without context, the subjects needed more time to evaluate the second sentence than the first, but after a sentence like "Harry threw the basketball in the swimming pool," they were able to evaluate both sentences equally quickly. According to Barsalou, it is the context – in this case that of a swimming pool – that activates certain characteristics of the concept, which are not activated without the context.

## Concepts as Chameleons

Barsalou's experiment led to a whole new view of concepts. Since the time of the Greek philosophers, it has been assumed that our concepts contain only characteristics that are fixed and, therefore, common to all examples belonging to a given concept. For example, our concept of dog contains only the characteristics that are common to dogs (and not common to cats, toasters, or mothers-in-law). Thus, the traditional assumption is that our concepts are built around fixed essential characteristics.

*Concepts are not unchangeable. They are more like a chameleon whose skin adjusts continuously to the situation.*

But Barsalou has shown that concepts are not as stable as we think. The characteristics of a concept, as well as the prototypes and typical examples of a concept, are not fixed in our brain, but are created on the fly as a function of the context. Remember the book we spoke about in the beginning? In specific contexts, like that of an annoying insect or pouring rain, our brain activates certain characteristics of a book that do not belong to the standard characteristics of a book (reading, letters, etc.). In these contexts, a book has commonality with things that are not books at all, such as a flyswatter or an umbrella.

According to Barsalou, our concepts contain two kinds of properties. On one hand, there are the concept-specific properties – characteristics that are specific to the concept. Concept-specific characteristics are context independent. That is, they typify something regardless of which context an item is in, like the four paws of a dog or the letters in a book (and even these so-called fixed characteristics are managed flexibly. For example, it is not very likely that you won't be able to recognize a dog with only three paws as being a dog). On the other hand, our concepts also have variable, context-dependent properties. These are only activated within a certain context, like the "killing" ability of a book. The difference between context-independent and context-dependent properties is similar to the distinction made in the last chapter between the fixed vocabulary meaning and the changing world meaning of words. Thus, concepts are not unchangeable. Instead, they look like chameleons, whose skin color changes continuously to its surroundings.[43] Or, as stated in the introduction of this book, **there are no absolute meanings**.[44]

Concepts help us give meaning to situations. In turn, situations give meaning to concepts.[45] For example, we have a concept of dog that is not fixed. It only gets meaning within a certain context. Change the context, and you get a different version of the concept dog. Moreover, concepts not only contain characteristics about themselves, whether variable or fixed, but also characteristics about the context, the contextual characteristics. Our concept of dog also contains contextual elements of a leash, a bag of dog food, avoiding dog poop on sidewalks, and fire hydrants against which male dogs lift their legs. So, our knowledge of dogs contains information about characteristics that are external to the dog. For example, ask people to describe the characteristics of a certain concept, like car, and they spontaneously also mention a few contextual elements that are connected to cars, such as gas station, garage, and highways.[46]

*Concepts are by definition contextual: They also contain information about context.*

The Israeli psychologist Nurit Gronau[47] speaks of contextual representations: Concepts contain information about what things are and also about the context(s) in which things normally occur, or to which they are related. In short, concepts do not exist in a vacuum. They are part of a complex network of concepts, normally referred to as a semantic network. Thus, by definition, concepts are contextual.[48]

It is logical to assume that our concepts do not exist apart from context. They are based on our experiences and perceptions that constantly occur within a certain context. Even when we zoom in on something, we subconsciously also take the context into account. (See Chapter 3 about the influence of context on visual perception.) We do that even when the context seems to be unimportant, or is disturbing. For example, students who have studied an assignment under noisy circumstances perform better on an exam that takes place in a noisy location than students who have studied in silence.[49] (Don't tell this to your student daughter or son!)

So we do not perceive things in isolation, but always in situations. When our concepts are the reflection of our experiences, they must contain contextual information. Psychologists use different terms for this phenomenon. Aside from *contextual representations*, the contextual character of concepts is also referred to as *situated concepts*,[50] *the ecological theory of concepts*,[51] and *situated cognition*.[52]

## Context and Memory

Concepts are pieces of knowledge of the world that are stored in our memory. In addition to categorization tasks, research on memory also sheds light on how people store and activate concepts. Thus, memory research provides evidence that concepts are contextually stored in our memory. For example, Henry Roediger and Kathleen McDermott,[53] two American psychologists, asked a group of subjects to listen to lists of carefully chosen words. All the words were related to a certain word, a so-called index word. For example, a list of words all had something to do with *needle*, such as *sharp, point, to sting, hay stack,* and *injection*. Another list contained words such as *snoring, dreaming, bed, awake, blanket, doze, nap*, and *rest*, all related to the index word *sleep*.

The subjects did not hear the index words. After listening to the list, they had to recite the words that they could remember. In more than half of the cases, when reciting the list of words, the subjects also mentioned the index word, even though it was not on the list of words they had heard. They were strongly convinced that they had heard the index word earlier. Clearly, the activation of contextually related meaning is so strong that it leads to false memories. Thus, despite its many advantages, context sensitivity does have some less desirable side effects.

Those who are less context sensitive have fewer false memories. The American neurologist David Beversdorf[54] and his team studied a group of adults with autism, repeating the experiment with the index words. These subjects showed fewer false memories than did the nonautistic control group. According to Beversdorf, this points to the fact that people with autism are less sensitive to the influence of contextually related terms and that the autistic brain has a reduced contextual or distributed semantic network.[55] The positive news is that the memory of people with autism does not seem to be contextually compromised. That is, when they repeat what someone told them, they are likely be very accurate.

*Context-related terms are stored together in our brain.*

Beversdorf's conclusion is not new. It is fully in line with the research results of Beate Hermelin and Neil O'Connor[56] from the 1960s. These showed that despite their excellent memory skills, children with autism did not recall a sequence of related words (*rabbit, horse, cow, pig*) better than a random sequence of words (*bus, apple, rabbit, fork*) unless they got a hint or visual support.[57] By comparison, children without autism did much better on a sequence of related words vs. unrelated words, and even reproduced words together that were related to each other.

Recent research on memory in autism[58] confirms that the network of concepts in people with autism is not as extensive and distributed as it is in people without autism. As mentioned before, concepts not only contain information about a given item itself but also about the context. For example, when we think about doctor, we also spontaneously think of nurse (see Chapter 5). When we think of apple, we also think of tree, Snow White, and apple pie.

But that contextual loading of concepts is far less present in people with autism. In developing concepts, it appears that they only store the item-specific information and not the contextual information (the relationship with other concepts).[59] Thus, their concept of chair contains only characteristics of the chair and not all types of information about contexts in which chairs occur and what you can do with chairs in those different contexts. What individuals with autism miss is the spontaneous organization of concepts in a network of meanings that can be flexibly reorganized and adjusted to the context.[60]

Another memory study provides evidence for decreased context sensitivity in the storage of knowledge of people with autism. For example, children with autism have difficulty remembering the context and the order of recent activities in which they participated.[61] Psychologists call this type of memory *episodic memory*. The episodic memory is our memory for episodes in our life – or personal happenings and how we experienced them.

Researchers have identified another form of memory called *semantic memory*. The semantic memory is our memory of facts we have learned – where we lived when we were 5 years old, what we played when we were 10 years old, which car our parents had, and so on. These are all stored in the semantic memory. On the other hand, memories about how much you liked the games that you played when you were 10 years old or how you enjoyed certain rides in the car with your parents are part of your episodic memory. Thus, episodic memory is the memory for the personal context of the facts and knowledge that we store during our experiences. Various studies[62] have shown that, despite a relatively good memory for facts and things, even higher functioning people with autism have a reduced episodic memory.

In light of our recent knowledge about concepts, especially the fact that they are contextual, we can no longer see semantic and episodic memory as detached from each other. If we always take context into account when forming concepts, then inside every concept in our semantic memory is also a piece of episodic memory. That both types of memory are not independent from each other was shown by a study at the research lab of psychologist Dermot Bowler.[63]

Bowler and his colleagues showed adults without autism a number of words on a computer screen and then asked them to remember them. After a break, subjects were shown a series of words containing words that they had seen in the first sequence as well as words that were new. They were asked to indicate if they recognized each word using the following two response formats[64]:

A. I am sure that I saw the word in the first series because I remember something about when I saw the word the first time, like where the word was located on the screen, a thought, or an image that I associated with the word.
B. I am sure that I saw the word in the first series. I know that without a doubt, not because I remember something like the location of the word, a thought, or an image I had when seeing the word.

The first answer indicates that someone is remembering something about the context of the word in the first series. The second indicates there is no memory of a context. Subjects indicated four times more often that they recognized the word by something in the context than without the context, thus providing evidence of the influence of context and episodic memory on semantic memory.

Bowler and his colleagues presented adults with autism with the same test. They remembered as many words correctly as the subjects without autism; however, in response to the question about why they recognized the words, they more often answered, "Just because I know it," and less often because they remembered something from the context.

Along with Bowler's, studies showing an impaired episodic memory deliver additional evidence for the hypothesis that the memory of people with autism is less contextualized.[65] What is in their memory is much less contextually embedded. It appears that the difficulty of utilizing context is a retrieval rather than an encoding problem. That is, in more supported conditions, when we "push the context button" and present the context more explicitly, people with autism find it easier to recall (contextual) details.[66]

## Context Blindness and Resistance to Change

When the concepts of people with autism contain item-specific information rather than contextual information, they are different from those of people without autism. Their mental world must look rather different.

> *Stephen, a man with autism, thought as a child that the world did not have color until the second half of the 20th century. He thought that in the early times everything was black, white, and grey. Only when he learned about photography and the invention of color photography did he understand that the world always had colors, but in the past, they could not be photographed. He had not spontaneously placed pictures, particularly black-and-white pictures of earlier times, in this context (that things have always had colors.*

The hypothesis that the concepts of people with autism are more acontextual would explain why they have so much trouble categorizing the atypical examples of a certain concept. (In the case of atypical examples, you cannot use much item-specific information.) For example, when you take into account just the appearance of a river eel, it looks more like a snake than a fish.

People without autism categorize atypical examples based on the contextual information of a concept (i.e., by context, they recognize an eel as a fish and not a snake). If an eel were found on dry land, somewhere under the bushes, it would make you take a step backwards ("Yikes, a snake!!").

If you see a river eel on dry ground, you think you see a snake.

On the other hand, when your concepts contain little or no contextual information, you will, in the case of atypical examples, have a very difficult time categorizing or recognizing them. This is what we often see in people with autism (see the earlier part of this chapter).

*At a summer camp for children with autism, a boy did not want to go to the toilet. Every time the supervisor said to him, "Come on, Marc, go to the toilet," he became afraid. He resisted and did not want to enter the restroom. They tried every toilet but to no avail. The boy's parents were consulted. Did Marc also do that at home? Is he sick? Why does he not want to go? No immediate answer emerged. Then they asked the parents, "What does the toilet look like in your house? And what does the one at Mark's school look like?"*

*After a long interview in which colors and forms of toilets were extensively discussed, the toilet mystery was solved. At home and at school, all toilet seats were white. At camp, all of them were black. Mark did not recognize the toilets at camp as being toilets. Something with a black seat cannot be a toilet!*

While Marc has a concept of a toilet, it is built only around characteristics of the toilets that he knows, not their context. The toilet concept of people without autism, on the other hand, contains not only characteristics of the toilet itself but also characteristics about contextual elements. Even when a toilet looks very different from all the toilets that we have ever seen, we recognize it by the context: the bathroom in which the toilet is located, the presence of toilet paper, a place for the soap, and so on. That is, because our concepts also contain contextual information, we are less dependent on item-specific characteristics when recognizing and categorizing things that are more or less different from the examples we already know. Put differently, we do not have great difficulty with changes in item-specific characteristics.

However, somebody who stores only item-specific characteristics in his concepts is easily confused when those characteristics change, and, as a result, develops resistance to change. Assume you only recognize people by how they look, like the clothes they wear or their hairstyle. If that were the case, you would probably hate it when people change the way they dress or their hairstyle. Or you would be confused, as I have seen several times in my career in children with autism who had difficulties recognizing certain people because of changes in their appearance, such as wearing glasses or changing hairstyle.

Resistance to change is a known characteristic of autism and is an expression of difficulty with generalizing. Meanings (and the reactions caused by the meanings) become connected to item-specific characteristics instead of context-specific characteristics. Generalization problems are common in people with autism.

*Paul has just been hired as an assistant at a company. His assignment is to do various jobs, among them to mow the lawn around the building. The first time he did the mowing, he checked the lawnmower and said, "I can't mow the lawn with this lawnmower!" Paul recognized that it was a lawnmower, so he has a clear concept of lawnmower, but he was confused because the company's lawnmower was different from the lawnmower he had at home. Specifically, the company lawnmower did not sound the way his does.*

*In the end, he used the company lawnmower, but only after his coach reminded him over and over that the lawn mower would do the job, even though the sound was different from what Paul associated with lawnmowers. Paul will become accustomed to this new lawnmower. He will add this new sound to his concept of lawn mower.*

Perhaps that is what people with autism do. Due to a lack of contextual information in their concepts, they make extended collections of all types of examples belonging to a concept, like the collections of examples that Temple Grandin uses.

When you store contextual information, you do not have to store so much item-specific information. That is why most of our concepts are vague and have fuzzy definitions. The ability to abstract (disconnect the concrete, observable characteristics) is also dependent on the ability to use context in concept formation.

## Context Activates Concepts

Context plays a role, not only in the development of concepts, but also in the use of concepts in everyday life. The application or concretization of concepts is very much contextually determined.[67] Without context, in relation to the concept bird, for example, people think about a prototypical bird such as a sparrow, blackbird, finch, or a robin. However, when they hear the sentence, "The bird walked around the farm," most would automatically think about a chicken.[68]

A house often has several doors. Which door are you referring to when you ask someone to open the door? To know the answer, we check the context. When someone is standing in front of the door with his arms full, it is clear that the reference is to that door and not another door in the house. And when the doorbell rings and you are asked to open the door, you know without much thought that the reference is to the front door. In contrast, people who are less context sensitive have to think quite a lot to know which door is referred to, and often end up choosing the wrong door, as does Jake in the following example. When the doorbell rings, his mother asks Jake, who has autism, to open the door. Jake opens the door to the closet instead of the front door.

A group of Belgian and American researchers[69] discovered that, depending on the context, we not only think about different concrete things but also about different characteristics. When people are presented with the word *game* in different contexts, like "games that you play with the family" or "games for smart people," they not only mention different games (*Monopoly*, chess) but also different characteristics of games (fun, competitive).

*Context not only activates our concepts, but also their characteristics.*

Concepts can be filled in differently depending on the context. In more technical terms, context changes the activation states of concepts and their characteristics. For example, when you talk about a tree in Canada, the idea of a pine tree is most likely what will be activated in a listener's brain. In the context of a tropical island, however, the idea of a palm tree is more likely to be activated.

Similarly, in the context of "the cat is hungry and is asking for food," the characteristic of a cat meowing is activated, but other cat characteristics like chewing are only potentially activated. This changes when the context is changed, as in "The cat is eating." The characteristic of chewing now becomes active. (Think again about the characteristic of a book as a flyswatter, which only becomes active in the context of an annoying insect.)

When we retrieve a concept from memory, not all of the concrete examples and characteristics of that concept become activated, only those that are contextually useful or relevant to us in that moment. For example, the brain does not activate a general idea of a bike, but only the examples and characteristics of a bike that match the present situation. Thus, the characteristics of bike that become activated when we want to repair a bike are different from those activated when we want to ride a bike.

According to Barsalou,[70] there is not *a* concept, but in every situation we create "ad hoc" concepts. For example, you have a concept for "what you take on an airplane trip" or a concept of "suitable excuses to escape doing the dishes." The fact that the properties of a concept are not determined up-front, but change according to the context, makes it possible to be flexible in the utilization and concretization of concepts; however, those who are less context sensitive rely more on fixed properties.

A typical example is a scene in the movie *Rain Man,*[71] where the main character, Raymond Babbit, a man with autism, crosses the street. When he is halfway across the street, the traffic light changes to "Don't walk." He complies. He stops walking halfway across street, to the annoyance of drivers whose lights have changed to green. The meaning of a red light changes much more than we are spontaneously inclined to believe. We have all learned that a red light means stop, but that is not always the case. That is only valid in a certain context when you have not yet started crossing the street. In a context where you are halfway across the street already, the red light means something totally different; namely, that you have to keep walking quickly. And in another context, when you have taken only two steps into the crosswalk of a very broad street during heavy rush hour traffic, a red light means "Go back!"

*Bob, a man with autism, rides a motorcycle and is a member of a motorcycle club. He often goes to meetings and on motorcycle rides with other members of the club. Bob is one of the people involved in making our movie about adults with autism,* Autimatically. *It is the day on which we film him. To give the film more action and because his motorcycle is his passion, we decided to film a scene that shows Bob riding his motorcycle. Because it is too difficult to send the entire film crew to a motorcycle event, we persuaded him to take a ride with me, a few colleagues, and some members of Bob's club. To make it easier for the film crew and to make multiple shots without having to relocate continuously, we drove several laps in Bob's neighborhood. After that we went to lunch, followed by an interview with Bob in his home. After the interview, Bob asked when we would go for the ride.*

*Bob has a concept of a motorcycle ride that has a few fixed, item-specific characteristics. More specifically, a ride is at least 100 kilometers. A few short laps in his neighborhood are, in Bob's mind, not a ride. Bob was not able to make an adjustment of his concept of motorcycle ride to the context (the making of a movie).*

Context is especially important in concretizing general, abstract concepts, like fruit, honesty, romance, work, a game, and a drink.[72] It is impossible to imagine something about the concept of a drink without a context. You can imagine something for "drink during breakfast," because you will spontaneously think about drinks like coffee, tea, or fruit juice. In the context of a pub, other pictures arise, like a beer or a whiskey. When you go to someone's house in the morning and are asked what you want to drink, the question activates only examples of the concept of drink that belong in the morning context. When you ask someone to play a game, he determines a concrete meaning of "game" by taking the context into account.

*During a short coffee break in a course for adults with autism, Jim does not know what to do. Because difficulty coping with free time and breaks is very typical for people with autism, the supervisors have arranged for an autism-friendly offering of free-time materials, like newspapers, magazines, and games. A supervisor proposes to Jim that he play a game during the break, because Jim likes to play games. To the question of which game Jim likes to play, he answers, "*Risk.*"* Risk *is a game with multiple players, and it usually takes a fairly long time to play; however, there were only 15 minutes to play, and all the other members of the group were already doing something else. In his concrete concept of "game," Jim was context blind: He neither took into account the available time, nor the availability of co-players. Jim was not able to concretize the abstract concept of game based on the context to the ad-hoc concept of games that you play on your own that do not take longer than 15 minutes to play.*

Higher functioning people with autism can – most of the time – describe abstract concepts, but their definitions often contain only item-specific information and not the contextual characteristics. This is because, although they seemingly know the terms, they have problems concretizing them in real life.

*During a course about relationships, I asked a group of high-functioning adults, most of whom were married or had been married, what the term* romance *meant to them. All of them knew the term, and they gave examples: a nice dinner, a romantic atmosphere, hugging, a nice present, or giving flowers. Then I asked them when they last had a romantic event with their partner. Not unexpectedly, one romantic blunder after another was disclosed. A number of their romantic initiatives were not successful, not because what they did was not romantic, but because they did not take context into account. For example, one of them told me that he was in a romantic mood and he wanted to surprise his partner, who did not live with him, with flowers. He took a bouquet of flowers to her home late in the evening, after she was in bed and asleep. He did not take into account the time. Another participant told me that he cooked a nice meal for his wife on an evening when she had been to a company party at which she had already eaten (he knew about the party).*

## Contexts and Scripts

Context is essential for abstracting concepts as well as concretizing them. In the literature, you often read that people with autism have difficulty with the abstract, but from the previous discussion it is clear that they also have problems with concretizing. They do not seem to spontaneously take context into account when concretizing concepts. It is difficult for them to get an idea of what something means **in a given context**. This leads to a lot of other problems with language and communication, extensively described in Chapter 5, but also to a lack of flexibility in behavior. When concepts contain little contextual information, and thus are reasonably stable and unchanging (a motorcycle ride is at least 100 kilometers, a game is a game like *Risk*, a red light means stop, and so on), the behavior related to these concepts is not very flexible.

In addition to concepts of animals, natural phenomena, objects, abstract ideas, and so on, we have concepts of events and situations. Psychologists call these types of concepts

*Our knowledge of events (called scripts) is context sensitive.*

scripts because they contain a description of how people behave in particular situations. Examples of scripts include a visit to the cinema, a bank robbery, a wedding party, a picnic, or an argument. In addition to a number of item-specific properties (a visit to the cinema without seeing a movie is no visit to the cinema; a marriage without the groom and the bride is not a wedding) scripts contain, just like every other concept, changing contextual characteristics. Popcorn and cola belong in a visit to the cinema but not necessarily. Whether you eat or drink something during the visit to the cinema is not fixed in the script but is determined by the context.

The script of a wedding party often contains dancing, but if you dance, how long you dance and with whom you dance changes depending on the context, such as the availability of dance partners, the sort of music being played, and your physical and mental condition. No matter how much grandfather and grandmother like to dance, if at their grandson's wedding primarily hardcore jump-style music is played, they may not follow the script and dance. (If you don't know what jump style is, just take a look on YouTube and you will understand why this dancing style is not very popular among grandparents.)

So, like all our other concepts, our scripts are reasonably vague and, most important, contextually very flexible. People with autism may learn many scripts. What is true for other concepts holds true here: Their scripts often lack context sensitivity and are, therefore, less flexible. When the context differs from the standard script, the lack of flexibility becomes apparent.

*For Ben, the script "Go to your room" includes Ben putting on his slippers. One day, the family was running late and preparing to leave the house. Ben had forgotten something in his room, and Mother told him to go to his room quickly. When Ben did not return after a few minutes, Mother went to Ben's room and found him sitting on his bed, putting on his slippers. When he went to his room, Ben put his slippers on, because that was the script he knew. He did not adjust the script to the context of being short on time and preparing to leave the house.*

## Context and Intelligence

People with autism have difficulty being flexible in their behavior. This is due to reduced cognitive flexibility. They form concepts, including abstract concepts, but their concepts are not contextualized enough. According to Rand Spiro and Jihn-Chang Jehng,[73] two American psychologists who specialize in cognitive flexibility, cognitive flexibility refers to the skill of spontaneously adjusting knowledge to the ever-changing context. Such flexibility is necessary to solve problems in complex situations (which encompasses most situations).

Context sensitivity is essential in gathering and applying knowledge. Intelligence is the cognitive ability to use this knowledge to solve problems. But does this mean that persons who are context blind, like people with autism, are less intelligent? Absolutely not!

Autism exists at every level of intelligence. Some people with autism perform especially well on intelligence tests and have higher IQs than the average person. But when we look more closely at their performance on intelligence tests, many of them score better on certain parts of these tests than on others. Even higher functioning adults with autism have more problems with tasks that require processing contextual information than with other tasks presented during intelligence tests.[74]

Uta Frith[75] differentiates between test intelligence and world intelligence, between school wisdom and world wisdom. She illustrates this distinction using a study of Brazilian street vendors. Despite their ability to quickly calculate prices and exchange money, they failed in similar calculations on a test that was part of a research study. Frith writes: "To be able to score well in a test environment, you just have to be good at solving problems outside the context of real life. People who have never gone to school have problems with the neutrality and the lack of context at solving abstract problems."

According to Frith, school wisdom has to do with being able to solve abstract problems – exercises that are separate from concrete life situations and thus separate from the context. World wisdom means that you can solve practical daily problems that are always embedded in a certain context. People with autism can be very school wise and may even excel in logical reasoning.[76] The exceptional talents of some people with autism, such as an excellent memory for data or outstanding calculation skills, are often acontextual.

*Donald, a very bright man with autism, has an unusual gift related to calendars. He can tell you exactly on which day February 14, 2018, will fall. He also knows that he met Ellen, his therapist, for the first time on Thursday, November 27, 2008. Still Donald has problems planning his activities. He does not show up to appointments because he forgets about them. His acontextual memory is better than his memory for things that are embedded in a context.*

Many people with autism of average or above-average intelligence are amazingly good at logical analysis of complex problems; however, such analysis applied to their daily activities sometimes fails them. The difference is the practical, everyday context. The difference between pure (test) intelligence and world intelligence (most often referred to as common sense) is that the latter requires far more context sensitivity. According to cognitive psychologist Douglas Hofstadter, common sense is characterized by the flexibility with which we use our concepts and the ability to tell the difference between the important and the unimportant.[77] What is important is neither absolute nor fixed.

Some things are always important and others are unimportant in a certain context. To make the distinction between what is relevant and what is irrelevant, logical reasoning does not suffice. The well-known philosopher Daniel Dennett[78] illustrated this with an imaginary story about computer programmers.

A group of computer programmers wanted to program a robot to solve a practical problem, the disarming of a bomb. After the first robots came to an explosive end because they did not take into account the consequences of their actions, or because they lost themselves in all kinds of details, the programmers wanted a newer version, called R2D1, to learn the difference between relevant and irrelevant. When the programmers went to observe, they found the robot with the bomb in his robot arms. They shouted to him, "Do something!" after which the robot answered, "That is what I am doing! I am busy ignoring thousands of irrelevant things. As soon as I find something that is irrelevant, I put it on the list of things that I have to ignore, and ..." Then the bomb detonates. This story is my answer to all those people who have asked me how we can teach someone with autism the difference between relevant and irrelevant. To make a distinction between important and unimportant is not based on logic but on context-directed intuition.

To solve abstract and theoretical problems, it is sufficient to know rules and procedures and to apply them. In practice, however, we have to adjust those rules and procedures to all kinds of contextual elements, which are often unpredictable and incalculable. In *Autistic Thinking*,[79] I described extensively the difference between solving a mathematical problem and executing very simple daily actions in the chapter "Making Coffee Is Not 2+2." For those everyday actions, like making coffee, we also use a set of rules and procedures (i.e., first you place the coffee filter in the coffee pot, then the coffee. The other way around, although creative, is not very productive).

People with autism can learn that kind of rules and procedures perfectly, but they get into trouble when the rules have to be adjusted to a context. It is not the rules that they have problems with; it's those countless exceptions to the rules, especially the illogical exceptions.

A research group at Radboud University in the Netherlands[80] found that high-functioning people with autism, even though they were good at logical reasoning and could manage if/then reasoning, still had trouble with exceptions. The researchers used questions like the following:

> When Mary has an exam, she studies in the library.
> Mary has an exam.
> Will she study in the library?

To arrive at a correct answer to this question, it is sufficient to reason in a classical, logical way. That type of reasoning is acontextual. When Mary has an exam, she will study in the library. With this type of question, the adults with autism did not have problems; however, this was not true with exercises like the next one.

When Mary has an exam, she studies in the library.
When the library is open, she studies in the library.
Mary has an exam. Will she study in the library?

The answer to this question is not a simple "yes." It depends on whether or not the library is open. That context influences the answer. The adults had far more trouble with this type of exercise. The researchers explained this by referring to the reduced context sensitivity of people with autism.

The problems that people with autism have with exceptions are related to what we discussed earlier about closed and open systems (see Chapter 4). Classical logic is, like mathematics, a closed system. As such, a closed system is not subject to contextual influences. One plus one always equals two. Context plays no role in that simple addition. If humans are mammals and Peter is a human, Peter is a mammal. It does not matter who Peter is, and in which context he is located. Analyzing and reasoning about closed systems is not problematic for people with autism. On the contrary, they often perform even better in logical and abstract problems because they ignore the context.

People without autism are sometimes less logical because they take context too much into account.

*Three men each order a snack in a snack bar. The snack costs 9 dollars per person. They each give the waiter a 10-dollar bill. Because the men are good customers, the manager decides to give them a discount. He gives the waiter not 3 dollars, but 5 dollars back. The waiter considers that awkward because 5 dollars cannot be divided by 3. He decides to give each man 1 dollar back and to put the remaining 2 dollars in his own pocket. As a result, the men did not get a discount and each paid 9 dollars for their snacks, a total of 27 dollars. Add to that the 2 dollars that the waiter put in his pocket, and you have 29 dollars. But the three men together paid 30 dollars (three 10 dollar bills). Where is the remaining dollar?*

People without autism sometimes have to think a lot before they find the answer, because they "lose" themselves in the story, the context. Think all the context away, apply simple calculus, and the problem is solved.

When people reason and make decisions, they use both logic analysis and intuition.[81] Analytical and logical reasoning has the advantage of being more accurate, but the disadvantage is that it is slower. Because we need to make quick decisions in everyday life, our brain corrects the slowness of the logical reasoning with a faster form of reasoning that is capable of processing large quantities of information simultaneously, quickly and, in large part, subconsciously. That form of reasoning and decision making is called *intuition*. Intuition is very context sensitive and is especially important when making decisions in open systems.[82]

*Common sense = intellect + context sensitivity.*

Most daily situations, like making coffee, having a conversation, putting the children to bed, or studying for an exam, are not closed, but open systems. The rules in these situations are influenced by numerous contextual influences and exceptions. In order to solve problems in open systems, we need a fair amount of context sensitivity in addition to logic. Common sense is more than intelligence: It is a combination of intellect and context sensitivity.

Because of the need for context sensitivity, the decisions and choices people make are not always consistent and purely logical. The influence of context on decisions, along with the lack of logical consequence, is known by psychologists as the *framing effect*. This effect has been studied primarily by the Israeli psychologists Amos Tversky and Daniel Kahneman[83] (who received the Nobel Prize for economics in 2002 for the economical application of the effect). Tversky and Kahneman showed their subjects situations like these:

> Assume that there is an outbreak of a very deadly disease among 600 persons. Scientists have come up with two treatments to fight the disease. With the first treatment, 200 people can be saved. With the second treatment, there is a one in three probability of saving all 600 people but a two in three chance that they all die. You have to decide which treatment people will apply. Eight out of 10 people chose the first treatment.
>
> Then the test leaders change the context. Although the consequences of the first treatment remain identical (two thirds die), they word it differently: In the first treatment, 400 people will die. In this condition, the majority chose the second treatment. Although the effects of the two treatments are the same in both scenarios, people made a different decision in the two conditions. Context is stronger than logic.

British researchers[84] showed a variation of this experiment to a group of adults with and without autism. A standard research measure of level of emotional response, skin conductance responses (SCRs), was used. Subjects were shown situations like the following:

Assume you have $50. You can choose between two options:

A. You gamble. There is a 60% chance that you will keep the $50 and a 40% chance that you will lose it.

B. You do not gamble and choose certainty. You keep $20.

Another situation was as follows:

Assume you have $50. You can choose between two options:

A. You gamble. There is a 60% chance that you keep the $50 and a 40% chance that you will lose it.

B. You do not gamble and choose certainty. You lose $30.

Note that in both situations the consequences are identical, but the wording is different. In the first situation, the context in option B is that you *keep* money, in the second situation, you *lose* money. Subjects without autism responded differently, depending on the situation. They chose the gambling option more for the "losing" condition than for the condition where they got to "keep" part of the money. This was consistent with the findings in the experiments of Tversky and Kahneman. Subjects with autism, on the other hand, were less susceptible to this contextual effect. In both situations, they tended to choose certainty and not gambling, a reaction that is fully in line with the need for predictability in people with autism. The autism group failed to integrate emotional contextual cues into the decision-making process. Their emotional responses (as measured by the SCRs) did not differ depending on the context. The opposite was true for the subjects without autism.

Additional evidence for a reduced context sensitivity in the reasoning of individuals with autism (and the advantage of it!) came from a recent British study.[85] In this study it was assessed whether adolescents with autism would also be susceptible to the so-called *conjunction fallacy,* a logic error that is seen as a classic example of the automatic contextualization of problems. The conjunction fallacy occurs when you assume that two specific conditions (in conjunction) are more probable than either of them occurring alone.

The classical example of this fallacy comes – again – from Tversky and Kahneman:[86]

> Linda is 31-year-old, smart woman who is single and outspoken. She majored in philosophy. As a student, she was deeply concerned with issues of discrimination and social justice and participated in antinuclear demonstrations.
>
> Which is more probable?
> 1. Linda is a bank teller.
> 2. Linda is a bank teller and is active in the feminist movement.

Remarkably, the majority of the people judge the second statement as more likely than the first, although the likelihood of Linda having both characteristics in conjunction is logically less than the likelihood of her having only one of those characteristics. People do so because the second statement seems more representative of Linda based on the description of her (the context that was given), even though it is clearly mathematically less likely. The adolescents with autism in the study were less susceptible to this conjunction fallacy than a control group, although fallacy rates were high in both groups.

Both studies support the hypothesis that people with autism are less influenced by contextual factors in their reasoning, but at the same time they also show that people with autism are sometimes more logical, consistent, and rational in their decision making. Pure logical thinking, for which it is an advantage to limit attention to all types of contextual factors, is often a strength in people with autism. Thus, context blindness has its advantages.

## Summary

Our knowledge of the world is contained in concepts. Concepts are not fixed, but vague. And, above all, they are flexible, changing – adjusting themselves like a chameleon to every context. This is because, in addition to item-specific information, they contain contextual information. Concepts are not separate from each other, but are related to each other in contextual semantic networks in our brain. Context plays a role in both the development of concepts (abstracting) and in the use and application of those concepts (concretizing).

Context is essential for the development of common sense or the ability to cope flexibly with the knowledge we have of the world. Flexibility in thoughts and actions is synonymous with context sensitivity. Until now, there has been little research into the concept development of people with autism. Research of concepts and their development in autism is sparse, and the few studies that have been conducted addressed the concepts of people with autism in circumstances that rather lacked context.

Both experience and scientific research demonstrate that people with autism have difficulties with the contextual aspects of concepts. Concepts that can be stated based on concrete rules in a closed system and with typical examples are generally understood by people with autism; however, atypical concepts and exceptions are often confusing to them. Further, they have little difficulty with the intrinsically unchanging and acontextual properties of concepts. Instead, they have difficulty adjusting concepts and their properties to the context, reflecting a reduced cognitive flexibility in autism. Taken together, this means that there are several qualitative differences between the concepts of individuals with and without autism. To state it differently, people with autism have a different view of the world than do people without autism.

# Endnotes - Context in Knowledge

1. In the literature, the difference between meaning and concept is not always clear; many psychologists consider them to be synonymous. For convenience, we follow the distinction that psychologist Barsalou et al. (1993) made. *Concepts* are our ideas of categories (like mother-in-law, football, or car). *Meanings* are the result of a connection that we make between a reference (a word that you hear or read, a symbol, or even an object) and our concepts. Although concepts and meanings are similar, they are not identical. When I say, for example, that I have a car, it is about my car (meaning) and not about a car (concept). Meanings are, in general, concretizations of concepts in a certain, specific, unique situation. Situations in which we address a category and not a specific example are exceptions to this. When I say "I have no idea what a computer can do," I am not referring to a certain computer but to the category or the concept of computer. In these cases, concept and meaning are interchangeable.
2. For a more extensive discussion, see, e.g., Ulrich Neisser (1987), who invented the term.
3. Eco (2001, p. 137).
4. Grandin (2000).
5. Grandin (2009).
6. Walton and Bower (1993).
7. Here we shortly summarize a series of publications. For those who want to read more, see, e.g., articles by Goldstone and Kersten (2003) and Machery (2007).
8. Hampton (2007); McCloskey and Glucksberg (1978); Rosch (1975).
9. This funny example comes from Steven Pinker (1997).
10. Pinker (1997, p. 22, in the Dutch translation).
11. The founder of the prototype theory was Eleanor Rosch (1975). That Prototype can be generated in different ways. For example, the prototype of dog can be the average dog, the most common dog, or the ideal dog. Is George Clooney the average bachelor or the ideal one? The labrador retriever is the most common dog, but is it also the ideal one?
12. Armstrong, Gleitman, and Gleitman (1983).
13. Wittgenstein (1953).
14. This is known as the exemplar theory of concepts. The best known example of this theory is that of Medin and Schafer (1978). Their

model was later extended to a generalized context model (GSM) by Robert Nosofsky (1986).

15. Aside from rules/criteria, prototype, and exemplar theories of categorization, there are also mixed theories. These state that our concepts are based on a combination of the most important principles of concept development; for example, a combination of criteria and examples (Erickson & Kruschke, 1998).
16. Hermelin and O'Connor (1970).
17. E.g., see Fay and Schuler (1980), Ungerer and Sigman (1987), and Waterhouse and Fein (1982). According to Fay and Schuler (1980), children with autism do form categories, but these categories are based on perceptual characteristics and not on functional criteria.
18. Grandin (2009, p. 1439).
19. Klinger and Dawson (1995, 2001).
20. Molesworth, Bowler, and Hampton (2005, 2008).
21. Plaisted (2000); Plaisted, O'Riordan, and Baron-Cohen (1998).
22. De Clerq (1999, pp. 27-28).
23. Gastgeb, Strauss, and Minshew (2006).
24. Froehlich, Miller, DuBray, Bigler, and Lainhart (2008).
25. Strauss et al. (2005).
26. According to Minshew, Meyer, and Goldstein (2002), people with autism do not have problems with identification of concepts based on clear rules; they do have difficulties with forming concepts based on more complex information.
27. Huart, Corneille, and Becquart (2005).
28. In reality, it is more complex. From the horticultural side, a tomato is a vegetable, because the tomato grows just like other vegetables on an herbal type of plant. However, botanically the tomato is a fruit, because fruit is produced by a wood-like plant.
29. Hampton, Dubois, and Yeh (2006).
30. Barsalou (2008).
31. Conference pear is the subordinate level and fruit the superordinate level. The most basic is that level on which there is an optimal equilibrium between similarities and differences. On the subordinate level, differences in details are taken into account (e.g., the distinction between a conference pear and a Doyenne pear). On a superordinate level, we abstract from many visible differences and group on a very abstract, functional level (although pears look totally dif-

ferent than grapes, they still belong to the category of fruit). Generally, it is assumed that in typical development, children first acquire the basic level and only later, by learning the order of things in the world, acquire the subordinate and superordinate levels (Mervis & Crisafi, 1982; Mervis & Rosch, 1981).

32. Mareschal and Tan (2007).
33. Fay and Schuler (1980).
34. This example is a variation on an example by Steven Pinker (1997).
35. Braisby and Franks (2000).
36. Noens, van Berckelaer-Onnes, Verpoorten, and Van Duijn (2006); Verpoorten, Noens, and van Berckelaer-Onnes (2007).
37. Moreover, language understanding plays an important role in the evolution of a conceptual or representative level of categorizing. After language training, a child with autism and an intellectual disability made many more semantic categorization mistakes than perceptual mistakes. In other words, when he chose a wrong picture to match a word, it was more often a picture that was conceptually and semantically related to the goal word than a picture that was perceptually equal (Boser, Higgins, Fetherston, Preissler, & Gordon 2002). Thus, children with autism and an intellectual disability appear not always to be perceptually concrete and hyper-selective as the first studies of Fay and Schuler (1980) would lead one to expect.
38. For this and the next example, we were again inspired by Steven Pinker (1997).
39. The WCST (Berg, 1948; Heaton, Chelune, Talley, Kay, & Curtiss, 1993) is a neuropsychological test for the executive functions and has been in use more than 50 years. There is now a computerized version available.
40. For an overview, but also a critical discussion, see Hill (2004). Although a lot of studies show an impairment in the performance of people with autism on the WCST, this is not the case in all studies. Besides differences in study design and samples, other factors can play a role in the research results. Performance on the WCST is not only a reflection of someone's cognitive flexibility (set shifting), other factors such as working memory, inhibition, and verbal intelligence also play a role.
41. Barsalou (1987).
42. Barsalou (1982).
43. There is a widespread misconception that the color of the chameleon's skin adjusts itself to its background. That is not true. Chame-

leons' skin color changes as a function of their emotional state (e.g., when they are stressed or frightened). When the color matches its background, it is purely coincidental.

44. One can discuss or talk about the general, universal meaning of concepts (like what is a dog?). Such a conversation also forms a context that activates certain characteristics of the concept, more explicitly the intrinsic example exceeding characteristics (Barsalou et al., 1993).
45. Gabora, Rosch, and Aerts (2008).
46. Barsalou (1993); Wu and Barsalou (2009).
47. Gronau, Neta, and Bar (2008). It is confusing, but the term *contextual representation* is also used by the language psychologist George A. Miller (Miller & Charles, 1991), but in that case, it has another meaning; specifically, the ability to understand in communication the different context dependent meanings of a word (see Chapter 5 on context and communication).
48. Barsalou (2008).
49. Grant et al. (1998).
50. Barsalou (2005, 2008, 2009).
51. Gabora et al. (2008)
52. Kirshner and Whitson (1997).
53. Roediger and McDermott (1995).
54. Beversdorf et al. (2000).
55. Beversdorf, Narayanan, Hillier, and Hughes (2007).
56. Hermelin and O'Connor (1970).
57. Tager-Flusberg (1991).
58. E.g., see Bowler, Gaigg, and Gardiner (2008, 2009).
59. Bowler, Gardiner & Gaigg (2008); Gaigg, Bowler, and Gardiner (2008).
60. This is a citation from Minshew et al. (2002). According to Minshew, Meyer, and Goldstein, people with autism do not have great difficulty with concept identification (like recognition of chairs, seats, etc.), but they have a problem with concept formation (the flexible organizing of concepts). This is equal to a reduced ability to store context-dependent information of concepts.
61. Boucher (1981).
62. See, e.g., Crane and Goddard (2008); Goddard, Howlin, Dritschel, and Patel (2007); Lind and Bowler (2008).

63. Bowler, Gardinier, and Grice (2000).
64. The two possibilities refer, respectively, to noetic consciousness (remembering) and autonoetic consciousness (knowing).
65. Bowler, Gaigg, and Gardiner (2008b) speak of a reduced ability to retrieve context. They state that a certain amount of encoding of the context takes place, but context is not used spontaneously when remembering things. However, when test subjects with autism were cued, the context had the same effect as for the persons without autism.
66. Maras and Bowler (2011), a study that confirms what is written in endnote 65.
67. Hampton (2003). See also Higgins (1996).
68. Roth and Shoben (1983).
69. Aerts and Gabora (2005a); Gabora et al. (2008).
70. This is what he calls situated conceptualizations (Barsalou, 2003).
71. *Rain Man*, the 1988 Oscar-winning film written by Barry Morrow and Ronald Bass, directed by Barry Levinson and featuring Dustin Hoffman in the role of Raymond Babbit, an autistic savant.
72. Murphy and Wisniewski (1989).
73. Spiro and Jehng (1990).
74. Vermeulen (2002). Specifically, the subtests Picture Arrangement and Picture Completion in the WISC-III (Wechsler, 1991). In the factor analysis of Lincoln, Courchesne, Kilman, Elamsian, and Allen (1988), the two subtests together account for Factor 3: the analysis of social and context-relevant information. Low scores on subtests with a high loading on contextual sensitivity have also recently been found by Goldstein et al. (2008).
75. Frith (1989, pp. 141-142).
76. Hayashi, Kato, Igarashi, and Kashima (2008).
77. Hofstadter (1985, p. 636, in the Dutch translation).
78. Dennet (1984).
79. Vermeulen (1996a).
80. Pijnacker et al. (2009).
81. See, e.g., Dijksterhuis and Nordgren (2006), and Evans (2008).
82. Stanovich and West (2002).
83. Tversky and Kahnerman (1974).

84. De Martino, Harrison, Knafo, Bird, and Dolan (2008).
85. Morsanyi, Handley, and Evans (2010).
86. Tversky and Kahneman (1983).

# Chapter 7
# Autism as Context Blindness: The Theory

Are people with autism truly into details?

Is context blindness the same as “not seeing the whole”?

Why do we not find it confusing that different people have the same first name?

What is the difference between context blindness and “autistic thinking”?

Is context blindness a new theory of autism?

Does context blindness offer a good explanation for autism?

Does context blindness also occur in people who do not have autism?

The previous chapters made it clear that a sense for context plays a vital role in several cognitive functions, such as perception of simple objects, understanding of language and human behavior, and development of world knowledge and common sense. We also described how a reduced context sensitivity can lead to the difficulties that are very typical for individuals with autism.

Can we then conclude that people with autism are context blind? What is context blindness, anyway? How does context blindness relate to other, more established, theories about autism? These questions are the subject of this chapter.

## Context Blindness and Central Coherence

The idea that people with autism have difficulties with context is not new. Although Leo Kanner, one of the pioneers in autism, did not actually use the word *context*, he mentioned in his famous 1943 article the problems that his patients had with adjusting meanings to changing contexts, especially with regard to understanding the meaning of language.

Kanner wrote about a girl named Elain C., "She uses sentences just like she has heard them, without adjusting them grammatically to the situation of the moment."[1] A few pages further, in a general discussion of his patients, Kanner wrote, "Apparently the meaning of a word becomes inflexible and cannot be used with any but the originally acquired connotation."[2]

Almost every article or book about autism mentions that people with autism have difficulty taking the context into account; but seldom or never do the authors explain the reason for these difficulties. One psychologist stands out as an exception, however. She was the first to give a lack of sensitivity to context an important place in the theory about the autistic way of processing information. I am talking about Uta Frith, one of the world's leading authorities on autism.

Uta Frith, a German psychologist, furthered her studies at the University of London. Under the auspices of co-specialists in autism, including Lorna Wing and Michael Rutter, Frith had an internship in the Maudsley Hospital, a psychiatric hospital in which a vast amount of research was being done at the time.

To say that Frith's contribution to the field of autism is impressive is an understatement. For example, she co-developed the theory that people with autism have difficulty imagining what others think, feel, or know (the idea of a weak theory of mind). Frith's name is especially connected to the theory of weak central coherence, a theory that she explains extensively in her book *Autism: Explaining the enigma*.[3]

Frith describes central coherence as "a built-in propensity to form coherence over as wide a range of stimuli as possible, and to generalize over as wide a range of contexts possible."[4] Generally, this definition is translated to mean that people with autism do not see the forest for the trees. Sometimes they do not even see the trees, but they do see the bark on the trees, the leaves, or even the veins on the leaves. It has been said that people with autism are detail thinkers and do not see "wholeness." However, this view does not fully cover what Frith meant by weak central coherence.[5] Although an orientation to details has been shown both in practice and in scientific research, it is not correct to equate autism with "thinking in details."

## Are People With Autism Detail Thinkers?

First, it appears not to be true that people with autism cannot see the big picture. Research findings in this area are sometimes conflicting, but it seems that people with autism, especially when cued, are capable of seeing the bigger picture.[6] In the opinion of Francesca Happé, a researcher who for years studied central coherence, it is still to be determined if they are always better at observing details. In an article that she wrote with colleague Rhonda Booth,[7] Happé relates that not every person with autism has a keen eye for detail.

Outcomes of a number of recent studies[8] appear to confirm Happé's idea. In these studies, people with autism, especially the higher functioning, did not always perform better than people without autism on tests for which a focus on details is an advantage. Remarkably, one of them is a test that has often been mentioned as evidence of focus on detail by people with autism, the so-called *Embedded Figures Test*.[9] In this test, subjects are instructed to locate details in a bigger picture, such as the triangle on the left in the next picture.

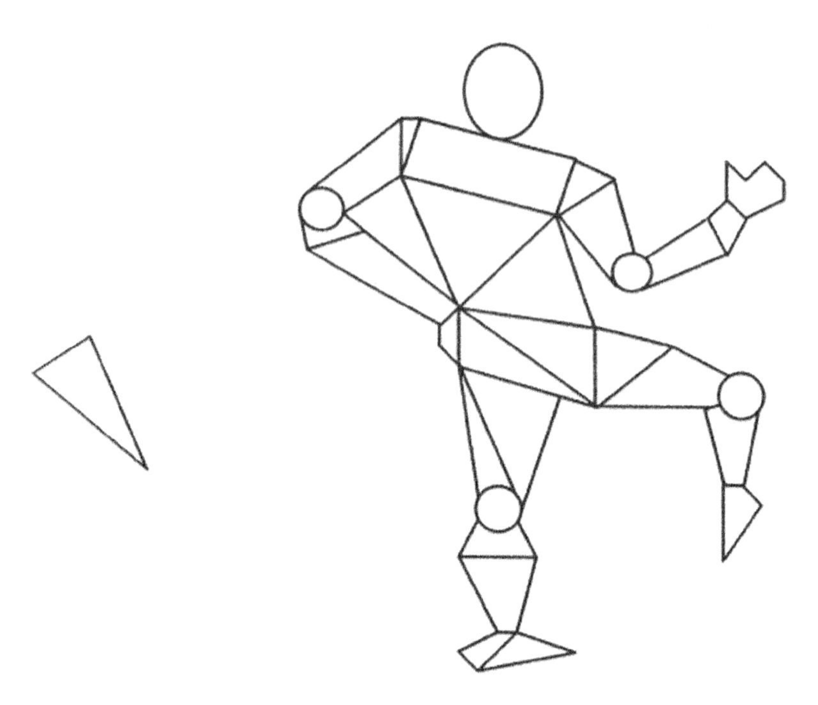

Search for the triangle on the left in the above figure. Contrary to what is usually assumed, people with autism do not always perform better on these types of tests.

Rhonda Booth found that global perception (seeing the bigger picture), on one hand, and local perception (focus on details), on the other, are not opposite processes. On the contrary, a person who is good with details is usually also good at seeing the connections.[10] This conclusion delivers a considerable blow to the common belief that people with autism are good with details and people without autism, in contrast, are good with the big picture. Moreover, two recent studies did not support the idea that people with autism are superior at attending to and recalling details.[11]

Nevertheless, there are many anecdotes about people with autism who notice minute details that no one else sees.

Are those stories true? Sure. The anecdotes and the recent scientific insights can be reconciled by looking more closely and more in detail (pun intended) at the perception of and attention to details.

First, not every detail is irrelevant and unimportant. Anyone who has entered a stage and only at that moment noticed that his fly was open or that he was wearing two different socks will fully acknowledge that. What is important is that you focus your attention on details that are important and ignore the unimportant details. That is what is difficult for people with autism: identifying what is important and what is not. For that reason, they sometimes notice details that people without autism are blind to, because these details are less important. And precisely because we did not notice those details, it strikes us that people with autism did. Hence, the impression that people with autism have a good eye for details. However, to conclude from this that people with autism notice more details than people without autism is presumptuous. The only thing that we can say is that they notice details that others do not see. In contrast, they do not notice (or do not notice as quickly) other details noticed by individuals who do not have autism.

Earlier in this book, we saw that people with autism have more difficulty than those without in determining which detail does not fit within a certain context.[12] In noticing contextually important changes in details, the subjects with autism did not do as well as subjects without autism.

Japanese scientists[13] showed children and adults of average intelligence, with and without autism, a series of drawings of easily recognizable everyday situations. One of the drawings depicted two children eating while a dog looks at them, drooling, because he is hungry. Participants were told to remember as many elements in the drawings as possible.

Subjects were then shown the same drawings again, but this time one detail was changed. In some drawings, the changed detail was related to the theme of the drawing; for example, the dog did not drool. In other drawings, the change involved a detail that was not related to the situation, such as a different pair of shoes. When the detail did not have anything to do with the theme, there was no difference in the responses of the participants with and without autism: Less than half of the changes were noticed.[14] However, when a detail connected to the theme of the drawing was changed, the subjects without autism performed significantly better than those with autism.[15]

A recent Canadian study showed that during development, children with autism improve less in the ability to detect changes in detail than children without autism.[16] So it seems that people with autism do not have a keen eye for all details and do not always notice details as quickly or as well as people without autism. In fact, they seem to notice especially important details less frequently than do people without autism.

It is generally known that people with autism have difficulties with distinguishing what is important and what is less important. As a result, for a lot of children and adolescents, comprehending what they read and summarizing texts is difficult. This difficulty lies in differentiating the critical information from the remainder of the text and results in a tendency to include everything. For example, book reviews written by children with autism are sometimes as long as the book itself, full of details the teacher views as unnecessary. Both children and adults with autism are subject to comments such as *boring* and *too detailed* when they report about something.

While it is generally assumed that people with autism are good with details, I dare say the opposite: People with autism have difficulty with details. That is, they have difficulty distinguishing important details from unimportant ones. Again, this is caused by context blindness. Which detail is relevant and which is not is context dependent.[17]

*Autism is not the same as thinking in details. People with autism do not notice important details as well as people without autism.*

Context and relevance go hand in hand.[18] Context dependence is the ability to discover among many elements the contextually relevant information and to ignore contextually unimportant information. In Chapter 3 about visual perception, we saw that context is the guide that tells us where to focus our attention. We use the context to make an instant estimation of the gist or the essence, and thus to direct attention to specific and relevant details. We notice contextually relevant details but not others.

An anecdote of Ros Blackburn,[19] a high-functioning woman with autism, illustrates the difference.

> *In her lectures, Ros often tells the story about a play that she attended with a group of people with intellectual disabilities. Ros tells that, contrary to the people with intellectual disabilities, after the show, she did not have a clue of what the play was about. Also contrary to her companions, she had seen everything, even the small feather that flew over the stage, all the shoes, lamps, and so on. Ros had seen everything, the total, but not the gist of the play, what the play was all about.*

This essence or gist is not a detailed description of a situation but a fast and crude summary of the essential elements in the total (refer to the pictures on pp. 104-105).[20] This grasp of the gist happens quickly and subconsciously, in a fraction of a second.[21]

Thus, noticing details and noticing particular details is strongly influenced by context. Perhaps because they have trouble with the gist, people with autism, like Ros, need to observe and store all the details as a sort of compensation strategy.[22] In other words, absence of speedy detection of the essence of a situation or context causes a failure to filter and results in the perception of numerous and tangential details. It is important to notice that the filtering does not occur *after* we see the whole. In the neurotypical individual, the perception of the gist or the essence provides an immediate filter, and the selection of details occurs based on that filter. (To explain how that filtering occurs would lead us too far from the topic at hand and is quite technical, but it has been the subject of numerous studies.[23])

That is not to deny the fact that people with autism are sometimes better at details than people without autism, but this is only the case in situations where the gist is not of importance and when attention must be paid explicitly to the details. For that reason, people with autism sometimes excel at tasks if the gist is not important, but details are.

*In the organization at which I work, Autism Centraal, we have a large database containing thousands of clients' email addresses. When inserting the email data of new customers, every detail counts. An email to peter.vermeulen@autismecentraal.com will not reach its destination when the proper address is petervermeulen@autismecentraal.com. The dot between the first name and the last name is "only" a detail. On a higher level of meaning, nothing changed. The first name and last name remain the same, and therefore refer to the same person. But for a computer, to which every symbol is of importance, this is different.*

*Employees of Autism Centraal have often made errors when inputting email addresses into the database. Focused as they are on the essence, they sometimes miss the details, like a silly dot between a name and a surname. However, since we have given an employee with autism the task of inputting our data, far fewer emails return as undeliverable, and our database is now well taken care of.*

Thus, people with autism are not always better at observing details and not always worse at observing the whole. All in all, it seems that using the term *central coherence* to denote whole versus detail (in the literature, this is often referred to as global vs. local processing of information) may not be very fruitful for retrieving the core of the autistic cognitive style. More important than seeing the whole or the details is picking up what is relevant and being able to flexibly switch one's attention between the whole and the details.[24]

## Central Coherence at Lower and Higher Levels

The idea is not new that people with autism do not differ that much from people without autism in terms of observing whole versus parts. Uta Frith suspected this from the beginning when she defined the term *weak central coherence*. In a personal conversation, Frith[25] even said that she regretted that a lot of people narrowed the term weak central coherence to "thinking in details."

In the first version of her book *Autism: Explaining the Enigma,*[26] Frith made a distinction between coherence at a low level (local cohesion) and coherence at a high level (central cohesion). To illustrate, she used the image of a powerful roaring river fed by many tributaries, which, for their part, are the result of the integration of numerous small creeks. Coherence at a low level is comparable to the creeks joining together to become a river. Frith describes this as an early stage of information processing. She refers to the perception of illusions and gestalt, such as seeing a triangle in the following drawing, as an example.

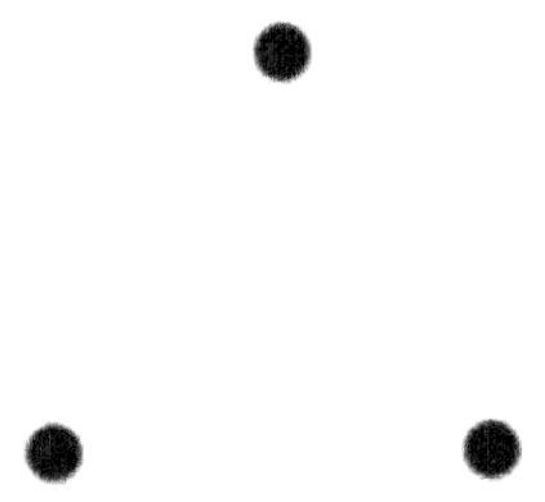

According to Frith, at this level of local cohesion, there is no difference between autism and nonautism.[27] To Frith, the essence of autism is situated at the higher level of coherence. That is what she means by weak central coherence. In relation to that higher level, Frith introduces the term **context independence**. She writes, "The need to slot information into a larger and larger context is another way to look at the effect of high-level central cohesion."[28] The revised version of her book from 2005 states, "A drive for coherence and the ability to make use of context are one and the same thing."[29]

Frith distinguishes between:

- Coherence at a lower level (local coherence): the seeing of totals; and
- Coherence at a higher level (or central coherence): the influence of context on meaning.

According to Frith, deficits in the latter (central coherence) are typical in autism.

From the beginning, Frith stressed the crucial role of context sensitivity in the term *central coherence*: "The ability to take account of context is what we take for granted in normal children, but not in autistic children. Here, instead, we might consider the ability *not to take account of context*"[30] (italics in the original text). In the revised edition of *Autism: Explaining the Enigma,* Frith equates central coherence with the "effect of context on meaning" and weak central coherence as "lack of an effect of context."[31]

The fact that Frith, more than 10 years ago, pointed to the lack of context sensitivity of people with autism means that the hypothesis of autism as context blindness that I suggest in this book is not new or original. I am indebted in large part to her. The hypothesis of context blindness is a rerun and further specification of the theory of weak central coherence.

Context blindness stresses an aspect of the term *central coherence* that has remained largely unnoticed and has not been well understood, specifically the *use* of context in the process of giving meaning. (This is different from *seeing* the context.) In addition, the term *context* in context blindness is not the same as the whole. With this, the connection between the terms context blindness and central coherence is shown. Having said this, the time is ripe for a definition of the term *context blindness*.

## Context Blindness: The Definition

**Context blindness is a deficit in the ability to use context spontaneously and subconsciously to determine meanings.** This definition deserves some explanation, especially of what is *not* meant by the term *context blindness*.

First, as we have discussed, context is not the same as "the whole." In Chapter 1, context and context sensitivity were defined as follows:

- *Context* is the totality of elements within the observing person and in the spatial and temporal surrounding of a stimulus that influence the perception of that stimulus and the meaning that is given to it.
- *Context sensitivity* is the ability to discover within the collection of elements contextually relevant information and to ignore unimportant things.

Thus, context is *the totality of contextually relevant elements* within both the environment and our memory. In a given situation, what is contextually relevant may be a detail. The context of the woman next door ringing your doorbell with a bloody knife in her hand is entirely different than if she was standing with a hundred-dollar bill in her hand. One detail can change the whole context.

Second, context blindness does not refer to *not seeing* the context, but more accurately to the *failure to use* context. Context blindness is not about "not seeing the forest for the trees" but about "not using the forest to see the trees as being trees." The difference between seeing and using context becomes clear with an example that is well known in the autism world as the ravioli example. The example is from a book by Francesca Happé.

Seeing the context, but being unable to use it. Used with permission.

In this example, a clinician is showing a high-functioning boy with autism a situation involving a doll bed. She asks him to describe what he sees. The boy correctly labels the bed, the mattress, the quilt, and the doll. The clinician then points to the pillow and asks, "And what is this?" The boy replies, "A piece of ravioli." Happé writes about this, "The child in this anecdote was not joking, nor was his sight impaired – indeed the clinician commented that the pillow indeed look like a piece of ravioli, *if taken out of context* "[32] (italics in original).

In a number of presentations, the ravioli anecdote has been used to illustrate the detail thinking of people with autism, along with the comment that the boy only sees fragmented pieces and does not see the total situation. But this is not true. The fact that he correctly names everything (bed, mattress, doll) proves that he did see everything. But he did not use the context he had seen to make the right choice out of the multiple possible meanings that the visual stimulus of a pillow could have.

Happé writes that subjects without autism "appear to be constrained in their interpretation of information by the context in which stimuli are presented. The central coherence theory suggests that autistic subjects are peculiarly free from such contextual constraints."[33] To see the context is imperative for contextualizing meanings, but it is not sufficient. Happé's anecdote clarifies that people with autism, even when they see the context, are still less context sensitive when they give meaning.

At this point, smart readers often remark that this means that people with autism are not context blind at all; the boy in the ravioli example did see the context! I agree. The term *reduced context sensitivity* is technically more accurate than *context blindness*. The choice of the term *context blindness* is a pragmatic one. Just as with classical blindness, *context blindness* implies that the challenges of people with autism in using context stem from an inability, particularly a perceptional inability. The term *context insensitivity* is easily associated with insensitivity in general, as in the meaning of "they could not care less." As if people with autism can take into account context, but do not care to do so. It would also imply that all we should do to "treat" autism is make people more sensitive to context. As we will see in the next chapter, theoretically this is correct, but it is practically impossible, just as it is impossible for a blind person to see. For those reasons, I chose the term *context blindness*.

*Context blindness is, specifically, a deficit in using context, more than it is a deficit in seeing the context.*

Third, context blindness is not the same as being unable to make connections. It is widely and erroneously believed that people with autism cannot make connections. The truth is that they do relate things. They are able to use logical reasoning (see Chapter 6). With his theory of autism as hypersystemizing, Simon Baron-Cohen[34] stresses the talent that people with autism have in reasoning according to "if x, then y" principles. People with autism also do not have a problem with one-to-one relationships (relationships between two entities). In fact, they have no problem giving meaning to single stimuli, like simple words or objects.[35]

All in all, people with autism do not always differ in their sense making: They often give the same meaning as people without autism. That can be confusing to professionals and parents – sometimes people with autism understand something correctly; sometimes they do not. More difficult for people with autism are the one-to-many relationships, when something is related to several different entities. In these types of open relationships, context plays a part in which relationship you choose out of all the possible relationships. And with that, we return to the foundation of this book: **Nothing has a fixed meaning.**

Meanings change according to the context. Every stimulus or sensation has many possible meanings. That causes problems for people with autism. While individuals with autism do make connections, those connections are fixed rather than context sensitive. Stated differently, people with autism tend to think in fixed one-to-one relationships, not in contextually changing one-to-many relationships. For example, to someone with autism, a book can only be a book. A world in which books can also be murder weapons, umbrellas, or stairs can be very confusing for people with autism.

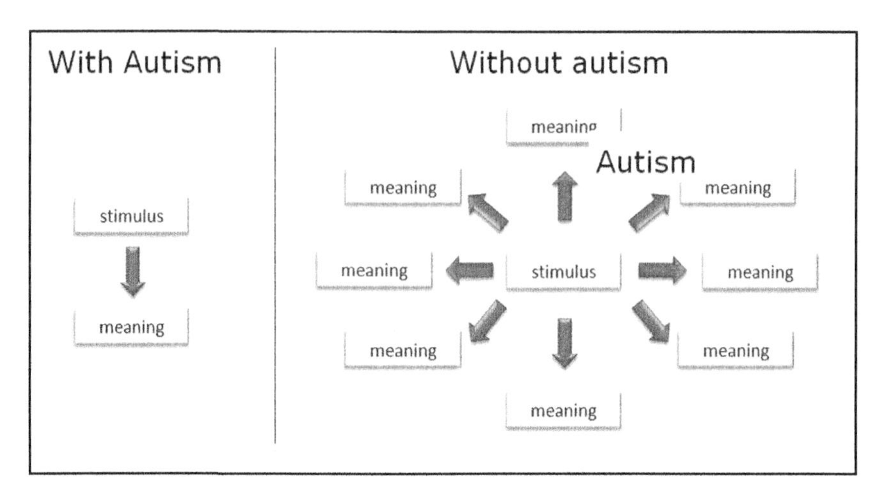


People without autism have an open collection of meanings and relationships. In contrast, people with autism tend to operate on fixed, single connections.

This characterizes not only people with so-called classic autism but also people with other diagnoses on the autism spectrum. For example, Uta Frith wrote, "Anecdotes suggest that difficulties tend to arise from the fact that people with Asperger syndrome see situations in fixed and absolute terms, rather than relative to context."[36]

We have also given a number of examples in this book. Think about *Rainman,* for whom a red light had only one meaning, STOP! Or think about the man who had difficulties with the fact that certain words, like *school*, have multiple meanings. Here is another example.

> *Matthew, a man with autism and a cognitive disability, works part-time in a retail store. One of his assistants is Katie. Matthew calls her by her name and also knows to whom it refers when people speak of Katie. Matthew is capable of making the connection between the name* Katie *and the person Katie. When a second assistant*

*with the name Katie arrives at the work place, Matthew is confused. Same name but belonging to a different person is really confusing; so he decides to call her Katie Vandenbos. This way there is no confusion with the first Katie. When a third Katie joins the scene, Matthew also invents an exclusive name for her, Katie Vandenbos Cornelis. Matthew's brain cannot handle that something, in this case a name, can refer to different people. Because of his autism, Matthew prefers fixed connections.*

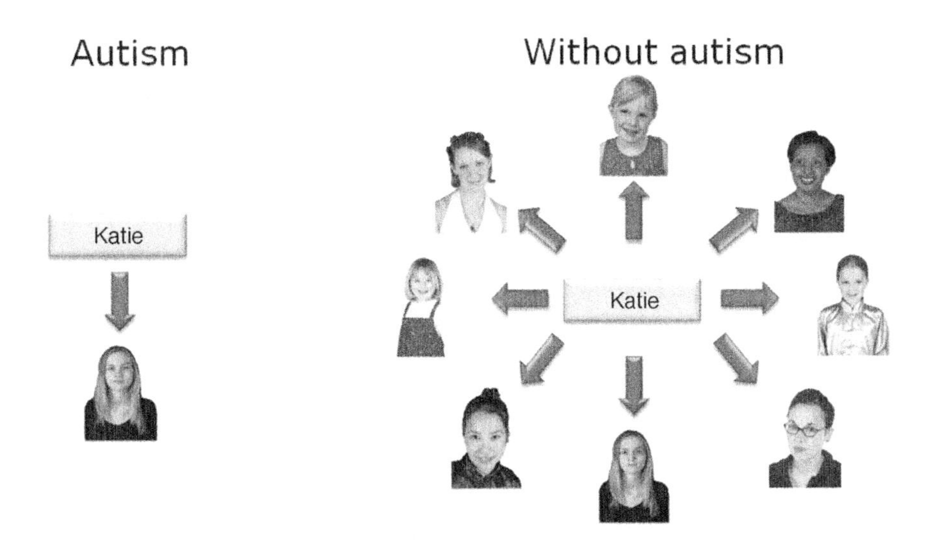


This example shows that people with autism do not have difficulty making a connection; Matthew can connect a name to a person. But the fact that one name can refer to different people is confusing to him. Matthew is not alone in this. In the more than 25 years that I have been working with people with autism, I have noticed that some of them prefer to always call people by their first name as well as their last name, even in informal situations and with people they have known for a long time. This has nothing to do with being polite.

The changing of meanings as a function of context is difficult for people with autism and makes them rigid in their thinking and behavior. The difference between people with and without autism is only noticeable when the connection between stimulus and meaning is not fixed. In fixed routines or when the context does not require a meaning to be revised, people with autism react pretty much like most other people.

*The receptionist in our office was absent for a week, so we trained our employee with autism to open the front door for people coming to our center to attend a workshop and accompany them to the conference room. We gave him a step-by-step plan for how to proceed and even did some role-play to practice. Everything went well until the last day of the week when a person came to the center for a meeting with our manager, as opposed to attending a workshop. Instead of adapting the routine to this new "context," the employee accompanied the person ... to the conference room.*

In addition to playing a part not only when different meanings are possible, context also plays a part when the meaning is not immediately clear – when our brain is receiving unclear, vague, or incomplete information. Consequently, people with autism do not have problems when information is clear, complete, and unambiguous. In such situations, they give the same meaning as people without autism, and their autistic thinking is not noticeable.

To conclude, when using the term *context blindness,* we do not mean that people with autism never use context to determine meanings. They can correctly pronounce words with multiple meanings (such as homographs) when it is pointed out that there is more than one possibility.[37] When the context is activated, they are also able to use it to name and explain emotions.[38] They also do well at explicit visual search tasks; their performance differs little from that of neurotypical subjects in the use of context.[39]

In each of these experiments, the researchers, in one way or another, pushed the "context button." It looks as if people with autism can use context in their information processing consciously but not on a subconscious level. They can use context, but do it less automatically and with more (conscious) effort.[40]

## Context Blindness and the Social Cognitive Theories About Autism

How context blindness is related to the theory of weak central coherence was discussed earlier in this chapter. How it relates to difficulties in mindreading and deficits in executive functions are additional areas to explore.

The relationship between context blindness and the theories that explain autism as reduced or low empathizing was extensively described in Chapter 4; therefore, only a short summary will be given here.

The ability to attribute mental states to others requires much more than theory of mind or empathizing. It also requires a great deal of context sensitivity. When people with autism have difficulty perceiving what others think, feel, want, or mean, a failure to involve the context, rather than an inability to empathize, is implicated. As soon as we activate the context, higher functioning people with autism do not perform poorly in terms of empathy. In addition, they seem to know numerous social scripts and can come up with solutions to social situations. However, as described in Chapter 4 on context and social interaction, there is a deficit in adjusting these scripts and solutions to context. And, unfortunately for people with autism, no two situations are identical.

The difference between a weak ability to empathize and a strong ability to systemize, a contrast that is the core of the theory developed by Simon Baron-Cohen,[41] can also be attributed to context blindness. People with autism can, as Baron-Cohen claims, reason very well systematically, but only within a closed system with fixed "when x, then y" rules. As soon as the system becomes open, and thus influenced by all types of contextual influences (when p, then q, but when y is present, then z), they make a myriad errors in their reasoning. No matter how skilled they are at systemizing, they have difficulties with the logic of exceptions and contextual changes in the system, whether a social situation or not.

Briefly, the typical characteristics of autism described by social cognitive theories seem to be the consequence of a deeper problem; in particular, context blindness. There is also some neurological evidence of this. Empathic reactions in the brain are influenced by context.[42] Those influences are fast and subconscious.

## Context Blindness and Executive Functions

The terms *use of context* and *flexibility in processing information* are more or less synonymous. Many scientists see the lack of flexibility in people with autism as evidence of a disorder in the executive system of the brain, a system that is primarily situated in the frontal lobe. *Executive functions* is the term used to describe a set of cognitive functions that are in charge of the oversight, control, and direction of our thinking and actions. Inhibiting impulses, foresight, and planning, and focusing and changing attention are only a few of the most important executive functions.

When the executive system does not function well, problems arise that typify autism, such as developing fixed routines (Saturday is French fries day), not being able to inhibit dominant associations (red light means STOP), difficulty planning and organizing activities, and not being able to shift attention (being busy for hours with a hobby or a task and not thinking about stopping to eat).

Because executive functioning incorporates multiple areas, it is referred to as an umbrella term. That is where we run into a bit of a problem: The theory is so broad that it not only explains the characteristics of autism but of many other disorders as well. Attention deficit-hyperactivity disorder (ADHD) is a case in point.[43] Additionally, only a few of the many functions within executive functioning are different for people with autism.[44] Particularly important among these are attention shifting and cognitive flexibility, not coincidentally functions that relate to context.

People with autism find it difficult to shift their attention and change their reactions in response to circumstances. Difficulty changing the topic of a conversation is a primary example. In the first study of executive functioning in autism, the neuropsychologist Judith Rumsey[45] stated that success in typical executive functioning tests like the *Wisconsin Card Sorting Test* requires attention to and integration of multiple contextual factors. In another domain, that of schizophrenia, researchers have made the connection between executive functioning and context sensitivity multiple times.[46] Given the overlap between context blindness and executive functioning, one is tempted to ask if context blindness is not just another word for the theory of executive dysfunction in autism. Yet, there is a clear difference.

Scientists connect executive functioning with the top-down system in our brain. Top-down has to do with all types of processes that supervise other systems, especially those having to do with processing what enters the brain, the so-called bottom-up processes. In this book, we have connected context sensitivity with these top-down processes.

But context sensitivity is more than top-down control from higher areas like the frontal lobes. Within the lower regions of information processing in the brain, like the thalamus and the primary visual cortex, contextual influence is also taking place. Indeed, we use context in the first milliseconds of information processing, at the stage at which we are not yet conscious of the incoming information. Think about the influence of context on the perception of size and color, like the perception of the size of the moon or the color of a white piece of paper in the shadow. Neurologists have discovered that even cells in the primary visual cortex (V1) are context sensitive[47] in the earliest phases of visual perception. These types of fast and early contextual influences on information processing differ from the executive functions, which are assumed to be higher mental functions, situated in the frontal lobes.

Whereas the theory of executive dysfunction primarily stresses differences in higher, often more conscious, top-down control, context blindness also involves differences in the lower subconscious levels of information processing. Consider the reduced sensitivity of people with autism to subconscious contextual effects at a low level such as the McGurk effect and the Ganong effect[48] (see Chapter 5 about communication). While they are more difficult to explain based on the theory of executive function, sensory problems such as oversensitivity and insensitivity to certain sensory sensations may also be linked to context blindness.[49]

## Context Blindness: A Subcognitive Problem

One problem with the theories of executive function, theory of mind, and systemizing is that they reach rather high. That is, they try to explain autism by a deficit in higher cognitive processes; however, personal stories and testimonials increasingly stress that autism is not as much a different way of *thinking* as a different way of *perceiving*. More advanced research techniques that enable us to map very closely how the brain works have shown that within a few hundred milliseconds after the input of information, the brains of people with autism work differently than neurotypical brains, even before the information reaches their consciousness.[50]

More and more, it seems that there is not something like "autistic thinking" (autistic cognition), but an *autistic subcognition*. Therefore, context blindness is not so much another way of defining the so-called autistic thinking, but an attempt to describe and explain challenges of people with autism in the lower levels of information processing. As we have said multiple times: Context sensitivity is a matter of the subconscious[51] and performs its work within the first milliseconds of information processing in the brain. Our subconscious can process 200,000 times more information than our conscious,[52] and a major part of that information is related to context.

We have seen that people with autism have problems selecting what is relevant. There is not a simple answer to the question "How do you know what is important?" This is because we select what is important in a certain context, in large part, subconsciously.[53]

It is widely known that autism, in essence, presents a challenge of sense making: People with autism often give an atypical meaning to what they experience. Further, it is becoming clearer and clearer that giving meaning is primarily the result of fast, subconscious processes in the brain. Nevertheless, it is still largely a mystery exactly what it is that happens in the brain (and where) that enables us to translate, in a fraction of a second, the millions of pixels from our retina into meanings like "book" or "mother." When we recognize that book or our mother (Hey, a book! Aha, my mother!), that is thought of as conscious cognition; but that recognition is the result of subconscious processes and not of conscious thought. As the cognitive scientist Douglas Hofstadter expressed it, "As if I recognize my mother by [consciously] comparing the scenery in front of me with stored memories of the appearances of tigers, cigarettes, hoolahoops, gambling casinos, and can openers (and, of course, all other things in the world simultaneously) and somehow instantly come up with 'what fits best.'"[54]

This quick but conscious and visual comparison is, according to her own writings, the way Temple Grandin[55] recognizes things. Could it be, therefore, that people with autism consciously have to reason through what people without autism know subconsciously (call it intuition, feeling, or instinct)?

This idea is not new. Thus, it has been suggested in relation to theory of mind that people with autism via conscious reasoning have to compensate for a lack of intuition.[56] For example, children with autism are capable, when they are urged and given time, of understanding others' emotions and of reacting appropriately; however, when emotions are presented in such a short time that they cannot be perceived consciously, they do not perform as well.[57]

Similarly, following gaze cues, a characteristic of joint attention, is known to be difficult for people with autism. How-

*What is typical for autism is not another way of thinking, but another way of subconscious information processing.*

ever, it seems that they are capable of following a gaze cue when the gaze is presented long enough to be seen consciously. But when the gaze cue is presented for such a short time that while the brain has received the information the person is still unaware of it, people with autism do not show the gaze cueing effect, in contrast with a neurotypical control group. So, there seems to be an impairment of unconscious, but not conscious, joint attention in autism.[58]

I am convinced that the difference between an autistic brain and a nonautistic brain is greater in the area of subconscious information processing than in conscious thought. Future research must focus more on autistic subcognition than on conscious autistic thinking. What differentiates the brain of someone with autism from the brain of someone without autism is a lack of quick, subconscious use of context.

## Context Blindness: A Good Theory?

As previously stated, context blindness is not a totally new theory about autism. It is an adjustment of the existing theory of weak central coherence. To what extent does context blindness achieve the standard of a cognitive model of autism? To answer this, we put context blindness to the test of a good psychological theory about autism. That test consists of six criteria:[59]

1. The theory must be based on what we know of the so-called typical development and so-called typical functioning;
2. The theory must be able to explain all the behavioral characteristics of autism;
3. The characteristic that the theory describes must be universal; that is, it must be present in all people with autism;
4. The characteristic must be specific; that is, it must occur in people with autism but not in people with other disorders;
5. The theory must be consistent with what we know about the brains of people with autism;
6. The theory must provide concrete predictions that can be tested through scientific research.

Let us see if the hypothesis of autism as context blindness matches these criteria.

**Context Sensitivity in So-Called Typical Development**

The previous chapters presented numerous examples of context sensitivity in so-called typical perception and information processing. Within developmental psychology, the role of context in information processing has been extensively demonstrated. That is, we know that children at a very young age already use context, for example, to retrieve the meanings of the behaviors of others or to read emotions (see Chapter 4 about context in social interaction).

There is overwhelming evidence for context sensitivity and its role in a number of cognitive processes. Although the term *context sensitivity* is very broad, and although until now there has been no agreement on its definition, the role of context sensitivity in different important areas of information processing is, within psychology and neuroscience, not subject to discussion. Or, as Kokinov phrased it, "Context-sensitivity is an important characteristic feature of every cognitive process and therefore should be reflected in every architecture pretending to explain human cognition."[60]

We know virtually nothing about the way context sensitivity develops, because there has been no research in that area; however, it seems logical to assume that, like so many other cognitive abilities, it develops gradually and through the years. Thus, young children are less sensitive than older children to visual illusions in which context plays a role (see Chapter 2 about context in the brain).

## Context Blindness and the Characteristics of Autism

Throughout the chapters of this book, reduced context sensitivity has been connected with the whole range of characteristics of autism:

- The atypicalities in processing of sensory information and sensory over- and under-sensitivity
- The difficulties with assigning meaning to social information, like reading and understanding the emotions and intentions of other people
- The difficulties in reacting appropriately in social situations
- The abnormalities and difficulties in understanding language and communication
- The lack of flexibility in behavior
- The problems with generalization and the resistance to change
- The need for predictability
- The memory profile
- The difficulties in understanding what is important and what is not.

To date, no research has explicitly shown a relationship between context blindness and the behavioral characteristics typical of individuals with autism, but two studies suggest a positive relation: The less context sensitivity in the recognition of sounds, the higher the autism quotient.[61]

The hypothesis of context blindness offers not only an explanation of the challenges that are typical to autism, it also explains the strengths in autism, such as a good eye for details that nonautistic people overlook and excellent reasoning abilities within a closed system. Context blindness can also explain why people with autism can sometimes invent logical and rational solutions in situations where people without autism are distracted by all types of contextual elements, especially emotional ones.

## Context Blindness in Everybody With Autism?

The studies described in this book that show a reduced context sensitivity in people with autism included a varied group of people with autism: children, adolescents, and adults at all different levels of ability. In the majority of studies, because of the complexity of the tests used, subjects with autism were of at least average intelligence. Nonetheless, context blindness seems to be a problem for all people with autism, regardless of their level of intelligence.

Participants in these studies included people with different diagnoses along the autism spectrum, such as classic autism and Asperger Syndrome. Reduced context sensitivity was shown in each of these diagnoses. For now, there is no reason to assume that certain subgroups on the autism spectrum are more or less context sensitive. At this moment, it is unclear if there are gradations in context blindness and if there is a relationship to intelligence, diagnosis, and age. However, there does seem to be a positive correlation between context sensitivity and age in people with autism[62]: Context sensitivity seems to improve with age, but it remains unclear to what extent there is improvement and whether there is a difference compared to the progress made in neurotypical development.

**Context Blindness: Specific to Autism?**

Are people with autism the only ones who have difficulty with spontaneous use of context? The answer is no! It is unclear to what degree people with other developmental disorders are less context sensitive, but there is one disorder in which scientific research has also found difficulties in processing the context: schizophrenia,[63] a disorder that is primarily characterized by delusions and hallucinations. The suspicion that a disorder in context sensitivity is at the foundation of the symptoms of schizophrenia is not new but dates back to the 1970s.

To illustrate, here are some remarkable citations from the literature on schizophrenia:

> "Patients with schizophrenia show deficits on tasks that require subjects to use contextual variables in determining the appropriate responses."[64]

> "People that hallucinate fail to make use of contextual information which controls the activation of appropriate material."[65]

> "Several schizophrenic deficits may be related to a single function: an impairment in maintaining contextual information over time and in using that information to inhibit inappropriate responses."[66]

> "Patients with schizophrenia are characterized by a reduced contextual influence in functions such as memory, attention, and language processing."[67]

The husband of autism expert Uta Frith, Chris Frith, has also contributed to the theory of distorted context sensitivity in schizophrenia. As he wrote in an article from 1991, "Studying tasks that involve the processes by which context determines relevance will enable us to understand the symptoms of schizophrenia."[68] Additionally, in an overview article from 2005, psychologist David Hemsley[69] concluded, "There is convincing evidence for an alteration in the way that context exerts its influence in schizophrenia."

In relation to context blindness, autism seems to have a twin brother, and that brings us back to the early beginning of theories about autism. A long time ago, it was thought that autism was a form of schizophrenia – some even categorized it among the psychoses. But autism and schizophrenia can be clearly distinguished, especially with regard to behavioral aspects. Delusions and hallucinations are typical of schizophrenia, not of autism. But what about cognitive characteristics, especially context blindness?

First, cognitive deficits are rarely exclusive to a certain disorder. That is especially true for deficits that are not linked to a specific location in the brain but are caused by anomalies in processes that are spread over the entire brain or a large area of the brain, which is the case in context sensitivity. It is, therefore, to be expected that context blindness can overlap with other disorders; however, this is also true for other cognitive characteristics in autism. For example, the impairments in theory of mind and executive functioning commonly seen in individuals with autism are also seen in people with schizophrenia.[70] The same holds true for a weak central coherence: difficulties with perception of the "whole" and the tendency for local perception to be stronger than global perception have also been found in people with schizophrenia.[71]

Neuropsychological studies in schizophrenia and autism are remarkably similar. Often, the same tests are used in research on schizophrenia and autism, such as the homograph test, the *Wisconsin Card Sorting Test*, or the hidden figures test, and with similar results as we see in autism.[72]

The overlap between the cognitive explanations for autism and schizophrenia has not gone unnoticed. In 2003, psychologists Phillips and Silverstein published an article about the biological and psychological aspects of schizophrenia. Among other things, they described reduced top-down coordination in the brain and reduced use of context, referring to similar problems in autism.[73] In response, autism experts pointed out that the theory of Phillips and Silverstein shows a remarkable resemblance to the well-known autism theory of weak central coherence.[74]

The overlap between schizophrenia and autism in relation to context blindness is also possibly caused by the vagueness of the term *context* and the many different meanings that are given to the term. The terms *context* and *context blindness* can be so broad that they become all-inclusive and thus meaningless.[75] Perhaps context sensitivity cannot be pinned to one process but is a collection of brain processes, some of which are manifest in autism spectrum disorders, others in schizophrenia, and still others in people with other disorders.

I am convinced that the problems with context in schizophrenia and autism are different, but to show these differences it will be necessary for researchers to reach agreement on the definition of context sensitivity and to look at specific aspects of context sensitivity.

For example, it is possible that not being able to activate contextually appropriate meanings is especially typical for autism, while not being able to repress contextually inappropriate meanings is more characteristic of schizophrenia.[77] Research has shown that people with autism as well as those with schizophrenia find it difficult to predict the last word in a sentence based on the context.

This identical finding for both groups may have different causes. Perhaps people with autism cannot predict the last word because they process all the previous words in the sentence separately and do not build a context. For individuals with schizophrenia, the same inability to predict the last word may be caused by excessive activation of all types of inappropriate associations, activated by the previous words in the sentence.[78] Further, there may be a different neurological underpinning of the reduced context sensitivity in the two conditions.[79] For now, this is speculation, and we cannot go beyond the common conclusion in scientific articles: Further research is necessary!

## Context Blindness: Does It Fit With What We Know About the Brain?

In Chapter 2, I answered this question. On a neurological level, context sensitivity expresses itself primarily in a well-built network in the brain, especially the top-down processes in this network (not only the top-down processes from higher areas of information processing to lower areas, but also within and between certain areas of the brain). Thus, the hypothesis of autism as context blindness fits well in the widely accepted theory of reduced cortical connectivity in the autistic brain.

## Context Blindness: Scientific Evidence?

Until recently, of the three big theories about autism (theory of mind, executive function, central coherence), the theory of weak central coherence has received the least attention in scientific research. Similarly, context blindness has rarely been the subject of scientific experiments. At the close of writing the original Dutch version of this book (in 2009), I found slightly more than 60 studies in which aspects of context sensitivity in people with autism were investigated. And now, two years later, the number has still not reached 100, while yearly around 2,500 scientific articles are being published on autism.

Most of the studies that involve context sensitivity in autism are described in the previous chapters. In 90% of the studies, the researchers found evidence for reduced context sensitivity. In the remaining 10%, the performance on tasks requiring the use of context was not lower for the subjects with autism than for the control subjects without autism. When we closely examine the latter group of studies, they almost always appear to involve a methodology in which the investigators made it easy for the subjects to utilize the context, including:

- The context was being activated by the experimenters (i.e., they pushed the context button), and/or
- Compared to real-life contexts, the context was very simple (e.g., a geometric configuration, one or two sentences), and/or
- The subjects were given an explicit assignment to do something consciously, and/or
- More or less equal contexts were offered repeatedly, resulting in training effects.[80]

In short, the tasks in these studies rarely reflected context use in real life.

Scientists must control and systemize variables as much as possible. A casual conversation with subjects in the cafeteria on the university campus can be cozy and informative, but a scientist cannot do much with data derived that way. Statistics and coziness do not go hand in hand. The traditional experimental setting in scientific studies is sometimes miles away from the reality of everyday life, which results in oversimplification of the complexity and velocity with which various situations occur in daily life.

It is not surprising that individuals with autism sometimes perform well in laboratory conditions in which information is systematically simplified and often stripped of all distracting sensations such as those you would have in a cafeteria, for example. A similar phenomenon is seen in the research on theory of mind: Sometimes people with autism perform splendidly in test situations, but in real life, they appear to have significant difficulty.[81]

Because a person can neatly sort pictures of facial expressions or can name them in the distraction-free research room of a university, it does not mean that the same person can read the annoyance on his mother's face when she is cooking in the kitchen, while he sets the table with the radio blaring and the dog running around attempting to grab food off of the counter. Context is difficult to scientifically research. Context can refer to almost anything, and in real life there are no two identical contexts: Every context is unique. Every translation of the term *context* in an experiment falls short of reality.

You might wonder, then, if context blindness should not be studied scientifically? The answer is: It should. But researchers should as closely as possible adhere to the way context sensitivity is defined in this book; namely, **the spontaneous, quick, and subconscious use of context in giving meaning, when that meaning is not obvious, and in everyday situations**.

Based on the theory of context blindness, we can predict that people with autism will not do as well on tests that make use of naturalistic, realistic material (such as movie fragments or newspaper articles) or in which the meaning of so-called target stimuli is not immediately clear or can have different meanings.

The following is an example of a concrete prediction based on the theory of context blindness: People with autism will have more difficulties than people without autism in naming atypical facial expressions for which the context changes the standard meaning (e.g., someone who cries because he won the lottery). In this type of task, the performance of people with autism will be weaker than in tasks in which they are offered acontextual facial expressions to be identified, such as naming facial expressions on pictures of faces.[82] For future research, it will be also important to distinguish between *seeing* context and *using* context.

Because context sensitivity is subconscious and happens within fractions of a second, there is also a need for research on quick, unconscious reactions, as measured by, for example, eye tracking or electrophysiological measurements of the brain. Based on theory-of-mind research on people with autism, we can assume that when these subjects get enough time, they can "hack" the right answers consciously.

## Summary

It is reasonable to say that the hypothesis of context blindness does not do a bad job as a cognitive model of autism: (a) The theory has its roots in developmental psychology, (b) there is a neurological base for it, and (c) it explains many characteristics of autism. Above all, there is already a body of scientific evidence of reduced context sensitivity in autism. And, independently of my work, other authors have

*To research context blindness scientifically requires more realistic research situations.*

also introduced the idea of the autistic mind as decontextualized[83] or have tried to define the deficit in contextual information processing in autism.[84]

Nevertheless, a number of questions remain unanswered. Is context sensitivity a specific single ability or is it an umbrella term encompassing multiple processes, some of which are perhaps intact in autism and others not? (If that were the case, this would explain the conclusion drawn in some studies that people with autism are context sensitive.) Is it the speed with which context must be taken into account, more than the ability to see it and use it, that is challenging for people with autism? Is there any situation where people with autism do use context, and if so, where? Do people with autism use context differently than people without autism? For example, some British researchers found that people with autism are capable of learning a visual context, but they follow a different learning pattern.[85] Another British research team found that people with autism are sensitive to sentence context, but the reactions of their brains form different patterns than those in the brains of people without autism.[86]

Are there differences in context blindness among groups of people with autism; for example, between people with and without additional cognitive disabilities? Do some people with autism have more trouble with certain aspects of context sensitivity than others with autism? Is it possible to differentiate subtypes along the spectrum based on context blindness? Before we can call context blindness a valid theory, we must have answers to these questions backed by scientific evidence.

Autism has many faces: It expresses itself in many ways and has characteristics that, although they occur together, do not necessarily have one cause or explanation in common.[87] It is perhaps an illusion to even try to capture the diversity of autism in a single model. There may be several cognitive deviations in autism, but perhaps context blindness is the common pathway on which these deviations come to expression. It is up to researchers to address these questions.

My foremost ambition in putting forward the hypothesis of context blindness is not to contribute to building academic theories about autism. The international scientific scene is not waiting for the ideas of a simple educationalist from Belgium. My ambition is to help ensure that whoever is involved in autism, professionally or otherwise, has a better understanding of what is happening in the brains of those with autism.

What does context blindness teach us for everyday practice? That is the subject of the final chapter.

## Endnotes – Autism as Context Blindness: The Theory

1. Kanner (1943, p. 241).
2. Kanner (1943, p. 244).
3. Frith (1989, 2003).
4. Frith (1989, p. 100).
5. Personal comment by Uta Frith, August 9, 2006, London.
6. This is the final conclusion of an extensive review study about central coherence of Francesca Happé and Uta Frith (2006).
7. Happé and Booth (2008, p. 59).
8. High-functioning persons with autism do not perform better than do control subjects on the *Embedded Figures Test* and the Wechsler subtest block patterns, two tests in which a preference for local processing leads to better results. See, e.g., Chen, Lemonnier, Lazartigues, and

Planche (2008) and Kaland, Mortensen, and Smith (2007). Happé and Booth (2008) suspect that a bias for the local processing of information is especially typical for people with autism and a younger developmental age (younger and so-called lower functioning persons), something that is confirmed by the study of Reed, Broomfield, McHugh, McCausland, and Leader (2009).

9. *Embedded Figures Test* (Witkin, Oltman, Raskin, & Karp, 1971).
10. Booth (2006).
11. Tsatsanis, Noens, Illman, Pauls, Volkmar, Schultz and Klin (2011) and Kuschner, Bodner and Minshew (2009). Tsatsanis, Noens et al. did, however, find a tendency in adults with autism to process complex information by parsing it into its component parts. Noens (personal communication, November 29, 2011), therefore, makes a distinction between a bias towards perceiving local information (superior eye for details) and fragmented perception (processing information in a part-oriented way).
12. More specifically, the study of Therese Jollife (1997), in which the test subjects had to search for what did not fit in a certain situation, like a squirrel on the beach.
13. Nakahachi et al. (2008).
14. Surprisingly, the test subjects without autism performed even a little better than the test subjects with autism. This is a contraindication for the assumed excellent perception of details in people with autism. However, the difference was not significant.
15. The persons without autism could correctly name in 85% of the cases what had been changed, while the people with autism could name it correctly in only 65% of the cases. It was notable that all subjects without autism could name the themes of the pictures compared to only two out of three subjects with autism. Also, in another study, it appears that people with autism, to a limited degree, use context for the detection of changes (Fletcher-Watson, Leekam, Turner, & Moxon, 2006).
16. Burack et al. (2009).
17. In line with the Nakahachi et al. (2008) study, it is shown that the perception of detail changes is very context sensitive and top-down directed (Austen & Enns, 2000).
18. Sperber and Wilson (1995); Ekbia and Maguitman (2001).
19. Ros Blackburn, presentation in Antwerp, December 20, 2010.
20. Oliva and Torralba (2006).
21. To be exact, pictures shown for only 26 milliseconds were recognized accurately in more than 90% of the trials with a reaction time of less

than one half second (Rousselet, Joubert, & Fabre-Thorpe, 2005). This proves that we can extract the gist of a natural scene with high accuracy in less time than the blink of an eye.

22. Happé and Booth (2008).
23. A summary of the process is as follows: There is a fast, subconscious (pre-attentive) processing of the "gist" of a scene on low resolution (coarse representation), in which eye movements are directed based on the internal context (stored knowledge) as well as key elements in the scene (color, position, contours, and lines). Once the gist has been captured and we are conscious of it, a detailed, conscious analysis of elements within the focus of attention follows. This process is also known as the "reversed hierarchy theory" of Hochstein and Ahissar (2002). For more detailed descriptions, see Oliva (2005); Oliva and Schyns (2000); Oliva and Torralba (2001); and Rousselet et al. (2005). Although most research focuses on visual perception, perception of the gist is also found in auditory perception (e.g., Hardin, Cooke, & König, 2008).
24. See in relation to this also Iarocci, Burack, Shore, Morttron, and Enns (2006).
25. Personal communication, December 15, 2005.
26. Frith (1989, p. 97).
27. Frith (1989, p. 98).
28. The choice of the term is a bit unfortunate, because context independence resembles another well-known term in psychology: field independence (Witkin, Dyk, Faterson, Goodenough, & Karp, 1962). In the revised edition of *Explaining the Enigma*, Frith seems to equate a weak central coherence with field independence (p. 153). The term *field independence*, however, refers to consciously distancing oneself from, or ignoring, the field or context after it has been picked up subconsciously by the brain. In later publications (e.g., Happé & Frith, 2006, p. 17), Frith corrected herself and said that a weak central coherence cannot be equated with field independence. People who are strongly field independent, can perform well on tests like the *Embedded Figures Test*. But that is because they can resist the gestalt in the drawing. When people with autism perform well on that test, it is not because they consciously ignore the bigger picture or the gestalt, or that they resist it (what field-independent people do), but because they do not see it in the first place.
29. Frith (1989, p. 101).
30. Frith (2003, p. 158); Frith (1989, p. 90).
31. Frith (2003, p. 152).

32. Happé (1994, p. 118). The drawing is based on the original drawing by Axel Scheffer and is used by courtesy of Francesca Happé.
33. Happe (1994, p. 117).
34. Baron-Cohen (2003).
35. Noens and van Berckelaer-Onnes (2005).
36. Frith (2004, p. 680).
37. Brock, Norbury, Einav, and Nation (2008); Hala, Pexman, and Glenwright (2007); Lopez and Leekam (2003); Norbury (2005).
38. Balconi and Carrera (2007); Wright et al. (2008).
39. Fletcher-Watson, Leekam, Turner, and Moxon (2006); Kourkoulou, Findlay, and Leekam (2008).
40. Pijnacker, Geurts, van Lambalgen, Buitelaar, and Hagoort (2010).
41. Baron-Cohen (2006).
42. de Vignemont and Singer (2006).
43. Frith (2008).
44. For an overview, see Hill (2004).
45. Rumsey (1985).
46. See Cohen, Barch, Carter, and Servan-Schreiber (1999).
47. Gilbert, Ito, Kapadia, and Westheimer (2000).
48. The McGurk and Ganong effects were discussed in the chapter about communication (Chapter 5). The Ganong effect, which seems to be reduced in people with autism, is partly a subconscious perceptual process in the brain and not only a case of more conscious, executive frontal processes (Myers & Blumstein, 2008).
49. Context works like a filter on the sensory stimuli: Context makes certain sensations stronger and represses others. For example, context promotes the transmission of that information in the receptive field of a neuron that relates coherently to the context. A reduced contextual sensitivity can result in a lack of differentiation between the sensations because either all the signals are sent through (resulting in hypersensitivity) or none are sent through (resulting in hyposensitivity), or irrelevant stimuli are being processed and relevant stimuli are not. For more information, see Phillips and Singer (1997).
50. See especially the studies on differences in ERPs (event-related potentials, the electrophysiological reactions in the brain) in autism. They show that the brains of people with autism already react differently within the first 500 milliseconds of the presentation of a visual stim-

ulus or an auditory stimulus. For an overview, see Jeste and Nelson (2009).

51. For clarity, we use the terms *subconscious* and *unconscious* not in the psychoanalytical meaning, but with the meaning that is commonly used within cognitive psychology. It refers to all types of cognitive processes of which we are not conscious.
52. Dijksterhuis, Aarts, and Smith (2005).
53. Dijksterhuis (2008). Also the "weighing principle," the weighing of elements in a decision (Dijksterhuis & Nordgren (2006).
54. Hofstadter (1985).
55. Grandin (2000).
56. I described this extensively in *The Closed Book: Autism and Emotions* (Vermeulen, 2005).
57. Begeer, Koot, Rieffe, Meerum Terwogt, and Stegge (2008).
58. Sato, Uono, Okada, and Toichi (2010).
59. Bailey, Phillips, and Rutter (1996); Happé (1994).
60. Kokinov (1994, p. 502).
61. Huang (2007) and Stewart and Ota (2008). The subjects in these studies did not have autism.
62. Loukusa, Leinonen, Jussila et al. (2007).
63. For an overview of the development of the hypothesis of context blindness in schizophrenia, see Hemsley (2005a, 2005b).
64. Hemsley and Richardson (1980, p. 141).
65. Levitan (1996, p. 253).
66. Servan-Schreiber, Cohen, and Steingard (1996, p. 1105).
67. Silverstein and Schenkel (1997, p. 696).
68. Frith, C. D. (1991, p. 29).
69. Hemsley (2005b, p. 50).
70. E.g., see Phillips and Silverstein (2003).
71. Goodarz, Wykes, and Hemsley (2000).
72. Phillips and Silverstein (2003).
73. Phillips and Silverstein (2003).
74. Bertone, Mottron, and Faubert (2004). Phillips and Silverstein (2003) relate the deficits in context sensitivity in schizophrenia to an NMDA-receptor dysfunction, that is, an underactivity of NMDA (N-methyl-

Daspartate) glutamate receptor channels. Bertone, Mottron and Faubert argue that although NMDA-hypofunction may be responsible for perceptual impairments in schizophrenia and possibly autism, it is highly unlikely that NMDA-hypofunction is specifically responsible for the autistic behavioral symptomology.

75. Titone and Debruille (2003) (commentary on Phillips and Silverstein).
76. Faubert and Bertone (2004).
77. A hypothesis that is based on what Titone and Debruille (2003) suggested.
78. Ring, Sharma, Wheelwright, and Barrett (2007).
79. Bertone et al. (2004).
80. Kunar, Flusber, Horowtz, and Wolfe (2007) showed that research design has an influence on the measurement of context sensitivity, specifically in the context of research of contextual cueing in visual search tasks.
81. I described this extensively in *The Closed Book: Autism and Emotions* (Vermeulen, 2005); additional evidence came from recent studies such as Spek, Scholte, and van Berckelaer-Onnes (2010) and Roeyers and Demurie (2010).
82. This hypothesis is currently being researched at the Lessius Institute in Antwerp.
83. Morsanyi, Handley, and Evans (2010), who use the term *decontextualised minds*.
84. Skoyles (2011).
85. Kourkoulou, Findlay, and Leekam (2008, May).
86. Braeutigam, Swithenby, and Bailey (2008).
87. Happé, Ronald, and Plomin (2006).

# Chapter 8
# Autism as Context Blindness: Applied

Can context blindness be tested?

Can you teach context sensitivity?

Why can't you explain how you learned
to whistle, swim, or ride a bike?

What serves as the white cane and Braille
for someone who is context blind?

Why do social skills training and similar strategies
have so little effect on people with autism?

So far in this book, people with and without autism have been presented as distinguishable from each other by their ability to use context: People without autism are context sensitive, and people with autism are context blind. Of course, it is not that black and white. In the previous chapter, we saw that people with autism sometimes use context; specifically, when they are consciously thinking about it and when it concerns recognizable, clear, and known contexts. In this final chapter, we want to discuss the other side – the context blindness of people without autism.

## Looking at Autism in an Autistic Way: Context Blindness in People Without Autism

When people without autism examine autism, they sometimes lose sight of the context. It is as if they look at autism in an autistic way.[1] They pick details of someone's functioning and connect a fixed meaning to them without taking into account the context, a thought process that has a strong similarity to the fixed one-to-one relations that we observe in people with autism. A classic example (perhaps one of the causes of the overdiagnosis of autism[2]) is the fixed connection between social problems and autism. In the case of people who are somewhat socially isolated, have few friends, and seem to demonstrate little empathy, autism is sometimes quickly diagnosed, or at least strongly suspected, as in the following scenario: "My husband does not talk about his emotions, locks himself away from others, and does not have the ability to empathize."

Even though the man is exhibiting these behaviors, it does not automatically mean that he has autism. To fully understand his behavior, we need to place it into context. Was he always like that? Does he talk with other people about his feelings? Has he recently experienced some unfortunate event (lost his job, lost one of his loved ones) and become depressed as a result? It is well known that people who suffer from depression may withdraw from their social world.[3] Above all, autism is more than just a disorder of social interaction. In order to be diagnosed as having autism, in addition to significant difficulties with social interaction and social communication, a person must also demonstrate restricted, repetitive patterns of behavior, interests, or activities.

Another example of looking at autism in an autistic way was described in the Preface. Caregivers and parents sometimes only look at the behavior, without looking at the context of that behavior. That is, they fail to consider the behavior of concern in light of, or in the context of, the person's own understanding that underlies their behavior. The woman with autism who, after assertiveness training, repeatedly says "no" and starts fights is not stubborn or disobedient, as her parents or caregivers think. Her behavior is caused by the "autistic connection" she made and that she did not adjust to the context. In the assertiveness training, she learned to say "no" and speak up for herself. That is what she is now doing systematically. She enters into discussions, even when she is wrong and knows she is wrong. She says "no" even though she wants to say "yes."

We read earlier about the boy with autism who did not want to wear his retainer. A reward system based strictly on his behavior was consequently put in place. This reward system did not work because the boy's resistance to the retainer was caused by his fear of swallowing it.

*There is a lot of know-how about autism, but there is too little know-why.*

Despite an enormous increase in know-how, the autistic way of looking at autism has resulted in too little know-why. We have protocols for diagnostics and various methods of treatment, but the core of autism is sometimes missed, due to a tendency to focus too much on the behavior of people with autism (often even details of that behavior) without sufficiently taking into account the context of what is taking place in the minds of people with autism. **The essence of autism is in the mind, not in the behavior.** And in the autistic cognition, a reduced context sensitivity plays a crucial role. It is important to be mindful of context blindness as we engage in diagnosis and treatment.

## Diagnostics and Context Blindness

Diagnosing autism is not a simple matter. Although autism has an undeniable biological base, we lack a medical, biological litmus test for autism. Thus, autism remains a behavioral diagnosis: The diagnosis is based on a detailed analysis of a person's behavior and functioning. But behavioral diagnosis is subject to pitfalls and constraints. A major problem is that the same behavior may have multiple causes. For example, a person may experience social challenges or exhibit a lack of social skills because he is shy, has social phobia, is depressed, or just because he is not in the mood to be social at a given moment.

Although autism is a behavioral diagnosis, it is not sufficient to make an inventory of behavioral characteristics to make a diagnosis. It is of crucial importance to determine whether the behavioral characteristics that resemble autism can be related to an autistic style of perception and thinking. While there is no obvious test to measure autistic cognition, a number of tests allow us to get at least a glimpse of the autistic style of information processing, such as the *Strange Stories* or the *Dewey Stories*, described earlier.

This book has provided multiple examples of research findings that indicate that people with autism have difficulty using context. It follows that tests that measure context sensitivity can be valuable in the diagnostic evaluation of autism. It would lead us too afield to try to cover the entire battery of tests and tasks that could be used for context blindness, but here are a few examples:

- Homographs tests
- Identification and explanation of verbal and nonverbal behavior of people in films and stories
- Identification of blanked-out facial expressions in realistic pictures or drawings
- Making inferences based on texts and stories
- Identification of contextually relevant versus irrelevant details
- Identification of relevant versus irrelevant changes in realistic drawings and pictures

These suggestions are based on the tests that have been used in scientific research on context sensitivity described in this book. In addition, some of the tests often used in diagnostic evaluations contain elements that, on a certain level, measure context sensitivity, such as the *Wisconsin Card*

*Sorting Test* (described in Chapter 6) or the D-KEFS. A well-known test for the measurement of executive functions, the D-KEFS[4] contains the *Word Context Test*, in which test subjects have to retrieve the meaning of a nonexisting word (like "prifa") based on sentences that gradually sketch the context that uncovers the meaning of that word.

In addition to administering tests and assessment tasks, the clinician makes informal observations during the diagnostic evaluation process. It is important to note any behaviors that indicate that the subject has not taken into account context or has connected acontextual meanings to language. The following is an example. These are a young man's answers from a questionnaire.

Where do you live?

☒ Independent/alone
☐ With my parents
☐ In a group house
☐ In assisted living

If you live with your parents or independent/alone, do you have support?

☐ No
☒ Yes, I am supported by: the floor

Difficulty using context was also seen in the following assessment situation. During the introductory conversation at the diagnostic center, the psychologist asked about the living situation of a woman whom he suspected to have autism. When questioned about employment, she answered that for the last couple of months she had alternated between working at home and volunteer work. After that response, the psychologist asked, "And what are you doing at this moment?" The woman answered, "Having a conversation with you."

Currently, neither a specific test nor a battery of tests exists to measure context blindness. Because difficulty with context is typical in autism, it would be beneficial to examine how assessment of context sensitivity can contribute to the diagnosis of autism. Use of measures of context sensitivity has the potential to advance the understanding of autism and improve the diagnostic process.

In addition, it is of importance in the use of various test materials to be mindful of the difference between contextual and acontextual material, especially when measuring social cognition. (This was discussed in Chapter 4 about context in social behavior.) On acontextual tests of theory of mind, as in the identification of emotions in pictures of facial expressions, people with autism do not always perform poorly. Unfortunately, these types of tests are as useful for determining autism as a blood test is for measuring someone's intelligence. When someone performs well on that type of acontextual test, autism cannot immediately be excluded.

## Can Context Sensitivity Be Learned?

After lectures that I give about context blindness, the following is the most frequently asked question, "Can you teach or train context sensitivity to people with autism?" My answer is always, "No we cannot. But we can still do something about it" ... a classic example of a combination of good and bad news.

Let us start with the bad news. As impossible as it is for a blind man to learn to see, it is just as impossible for someone who is context blind to learn to be context sensitive. Why? To begin with, it is impossible to learn something that happens, in large part, on a subconscious level. As we have seen, context sensitivity primarily involves subconscious brain work. How do you use context? In the best case, you can say in retrospect that you used context, and maybe even which elements from the context you used, but as for "how" you did it, you will not be able to answer. Try it. Read the following sentence and answer the question.

> As soon as the machine was at cruising altitude, Eveline, a slim young woman with blond hair and the daughter of a well-known heart surgeon, began to serve drinks to the people in the business class. What is Eveline's profession?

Easy, you think: a flight attendant. But how did you arrive at that answer? You can say that you used certain words from the sentence, like *cruising altitude*, *serve*, and *business class*, but how did you manage to choose just those words? Why did you ignore the other words, like *slim*, *blond,* and even the word that refers to a profession, like *heart surgeon*. Which plan did you follow? You do not know, right? Besides, I bet that after the word *cruising altitude* you immediately thought of a plane, although the word *plane* was not mentioned. Still, before you read what Eveline was doing, you had grasped the context of a plane. How did you do it? No idea! It just occurred to you; you just knew it.

This is how context works: Incredibly quickly, without knowing how you do it, you pick from the many pieces of information those that are useful. Context sensitivity is pure intuition, no conscious thinking.[5]

How can you teach something that occurs so quickly and subconsciously? Experience has taught us that we can help people with autism to complete various types of assignments and tasks with a sort of step-by-step plan. A step-by-step plan describes, in a concrete and sequential way, how to do something, like setting the table or getting dressed. But how would you compose a step-by-step plan for using context? It would be impossible.

Because use of context happens on a subconscious level, learning to make use of context is a form of what psychologists call implicit learning. In implicit learning, you learn something without being conscious of how you learn it, and you know how to do it without clear instructions. Learning to walk, whistle, to snap your fingers, lie, and to ride a bike are forms of implicit learning. You just learn to do it, and afterwards you cannot say exactly how you did it.

At the University of Alabama,[6] researchers examined the level at which adolescents and adults with autism could make improvements in the implicit learning of context. (This study was mentioned in Chapter 3 about context and perception.) The subjects were shown pictures in which they had to search for Jiminy Cricket; the context predicted where Jiminy was located. After a learning phase, subjects with autism appeared to be only 10 milliseconds faster than at the start of the test, while a control group of subjects without autism improved their performance by more than one hundred milliseconds. The conclusion: Even after training, most people with autism do not use context more than before the training.

If this first argument does not convince you, here is another.

*I taught a group of young adults with autism how you could invite someone to your house in a socially appropriate way. I had shared, based on social norms, a social script contain-*

*ing a number of attention points: Welcome someone, shake hands, invite them to come in, take their jacket and put it on a hanger, ask them to sit down, offer a drink, and so on. All steps were extensively trained in role-play. And the participants acted perfectly!*

*The true test came in real life. For the last day of the course, we had invited a few guests for a dinner. Some of the participants did the welcoming. They awaited the guests at the front door. They did exactly what we had taught them. They welcomed them, they shook hands, invited them to come in, offered to take their jackets, etc. Unfortunately, it had been hot that day, and none of the guests wore a jacket. I pointed them to the context: When no one wears a jacket, you don't have to ask for it. The students immediately understood that.*

*A little later, the parents of one of the participants arrived. Just at the moment when his mother leaned in to kiss her son, he reached his hand out to shake her hand. I pointed out to him the changed context and that shaking hands is not always necessary. This was directly followed by the question of one of the other boys, "Say, how many of those exceptions are there?"*

You can point out to people with autism the importance of context, but the pertinent factors are different in every contex, and it is impossible to fully teach how to identify those elements. The exceptions not only confirm the rule, in the case of context sensitivity, they are the rule.

Further, context sensitivity itself is influenced by context. People without autism do not always use context to determine meaning, and how much and which context they use is, to a high degree, subject to change. It is not always necessary to use context; for example, when the intrinsic information of a stimulus is sufficiently clear to give meaning to it. Thus, to give meaning to words that you know and that do not have double meanings, you do not need context. And when you must use context, it depends on the context which context you can best use.

Do you remember the word *convalescent* in Chapter 1? Some people interpret that word by using their internal context (knowledge of Latin, knowledge of similar words); others use the external context (the sentences around the word). You must possess context sensitivity to flexibly learn to use context. Context sensitivity squared, in fact.

Still not convinced? There is one last argument for why context sensitivity is barely learnable. The use of context is not only subconscious; it is spontaneous. To urge someone to be context sensitive is an example of the well-known paradox: "Now do it spontaneously!" Can you call it "context sensitivity" if a person uses context only after being instructed to do so? The answer is no.

## Pushing the Context Button

But the news is not all bad. The result is what counts; not the method used to get there. So here comes the good news. Various studies[7] have shown that people with autism can, to a certain degree, take context into consideration, especially when you push their context button. They still do not do it spontaneously, but the end result appears to be fairly good – in these studies the individuals with autism performed as well as those without autism.

*Context sensitivity cannot be explicitly taught. But we can compensate for context blindness.*

We cannot teach people with autism the "real" way to reach context sensitivity; that is, spontaneous, fast, and subconscious context sensitivity, but we can offer them a side door to getting there. We first have to point to the arrows that lead to the detour. In professional terms, this type of technique is called a **compensation strategy**. We cannot teach people with autism intuitive context sensitivity. But we can teach them to compensate. In this case, the analogy with classic blindness is again valid: You cannot teach a blind man to read a book like everyone else does, but you can teach him Braille so that he can, by a detour, read with his fingers. He still cannot see, but he can read the same book as others – in Braille.

When we analyze the analogy with blindness, we see two components: learning a compensation strategy (to learn Braille) and adjusting the environment and material (books in Braille). These two components are also applicable when we want to help people with autism with context. First, we adjust the environment to make the context explicit and clear – we clarify the context that people with autism do not take into account spontaneously. But adjustment of the environment is not enough. We have seen that context blindness at the most basic levels of perception can lead to overexposure to sensations and sensory problems. The sensory filter difficulties of people with autism require an environment in which distracting sensations (such as sound or light) are reduced as much as possible and the relevant stimuli are accentuated.

In addition to important modifications of the environment, the second element is to learn to consciously think about context. Within the pages of this book, it is impossible to give a detailed description of how this is done. I restrict myself instead to some words of explanation and a few examples.

## Highlighting the Context

When people with autism do not use context spontaneously, we can help them by pointing out the context and which elements of it are relevant. By highlighting the context, we prevent people from falling back on learned, fixed connections and reacting acontextually.

For example, we could have helped the young man with autism who filled in the questionnaire about support with the answer "the floor" by making clear the context of the question. We wanted to know "what people or organizations" supported him. The word *support* can have different meanings. We did not mean physical support, but *financial, psychological* and *practical* support and assistance provided by support services. A better question would have been:

> If you live with your parents or live alone, do you receive support?
>
> ☐ No
> ☐ Yes, I get support from the following people or organizations:
>
> Still better would have been to use the phrase "financial, psychological, and practical support and assistance" instead of *support*.

Another example:

*Children with autism were learning about Phillip II and William of Orange. They first read a text with a description of both historical figures. One of them lived in Brussels, the other in Spain; one of them was Catholic, the other Reformed, and so on. The teacher wanted to prepare the students for a classical discussion by using a worksheet with questions about the differences between Phillip II and William of Orange. The teacher had received some training about autism and, thus, learned that visual supports are often important for students with autism. To support her students, she showed two drawings on the board that were representations of Phillip II and William of Orange. Then she asked the class, "And what are the differences between Philip II and William of Orange?"*

*Here are the answers of some of her pupils:*
- *They have different faces.*
- *Phillip II looks more like President Obama.*
- *William of Orange has a bigger white collar.*

This was not what the teacher was asking. Some pupils did not take into account the context of the text that they had just read and described only the differences that they saw in the drawing. The teacher could have highlighted the context of her question. To arrive at differences in politics, belief, and so on, she could have asked questions like:

- *What is the difference in the beliefs of the two men?*
- *Did they live in the same country?*

This example shows that strategies generally used with individuals with autism, namely, offering structure and visual support, are not sufficient. The lesson was structured, and the teacher had prepared a visual support with drawings and worksheets. Visualizing and structuring do help people with autism, but do not guarantee that they pick up the correct meanings. In Chapter 5 about communication, we saw that in interpretation of visual signs, context sensitivity is crucial.

*The parents of Rashid, a young man with autism, have taken a basic course in autism because they did not know how to handle him. They have trouble getting him out of bed in the morning, but they are patient. They urge him several times to get up, but it often takes a long time before he gets out of bed. Sometimes there is no solution other than pulling the covers off and physically removing him from the bed, something that Rashid, surprisingly enough, allows them to do.*

*In the introductory autism course, Rashid's parents learned that they have to be predictable and consistent; a fixed routine would help Rashid. They also learned that it is best to visually support communication with Rashid. "People with autism think visually," the instructor had said while she – loyal to the principle of visualizing – supported her PowerPoint presentation with a picture of Temple Grandin (who wrote a book about thinking in images).*

*Based on this information, Rashid's parents created a step-by-step plan for the process of getting out of bed and posted it on the door of his room so that he could see it from his bed:*

1. *Mom or dad knocks on the door and says, "Wake up."*

2. *Mom or dad knocks on the door a second time and says, "Wake up."*
3. *Mom or dad enters the room and says, "Wake up."*
4. *Mom or dad enters the room, pulls the covers off and says, "Wake up."*
5. *Mom or dad enters and gets you out of your bed.*

When I visited the family a few weeks later, Rashid's parents told me that visual supports had not helped. On the contrary, since the introduction of the step-by-step plan for Rashid, the morning routine of getting him out of bed had become worse. Now they had to help him physically out of bed every day, while before he sometimes did it himself, after repeated urging.

I asked them to show me the step-by-step plan, and immediately it became clear to me why Rashid stayed in bed. He understood the step-by-step plan perfectly, but the context was unclear to him. For him this was literally a step-by-step plan: It describes the different steps to waking up, and Rashid follows them accurately until the whole the plan is finished. Therefore, he waits for his parents to get him out of bed, because only in that moment has the plan been completed. What Rashid did not understand was that the step-by-step plan was not a step-by-step plan for him, but for his parents, so that they knew what to do. That context was not clear for Rashid.

## Context Clarification: Concrete Communication

Clarifying the context is a form of concrete communication. In Chapter 6 about context and knowledge, we saw that people with autism have difficulty with concretizing concepts: What does something mean here and now in this context?

Concrete communication means that we clarify, as much as possible, in our communication (through the questions we ask, the remarks we make, the instructions we give) the context of the words we use so that the person with autism does not have to search for the concrete meaning of those words, questions, and instructions in the here and now. Concrete communication is so concrete that someone with autism does not have to concretize the function of the context. In this case, it does not make any difference whether the information is offered visually or verbally.

*Carol, a young woman with autism, works at a computer company. During her lunch break, she disappears as soon as she has finished her sandwich. Her coach wants Carol to have more contact with her colleagues, so she gives Carol the assignment to stay longer during lunch. Carol complies; however, she brings a new software manual to the lunch room and begins to study it as soon as she finishes her sandwich.*

*Her coach immediately realizes that the instructions that she gave Carol were not concrete enough. Carol did exactly what her coach asked her to do – stay longer. But by staying longer, the coach meant for Carol to make contact with her coworkers, talk about something, and listen to what others say during lunch. "Longer" was not concrete: How long is that? That context was insufficiently explained to Carol.*

*The coach explained to Carol in concrete terms what it meant to stay longer. Now Carol does not bring her manual any more, and she remains sitting and listening until her coworkers clean the table and leave the lunchroom. Now and then she even joins the conversation.*

The speech and hearing therapist Roger Verpoorten uses the term *augmentative communication*[8]: a communication in which the information is not only adjusted in form (e.g., drawings when spoken language is too difficult), but everything is represented as clearly and as concretely as possible to help the person to understand the correct meaning or concept behind the word, drawing, or object. Verpoorten stresses that adjustment of the *form* of communication is not sufficient.

For example, you can clarify to a person with autism who has difficulty with spoken language that he is to drink by giving him a concrete object like a cup. But even then, the context of the information still remains unclear: Can he drink right away? Where will he get the drink? And especially, what he will drink and how much?

Verpoorten tells an anecdote about a boy with autism and severe cognitive disability who was given an empty plastic cup to show him that the sports activity was over and that he had to pause for a drink. The boy put the cup to his lips to drink and became very angry because there was nothing in it. The boy lacked the imagination to visualize together with the cup a context that was not present in the here and now; namely, the drink he was going to get a couple of minutes later.

## Contextual Reframing

In order to communicate clearly with someone with autism, especially when it is about new, vague, and ambiguous concepts like drink or work, we try to maximize the contextual concretizing of the concept (e.g., in which context does the person with autism have to understand the word *work*?). Concrete communication minimizes misunderstanding. It prevents the person

*Clarifying the context helps people with autism to find the correct meaning.*

from remaining fixed on a dominant or fixed connection (e.g., work is physical work, or work is working on a computer).

But even when we clarify the context via concrete communication, misunderstanding can still occur. Some contextual cues are so evident to us that we do not think about explicitly clarifying them. Therefore, there is no 100% guarantee for correct meanings even with concrete communication.

Even in an autism-friendly environment, characterized by concrete communication and clarification of the context, people with autism may still misunderstand something (read *acontextual* understanding). I often call this an autistic "twist": The person with autism does not involve the context to determine the meaning, but falls back on a fixed, one-to-one connection.

In correcting these types of misconceptions, we also have to clarify the context. We place the so-called incorrect meaning into a context so that we can correct it. We reframe the meaning whereby a more contextually appropriate meaning emerges. The first and most important question to ask is: To what is this person blind? Which context does he not see or is he unable to imagine?

The boy in the example in the Preface who was afraid of swallowing his retainer gave a fixed connection: What is in his mouth, he might swallow. He is missing the insight to picture the size of the retainer in the context of the size of his throat. To remove his fear, we clarify the context. We make a drawing of the mouth and the throat (or, when our drawing talents are not good we enlist help from the Internet). We point to the size of the throat and the size of the retainer, so that the boy literally can see that he can never swallow the retainer. If the drawing is still not concrete enough, we search for an anatomic model of the head (check with a doctor). We let the boy try to put his retainer through the throat of the model. That way he will not only visually but also by experience find out that swallowing the retainer is physically impossible.

*Tommy just got new glasses. His previous glasses were no longer adequate. But Tommy refuses to wear the new glasses. Resistance to change, we conclude – typical for autism. But why does Tommy resist his new glasses? Is it only because the glasses look different than the previous ones? Luckily, Tommy gives us some insight.*

*"The new glasses are no good," he says. "I see too much with them." From experience, I know that you have to get used to stronger glasses. But contrary to Tommy, I place the sharpness of the new glasses in a context: The previous glasses were not good enough any more, so what I see now is, in fact, what I should be seeing. Tommy does not see that context. For him, seeing more than what he saw with his old glasses is seeing too much. We clarify this for Tommy with a drawing:*

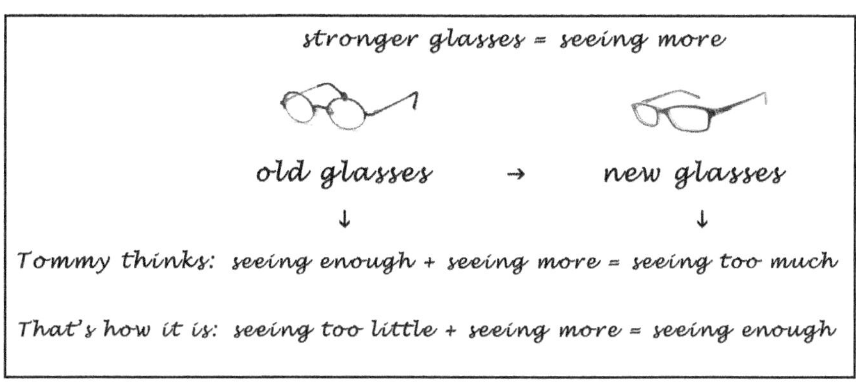


When we place things in the right context, we help people with autism to find the right meaning.

## "Braille" for Context Blindness

The scenarios of the boy with the retainer and Tommy are examples of how by means of Socratic method,[9] we can make people aware of the context, and thereby help them more easily retrieve correct meanings. We can help them to become aware of the context, but they will not be able to do it spontaneously. We compensate for the lack of implicit use of context via explicit instruction. The way we do this is by asking questions that focus their attention on the relevant contextual variables. Asking the right questions is what we might call "Braille" for context blindness.

Remember Jim who was annoyed during coffee break and replied to the suggestion of playing a game with a proposal to play *Risk*? It is difficult for people with autism to choose, not only because they cannot imagine alternatives, but also because choices must be adjusted based on the context. In practice, they tend to make unfeasible choices and, as a result, their suggestions are often rejected.

Choosing a free-time activity, as in the case of Jim, requires that you take the context into account: How much time do I have? Do I have a partner to play the game with? Are the necessary materials available at the moment? You can tell someone with autism to take into account the context or the situation, but that is still unclear. What should he take into account?

To help Jim make choices for his free time, we clarified important contextual elements. We let Jim write down on small pieces of paper the free-time activities he likes to do. Then we let him sort the pieces of paper into two boxes: things you do indoors and things you do outdoors. That is an important element in the context. You may want to play a game of badminton, but when the wind is strong and it is raining, this is not a good idea.

After that, we again let Jim sort the pieces of paper in the two boxes, this time according to the criterion: Can you do it by yourself? Once that has been completed, together with Jim, we make a note about how long a given activity will take (something with which Jim needs help because it is difficult for him to estimate). Finally, together with Jim, we make a free-time guide, a map in which the activities are neatly ordered. Part 1 contains the inside activities, subdivided into "Do by Yourself" and "Do With Others." Within those subdivisions, activities are also sorted by how much time they require (e.g., activities that take less than 15 minutes, 15-30 minutes, 30 minutes, etc.).

From now on, when Jim has free time, he gets a list of questions:

- Where can you spend free time? Indoors or outdoors? (Think about the weather!)
- Is there someone to do something with?
- How much time do you have?
- Is the material for the chosen activity available?

With those questions, Jim is able to make the correct choice, adjusted to the context, so that he more often hears "Good idea, Jim!" instead of "Good idea, Jim, but ..."

You may argue that this takes a lot of time. That is true, but in the end, it is a compensation strategy. Someone who is blind cannot scan in one blink of an eye an entire page but must feel the entire text before he can filter the essence of the text. The Braille for context blindness in making choices for free-time activities also takes time. But in time, Jim remembers the list of questions in his head and can internally evaluate them so that his choice is made faster. From that point on, he makes conscious use of context; he has compensated for context blindness in the choice of free-time activities.

However, Jim has not overcome his context blindness. There will be exceptions that cannot be covered with the questions (e.g., the material is available, but it is broken), and the list does not contain all the questions that you have to ask yourself (e.g., there may be someone with whom you can do something, but whether or not she wants to do it is another important contextual element). And there is no guarantee that Jim will spontaneously generalize the newly acquired compensation strategy to other choices, like what he wants to drink during a break or which clothes he wants to put on in the morning.

## Contextualized Skills Training

Generalization problems are common among individuals with autism.[10] They are the logical consequence of the fixed one-to-one relationships that they often make. Red light means stop, welcoming someone means taking their jacket, remember? These types of relationships often put a limit on the effects of skills training. That social skills training and training in theory of mind, including training in recognition of emotions, have only a minimal effect on social competence in real life has been proven.[11]

An important reason for the limited effects of many types of treatments and trainings is that they teach decontextualized skills.[12] That is, they take place in an artificial environment. This is comparable to learning to drive a car by taking a written course. You can learn to engage in chit-chat in the safe, adjusted environment of the training, but it does not guarantee success in real life, which is full of changing contexts. Similarly, recognizing emotions from a set of cards or drawings is anything but realistic. We know that progress on offline tasks does not necessarily mean that people can apply them online.[13]

*To increase the effectiveness of all types of training, we need to contextualize the skills. Situational trainings are preferable to skill trainings.*

Another important constraint of many types of skill training is in the generic (general) or acontextual learning of skills. When I look at programs, especially social skills training programs, the goals are almost always acontextual and abstract. To chat, to ask for help, to invite someone to a game, to listen to what someone is saying – those are typically the noble, but empty goals, stripped of the countless contextual variables that influence them in daily life.

This type of generic training is generally adequate for children without autism. Once you teach the child that a red light means stop, in real life, she will spontaneously adjust that connection to the context. The concept of being polite will also spontaneously be generalized and adjusted to fit all types of changing and unique contexts.

But for children with autism, it is necessary to contextualize the skills that we teach. This means that we must teach the skills in a situation-specific way. We avoid teaching concrete rules, such as a red light means stop. We teach instead that a red light means stop, *except when* ... If exceptions are the rule, then we include them *as much as possible* in our trainings. The italics in the last sentence are important: It is impossible to show all the exceptions, but we can show the most common ones.

Contextualizing skills is more than paying attention to the exceptions. Contextualized skill training not only teaches the skill (the how) but also when to apply that skill and, importantly, *when not to*.[14] This means that Social Stories™,[15] narratives that we write to teach a child with autism about his social world and what is expected of him within that world, preferably contain contextual variables. That can take the form of "if sentences" or "when sentences." For example, here is a script about how to welcome someone (the underlined sentences refer to important contextual elements):

When the person wears a jacket, you ask "May I take your jacket?"
When the person says "no," you invite the person to enter.
When the person says "yes," you wait until the person gives you the jacket, then you take the jacket and put it in the closet. If there is no closet, put the jacket neatly over a chair.

This type of contextualized script offers more flexibility but becomes a lot longer than fixed scripts. It is an art to find a balance between sufficient contextual flexibility and sufficient overview and clarity. Especially for children and for people with autism and an intellectual disability, it is important to keep scripts and step-by-step plans simple and clear in the beginning and to gradually add more contextual adjustments.

## Training Situations, Not Just Skills

I prefer *situational trainings* to skill trainings. Skill trainings look good on paper, but their goals are usually abstract, especially for people with autism. Here is a sample of the goals of some social skill training programs I found on the Internet:

- To learn how to recognize emotions
- To learn how to make a conversation
- To look someone in the face
- To wait for your turn
- To show interest in something
- To participate in a group
- To cope with winning and losing

These are sensible goals, but what does someone with autism understand from them, and what can that individual do with them?

When we did a trial for a course about relationships for adults with autism, we noticed that abstract themes and goals did not make much sense. The participants knew a lot of emotions by name and, in theory, they knew that emotions played a role in relationships, but the overall theme of emotions was too difficult and confusing for them. The problem with concretizing concepts was evident.

What was more successful was a session in which we started from concrete situations such as: "Imagine that you want to plan a trip in detail, but your partner only wants to buy the plane ticket and then to improvise the rest during the trip. How do you handle this situation?" Or "Who are your friends and what activities do you do with them?" In concrete situations and contexts, people with autism can more easily work with the concepts than in the case of abstract, generic skills.

Instead of formulating goals in terms of skills (e.g., learn to greet people, learn to have a conversation), we would do better to *set goals in terms of contexts*. The conversation that you have while you are waiting for your turn in the bakery is totally different from the conversation you have when you visit someone in the hospital. Context determines what is socially appropriate and effective. I prefer to set goals such as: What do you do when you visit someone in the hospital? How do you behave in a store? What do you do when you go to a birthday party? and How do you survive the breaks during your work day?

Within each of these contexts, we can work on different skills, such as having a conversation, waiting for your turn, recognizing emotions, and so on. Teaching competencies in terms of situations instead of skills has a number of advantages. First and foremost, because skills are connected to concrete situations, applying them in real life is easier. Working around concrete contexts increases the transfer of the learned skills to real life. Second, people with autism learn from the beginning that there are variations to every script or scenario, which increases their flexibility. Using this approach, we teach people to pay attention to the similarities and differences between situations. After teaching someone an appropriate subject for a conversation at a birthday party, we might ask if the same subject is also appropriate for a conversation when you visit somebody at the hospital.

Working on concrete situations also prevents us from placing too high expectations on the effects of our training. When the child learns to play a simple social game, including waiting for turns, we do not expect her to be capable of the general or generic skill of waiting her turn. She can play a certain social game but not more than that. To start from concrete situations makes us more alert to the need to explicitly focus our attention on generalization. When we have taught someone how to behave in a store, we cannot immediately expect him to react appropriately at a funeral.

Within this approach, exceptions are seen less as exceptions and more as variations or new situations that require a new learning process. What is true for social skills training is true for other skills: **Start from concrete contexts and focus the**

**attention of people with autism on relevant contextual elements**. For example, instead of teaching how to recognize emotions from pictures or drawings containing only the face, show pictures or drawings of situations. That is not only more realistic (in real life you never see a face without a context), but as we saw in Chapter 4 on context and social interaction, research has shown that in order to recognize emotions, we sometimes must involve more of the context than the face.

An example: You show a picture of someone who is moving to a new city. You can discuss what the person is doing, thinking, and feeling when she moves and that her feelings depend on certain things. That is, when someone is moving far away, she will probably lose a few good friends, and that probably makes her sad.

To avoid one-to-one connections (e.g., getting a gift = happy), offer variations (e.g., getting a gift you already have = not happy; getting a gift that you do not have, but wanted = happy). Here is an example involving teaching children independence skills: Teach children with autism to connect clothes to context variables like weather and planned activities. For example, when it is really hot, you do not wear a sweater; instead, a t-shirt would be appropriate. It may sound obvious, but during courses for adults with autism who are fairly high functioning, I have observed numerous times that in dressing themselves they did not take into account the context, but either fell back to routines or wore whatever they saw first in their wardrobe or suitcase.

And finally, an example involving teaching language: Teach children, adolescents, and adults with autism explicitly that words often do not have fixed connections and direct them to the context. Focus them on how words and sentences in a paragraph give clues to the meaning of a word that they do not yet know or a word that has multiple meanings.

All of this is not training in spontaneous and natural context sensitivity. It remains a compensation strategy, one that is externally directed, to encourage individuals with autism to think consciously about context. As is the case with scripts, it is important to find a balance between flexibility and clarity. Depending on the person's developmental age, it is sometimes better to focus on very obvious fixed relations. People with autism and severe cognitive disorders do not have the ability to process multiple context elements. You would only confuse them if you tried to teach them that it depends on the context if you can touch someone and where you touch. Instead, teach them a more generally valid, fixed routine, such as you shake people's hands.

Paying attention to the context requires effortful and conscious thought for people with autism, and they do not always have the required mental energy or ability. In crisis situations, for example, even with hints and tips, they are not able to process the context. This is not surprising; in moments of severe stress, we are all less context sensitive. The difference is that to involve context people with autism must engage in much more brainwork. Therefore, we should explicitly take the context into account when teaching context to people with autism.

## The Need for an Autism-Friendly Environment

Teaching compensation strategies and making people with autism aware of context will increase their flexibility,[16] but we need to be realistic in our expectations. There is not always enough time to consciously think about the context. As a result, we often have to push the context button. Most important, there are so many contextual elements and so many exceptions that it would be unreasonable to expect someone to use context spontaneously across situations. In a number of situations, people with autism will remain context blind.

The message here is: **Create an autism-friendly environment in which people with autism are offered clarity about the many changing meanings in our world.** Create an environment in which people with autism can find their way (context) blindly.[17]

## Context Blindness in Context

With this book I have tried to show that people with autism have difficulties with the many changing meanings in the world around us. They give meaning, but meanings are often not context sensitive. Expressed differently, people with autism think in fixed one-to-one relationships, not in contextually changing one-to-many relationships. The meaning of almost everything (objects, language, human behavior) depends on the context. This means that people with autism do not have much to rely on. For every stimulus or sensation, there are many possible meanings. It is challenging to live in a relative world when you think in absolute terms.

Let us end by placing the term *context blindness* into context. *Context* remains a vague term, and *context blindness* is also not absolutely defined. The meaning of a book about autism as context blindness is also relative. How could it not be? Context blindness is not THE explanation of autism. It would be outrageous to claim that with the term *context blindness* autism is finally understood.

There are still more questions than there are answers. With the term *context blindness,* I try to achieve a better understanding of the inside of autism, how people with autism experience and observe the world around them. That is the context in which this book is written. And now you are finished reading it, you are allowed to kill an insect with it, use it as an umbrella, or ... It is up to you, depending on the context!

## Endnotes – Autism as Context Blindness: Applied

1. Vermeulen (1996b).
2. More and more, it is becoming clear that the vagueness of certain autism criteria, especially in the social and communication realm, in combination with eligibility for funding and special services can also lead to overdiagnosing autism. See, e.g., Frances (2010), Matson and Kozlowski (2010), and Skellern, Schluter, and McDowell (2005).
3. In depression, social skills deficits are among the most restraining symptoms leading to social withdrawal, thereby aggravating social isolation and depressive affect (Derntl et al., 2011, p. 1).
4. Delis, Kaplan, and Kramer (2001).
5. Klinger, Klinger, Travers, and Mussey (2008).
6. Klinger et al. (2008).
7. See, e.g., Balconi and Carrera (2008); Hala, Pexman, and Glenwright (2007); Fletcher-Watson, Leekam, Turner, and Moxon (2006); Lopez and Leekam (2003); Kourkoulou, Findlay, and Leekam (2008, 2008 May); Wright et al. (2008).
8. Denteneer and Verpoorten (2007).
9. For an extensive description of the Socratic method for people with autism, see Vermeulen (2005b).
10. Jordan and Powell (1995).
11. E.g., see Brunner and Seung (2009); Hadwin, Baron-Cohen, Howlin, and Hill (1996); Howlin (1998); Swettenham (2000).
12. Bellini, Peters, Benner, and Hopf (2007).
13. See Vermeulen (2005a).
14. For people with autism of average ability, the context of why also plays a role.

15. Gray (1998).
16. From the study of Loukusa, Leinonen, Kuusikko, and others (2007), we can derive that a certain progression in the use of context is possible. Older and higher functioning children with autism were more capable of answering contextual questions than younger children. This suggests that the skill of using context increases during development.
17. Van der Gaag and van Berckelaer-Onnes (2000).

# References


Adolphs, R., Sears, L., & Piven, J. (2001). Abnormal processing of social information from faces in autism. *Journal of Cognitive Neuroscience, 13*, 232-240.

Aerts, D., & Gabora, L. (2005a). A state-context-property model of concepts and their combinations I: The structure of the sets of contexts and properties. *Kybernetes, 34*(1&2), 167-191.

Aerts, D., & Gabora, L. (2005b). A state-context-property model of concepts and their combinations II: A Hilbert space representation. *Kybernetes, 34*(1&2), 192-221.

Allen, M. L., & Chambers, A. (2011). Implicit and explicit understanding of ambiguous figures by adolescents with autism spectrum disorder. *Autism, 15*(4), 457-472.

American Psychiatric Association. (1994). *Diagnostic and statistical manual of mental disorders* (DSM-IV) (4th ed.). Washington, DC: Author.

Armstrong, S. L., Gleitman, L. R., & Gleitman, H. (1983). What some concepts might not be. *Cognition, 13*, 263-308.

Austen, E. L., & Enns, J. T. (2000). Change detection: Paying attention to detail. *Psyche: An Interdisciplinary Journal of Research on Consciousness, 6*(11). Retrieved from http://psyche.cs.monash.edu.au/v6/psyche-6-11-austen.html

Aviezer, H., Ran, H., Ryan, J., Grady, C., Susskind, J. M., Anderson, A. K., & Moscovitch, M. (2008). Angry, disgusted or afraid? Studies on the malleability of facial expression perception. *Psychological Science, 19*(7), 724-732.

Baddeley, A. D., & Woodhead, M. (1982). Depth of processing, contexts and face recognition. *Canadian Journal of Psychology, 36*, 148-164.

Baggett, P. (1975). Memory for explicit and implicit information in picture stories. *Journal of Verbal Learning and Verbal Behavior, 14*, 538-548.

Bailey, A., Phillips, W., & Rutter, M. (1996). Autism: Towards an integration of clinical, genetic, neuropsychological and neurobiological perspectives. *Journal of Child Psychology and Psychiatry, 37*(1), 89-126.

Balconi, M., & Carrera, A. (2007). Emotional representation in facial expression and script. A comparison between normal and autistic children. *Research in Developmental Disabilities, 28*(4), 409-422.

Balconi, M., Amenta, S., & Ferrari, C. (2012). Emotional decoding in facial expression, scripts and videos: A comparison between normal, autistic and Asperger children. *Research in Autism Spectrum Disorders, 6*(1), 193-203.

Baldwin, D. A. (1993). Infants' ability to consult the speaker for clues to word reference. *Journal of Child Language, 20*, 395-418.

Balkenius, C. (2003). Cognitive processes in contextual cueing. In F. Schmalhofer, R. M. Young, & G. Katz (Eds.), *Proceedings of the European Cognitive Science Conference 2003* (pp. 43-47). Mahwah, NJ: Lawrence Erlbaum Associates.

Bar, M. (2004). Visual objects in context. *Nature Reviews Neuroscience, 5*, 617-629.

Barcelo, F., & Knight, R. T. (2007). An information theoretical approach to contextual processing in the human brain: Evidence from prefrontal lesions. *Cerebral Cortex*, 17, i51-i60.

Barnes, J., & Baron-Cohen, S. (2011). The big picture: Storytelling ability in adults with autism spectrum conditions. *Journal of Autism and Developmental Disorders.* Published online November 1, 2011.

Baron-Cohen, S. (1991). Do people with autism understand what causes emotion? *Child Development, 62,* 385-395.

Baron-Cohen, S. (2002). The extreme male brain theory of autism. *Trends in Cognitive Sciences, 6*, 248-254.

Baron-Cohen, S. (2003) *The essential difference: Men, women and the extreme male brain.* New York, NY: Penguin/Basic Books.

Baron-Cohen, S. (2006). Two new theories of autism: Hyper-systemising and assortative mating, *Archives of Disease in Childhood, 91*, 2-5.

Baron-Cohen, S., Jolliffe, T., Mortimore, C., & Roberts, M. (1997). Another advanced test of theory of mind: Evidence from very high functioning adults with autism or Asperger Syndrome. *Journal of Child Psychology and Psychiatry, 38*, 813-822.

Baron-Cohen, S., Leslie, A. M., & Frith, U. (1985). Does the autistic child have a "theory of mind"? *Cognition, 21*, 37-46.

Baron-Cohen, S., O'Riordan, M., Stone, V. E., Jones, R., & Plaisted, K. (1999). Recognition of faux pas by normally developing children with Asperger syndrome or high-functioning autism. *Journal of Autism and Developmental Disorders, 29*(5), 407-418.

Baron-Cohen, S., Richler, J., Bisarya, D., Gurunathan, N., & Wheelwright, S. (2003). The systemising quotient (SQ): An investigation of adults with Asperger Syndrome or high functioning autism and normal sex differences. *Philosophical Transactions of the Royal Society, Series B* [Special issue on autism: Mind and brain], *358*, 361-374.

Baron-Cohen, S., Spitz, A., & Cross, P. (1993). Can children with autism recognize surprise? *Cognition & Emotion, 7*, 507-516.

Baron-Cohen, S., Wheelright, S., Hill, J., Raste, Y., & Plumb, I. (2001). The "Reading the mind in the eyes" test revised version: A study with normal adults and adults with Asperger syndrome or high-functioning autism. *Journal of Child Psychology and Psychiatry, 38*, 813-822.

Baron-Cohen, S., Wheelwright, S., & Jolliffe, T. (1997). Is there a "language of the eyes"? Evidence from normal adults and adults with autism or Asperger syndrome. *Visual Cognition, 68*, 48-57.

Baron-Cohen, S., Wheelwright, S., Scahill, V., Lawson, J., & Spong, A. (2001). Are intuitive physics and intuitive psychology independent? *Journal of Developmental and Learning Disorders, 5*(1), 47-78.

Barsalou, L. W. (1982). Context-independent and context-dependent information in concepts. *Memory & Cognition, 10*, 82-93.

Barsalou, L. W. (1987). The instability of graded structure: Implications for the nature of concepts. In U. Neisser (Ed.), *Concepts and conceptual development: Ecological and intellectual factors in categorization* (pp. 101-140). Cambridge, UK: Cambridge University Press.

Barsalou, L. W. (1993). Flexibility, structure, and linguistic vagary in concepts: Manifestations of a compositional system of perceptual symbols. In A. C. Collins, S. E. Gathercole, & M. A. Conway (Eds.), *Theories of memory* (pp. 29-101). London, UK: Lawrence Erlbaum Associates.

Barsalou, L. W. (2003). Situated simulation in the human conceptual system. *Language and Cognitive Processes, 18*, 513-562.

Barsalou, L. W. (2005). Situated conceptualization. In H. Cohen & C. Lefebvre (Eds.), *Handbook of categorization in cognitive science* (pp. 619-650). St. Louis, MO: Elsevier.

Barsalou, L. W. (2008). Situating concepts. In P. Robbins & M. Aydede (Eds.), *Cambridge handbook of situated cognition* (pp. 236-263). New York, NY: Cambridge University Press.

Barsalou, L. W. (2009). Simulation, situated conceptualization, and prediction. *Philosophical Transactions of the Royal Society of London: Biological Sciences, 364*, 1281-1289.

Barsalou, L. W., Yeh, W., Luka, B. J., Olseth, K. L., Mix, K. S., & Wu, L. (1993). Concepts and meaning. In K. Beals, G. Cooke, D. Kathman, K. E. McCullough, S. Kita, & D. Testen (Eds.), *Chicago Linguistics Society 29: Papers from the parasession on conceptual representations* (pp. 23-61). Chicago, IL: University of Chicago, Chicago Linguistics Society.

Begeer, S., Koot, H., Rieffe, C., Meerum Terwogt, M., & Stegge, H. (2008). Diagnostiek en ontwikkeling van emotionele vaardigheden bij kinderen met autisme [Diagnosis and development of emotional skills in children with autism]. In R. Didden & B. Huskens, (Eds.), *Begeleiding van kinderen en jongeren met autisme: Van onderzoek naar praktijk* [Treatment of children and youngsters with autism: From theory to practice] (pp. 84-101). Houten, Netherlands: Bohn Stafleu.

Begeer, S., Rieffe, C., Terwogt, M. M., & Stockmann, L. (2006). Attention to facial emotion expressions in children with autism. *Autism, 10*(1), 37-51.

Bellini, S., Peters, J. K., Benner, L., & Hopf, A. (2007). A meta-analysis of school-based social skills interventions for children with autism spectrum disorders. *Remedial and Special Education, 28*, 153-162.

Belmonte, M. K., Allen, G., Beckel-Mitchener, A., Boulanger, L. M., Carper, R. A., & Webb, J. (2004). Autism and abnormal development of brain connectivity. *Journal of Neuroscience, 4*, 9228-9231.

Bentin, S., Allison, T., Puce, A., Perez, E., & McCarthy, G. (1996). Electrophysiological studies of face perception in humans. *Journal of Cognitive Neuroscience, 8*, 551-565.

Berg, E. A. (1948). A simple objective technique for measuring flexibility in thinking. *Journal of General Psychology, 39*, 15-22.

Berger, J., Meredith, M. & Wheeler, S. C. (2008). Can where people vote influence how they vote? The influence of polling location type on voting behavior. *Proceedings of the National Academy of Sciences, 105*(26), 8846-8849.

Bertone, A., Mottron, L., & Faubert, J. (2004). Autism and schizophrenia: Different neurobiological etiology, similar perceptual consequence? *Behavioral and Brain Sciences*, 7, 592-593.

Bertone, A., Mottron, L., Jelenic, P., & Faubert, J. (2005). Enhanced and diminished visuo-spatial information processing in autism depends on stimulus complexity. *Brain, 128*, 2430-2441.

Best, C. S., Moffat, V. J., Power, M. J., Owens, D. G., & Johnstone, E. C. (2008). The boundaries of the cognitive phenotype of autism: Theory of mind, central coherence and ambiguous figure perception in young people with autistic traits. *Journal of Autism and Developmental Disorders, 38*(5), 840-847.

Beversdorf, D. Q., Narayanan, A., Hillier, A., & Hughes, J. D. (2007). Network model of decreased context utilization in autism spectrum disorder. *Journal of Autism and Developmental Disorders, 37*, 1040-1048.

Beversdorf, D. Q., Smith, B. W., Crucian, G. P., Anderson, J. M., Keillor, J. M., Barrett, et al. (2000). Increased discrimination of "false memories" in autism spectrum disorder. *Proceedings of the National Academy of Sciences in the United States of America, 97*(15), 8734-8737.

Bezuidenhout, A., & Sroda, M. S. (1998). Children's use of contextual cues to resolve referential ambiguity: An application of relevance theory. *Pragmatics and Cognition, 6*, 265-299.

Biederman, I. (1981). On the semantics of a glance at a scene. In M. Kubovy & J. Pomerantz (Eds.), *Perceptual organization* (pp. 213-253). Hillsdale, NJ: Lawrence Erlbaum.

Bird, G., Catmur, C., Silani, G., Frith, C., & Frith, U. (2006). Attention does not modulate neural responses to social stimuli in autism spectrum disorders. *Neuroimage, 31*(4), 1614-1624.

Blakemore, S. J., Tavassoli, T., Calo, S., Thomas, R. M., Camur, C., Frith, U., et al. (2006). Tactile sensitivity in Asperger Syndrome. *Brain and Cognition, 61*(1), 5-13.

Bonnel, A. C., Mottron, L., Peretz, I., Trudel, M., Gallun, E., & Bonnel, A. M. (2003). Enhanced pitch sensitivity in individuals with autism: A signal detection analysis. *Journal of Cognitive Neuroscience, 15*, 226-235.

Bonte, M., Parviainen, T., Hytönen, K., & Salmelin, R. (2006). Time course of top-down and bottom-up influences on syllable processing in the auditory cortex. *Cerebral Cortex, 16*, 115-123.

Booth, R. (2006). *Local-global processing and cognitive style in autism spectrum disorder and typical development*. London, UK: King's College London.

Booth, R., & Happé, F. (2010). "Hunting with a knife and … fork": Examining central coherence in autism, attention deficit/hyperactivity disorder, and typical development with a linguistic task. *Journal of Experimental Child Psychology, 107*(4-5), 377-393.

Boraston, Z., Corden, B., Miles, L., Skuse, D., & Blakemore, S. J. (2008). Perception of genuine and posed smiles by individuals with autism. *Journal of Autism and Developmental Disorders, 38*(3), 574-580.

Bosco, F. M., Bucciarelli M., & Bara B. G. (2004). The fundamental context categories in understanding communicative intention. *Journal of Pragmatics, 36*, 467-488.

Boser, K., Higgins, S., Fetherston, A., Preissler, M. A., & Gordon, B. (2002). Semantic fields in low functioning autism. *Journal of Autism and Developmental Disorders, 32*(6), 563-582.

Boucher, J. (1981). Memory for recent events in autistic children. *Journal of Autism and Developmental Disorders, 11*, 293-301.

Bowler, D. M., Gardiner, J. M., & Grice, S. J. (2000). Episodic memory and remembering in adults with Asperger Syndrome. *Journal of Autism and Developmental Disorders, 30*(4), 295-304.

Bowler, D. M., Gaigg, S. B., & Gardiner, J. M. (2008a). Subjective organisation in the free recall of adults with Asperger's Syndrome. *Journal of Autism and Developmental Disorders, 38*, 104-113.

Bowler, D. M., Gaigg, S. B., & Gardiner, J. M. (2008b). Effects of related and unrelated context on recall and recognition by adults with high-functioning autism spectrum disorder. *Neuropsychologia, 46*, 993-999.

Bowler, D. M., Gaigg, S. B., & Gardiner, J. M. (2009). Free recall learning of hierarchically organised lists by adults with Asperger's Syndrome: Additional evidence for diminished relational processing. *Journal of Autism and Developmental Disorders, 39*(4), 589-595.

Bradley, N. A., & Dunlop, M. D. (2005). Towards a multidisciplinary model of context to support context-aware computing. *Human-Computer Interaction, 20*, 403-446.

Braeutigam, S., Swithenby, S. J., & Bailey, A. J. (2008). Contextual integration the unusual way: A magnetoencephalographic study of responses to semantic violation in individuals with autism spectrum disorders. *The European Journal of Neuroscience, 27*(4), 1026-1036.

Braisby, N. R., & Franks, B. (2000). *Perspectives and categorization.* Unpublished manuscript, Open University, UK.

Brewer, W. F., & Treyens, J. C. (1981). Role of schemata in memory for places. *Cognitive Psychology, 13,* 207-230.

Brock, J., Brown, C. C., Boucher, J., & Rippon, G. (2002). The temporal binding deficit hypothesis of autism. *Development and Psychopathology, 14,* 209-224.

Brock, J., Norbury, C. F., Einav, S., & Nation, K. (2008). Do individuals with autism process words in context? Evidence from language-mediated eye-movements. *Cognition, 108,* 896-904.

Brockmole, J. R., & Henderson, J. M. (2006). Using real-world scenes as contextual cues for search. *Visual Cognition, 13*(1), 99-108.

Brockmole, J. R., Castelhano, M. S., & Henderson, J. M. (2006). Contextual cueing in naturalistic scenes: Global and local contexts. *Journal of Experimental Psychology: Learning Memory and Cognition, 32*(4), 699-706.

Brosnan, M. J., Scott, F. J., Fox, S., & Pye, J. (2004). Gestalt processing in autism: Failure to process perceptual relationships and the implications for contextual understanding. *Journal of Child Psychology and Psychiatry, 45,* 459-469.

Brunner, D. L., & Seung, H. K. (2009). Evaluation of the efficacy of communication-based treatments for autism spectrum disorders: A literature review. *Communication Disorders Quarterly OnlineFirst.*

Burack, J. A., Joseph, S., Russo, N., Shore, D. I., Porporino, M., & Enns, J. T. (2009). Change detection in naturalistic pictures among children with autism. *Journal of Autism and Developmental Disorders, 39*(3), 471-479.

Burke, P. (2002). Context in context. *Common Knowledge, 8*(1), 152-177.

Cain, K., Oakhill, J., Barnes, M., & Bryant, P. (2001). Comprehension skill, inference-making ability, and their relation to knowledge. *Memory & Cognition, 29,* 850-859.

Capps, L., Yirmiya, N., & Sigman, M. (1992). Understanding of simple and complex emotions in non-retarded children with autism. *Journal of Child Psychology & Psychiatry, 33,* 1169-1182.

Carroll, J. M., & Russell, J. A. (1996). Do facial expressions signal specific emotions? Judging emotion from the face in context. *Journal of Personality and Social Psychology, 70,* 205-218.

Carruthers, P., & Smith, P. K. (Eds.). (1996). *Theories of theories of mind*. Cambridge, MA: Cambridge University Press.

Castelli, F., Frith, C. D., Happé, F., & Frith, U. (2002). Autism, Asperger Syndrome and brain mechanisms for the attribution of mental states to animated shapes. *Brain, 125*, 1839-1849.

Channon, S., Charman, T., Heap, J., Crawford, S., & Rios, P. (2001). Real-life-type problem-solving in Asperger's Syndrome. *Journal of Autism and Developmental Disorders, 31*(5), 461-469.

Chen, F., Lemonnier, E., Lazartigues, A., & Planche, P. (2008). Non-superior disembedding performance in children with high-functioning autism and its cognitive style account. *Research in Autism Spectrum Disorders, 2*(4), 739-752.

Chun, M. M. (2000). Contextual cueing of visual attention. *Trends in Cognitive Science, 4,* 170-178.

Chun, M. M., & Jiang, Y. (1998). Contextual cueing: Implicit learning and memory of visual context guides spatial attention. *Cognitive Psychology, 36*, 28-71.

Clark, H. H., & Carlson, T. B. (1982). Hearers and speech acts. *Language, 58*, 332-373.

Cohen, J. D., Barch, D. M., Carter, C., & Servan-Schreiber, D. (1999). Context-processing deficits in schizophrenia: Converging evidence from three theoretically motivated cognitive tasks. *Journal of Abnormal Psychology, 108*(1), 120-133.

Cohen, J. D., & Servan-Schreiber, D. (1992). Context, cortex and dopamine: A connectionist approach to behaviour and biology in schizophrenia. *Psychological Review, 99*, 45-77.

Cole, R. A., & Jakimik, J. (1978). Understanding speech: How words are heard. In G. Underwood (Ed.), *Strategies of information processing* (pp. 67-116). New York, NY: Academic.

Corden, B., Chilvers, R., & Skuse, D. (2008). Emotional modulation of perception in Asperger's Syndrome. *Journal of Autism and Developmental Disorders, 38*(6), 1072-1080.

Cornsweet, T. (1970) *Visual perception*. New York, NY: Academic Press.

Courchesne, E., Campbell, K., & Solso, S. (2010). Brain growth across the life span in autism: age-specific changes in anatomical pathology. *Brain Research, 1380*, 138-145.

Courchesne, E., & Pierce, K. (2005). Why the frontal cortex in autism might be talking only to itself: Local over-connectivity but long-distance disconnection. *Current Opinion in Neurobiology*, *15*(2), 225-230.

Courchesne, E., Pierce, K., Schumann, C. M., Redcay, E., Buckwalter, J. A., Kennedy, D.P., et al. (2007). Mapping early brain development in autism. *Neuron, 56*(2), 99-413.

Crane, L., & Goddard, L. (2008). Episodic and semantic autobiographical memory in adults with autism spectrum disorders. *Journal of Autism and Developmental Disorders, 38*(3), 498-506.

Da Fonseca, D., Santos, A., Bastard-Rosset, D., Rondan, C. Poinso, F., & Deruelle, C. (2009). Can children with autistic spectrum disorders extract emotions out of contextual cues? *Research in Autism Spectrum Disorders, 3*(1), 50-56.

Dalton, K. M., Nacewicz, B. M., Johnstone, T., Schaefer, H. S., Gernsbacher, M. A., Goldsmith, H. H., et al. (2005). Gaze fixation and the neural circuitry of face processing in autism. *Nature Neuroscience, 8*, 519-526.

Dapretto, M., Davies, M. S., Pfeifer, J. H., Scott, A. A., Sigman, M., Bookheimer, S. Y., et al. (2006). Understanding emotions in others: Mirror neuron dysfunction in children with autism spectrum disorders. *Nature Neuroscience, 9*(1), 28-30.

Dascal, M. (1989). On the roles of context and literal meaning in understanding. *Cognitive Science: A Multidisciplinary Journal, 13*(2), 253-257.

Dawson, G., & Fernald, M. (1987). Perspective-taking ability and its relationship to the social behavior in autistic children. *Journal of Autism and Developmental Disorders, 17*(4), 487-498.

Dawson, G., Webb, S. J., & McPartland, J. (2005). Understanding the nature of face processing impairment in autism: insights from behavioral and electrophysiological studies. *Developmental Neuropsychology, 27*(3), 403-424.

De Clercq, H. (1999). *Mama, is dat een mens of een beest?* [Mom, is that a human being or an animal?] Antwerpen/Amsterdam, Netherlands: Houtekiet.

de Gelder, B., Meeren, H.K.M., Righart, R., Van den Stock, J., van de Riet, W.A.C., & Tamietto, M. (2006). Beyond the face: Exploring rapid influences of context on face processing. *Progress in Brain Research, 155*, 37-48.

de Gelder, B., & Vroomen, J. (2000). The perception of emotions by ear and by eye. *Cognition & Emotion, 14*(3), 289-311.

de Gelder, B., Vroomen, J., & Van der Heide, L. (1991). Face recognition and lip-reading in autism. *European Journal of Cognitive Psychology, 31*, 69-86.

De Graef, P. (2005). *Context effects on object perception in realistic scenes.* Unpublished doctoral dissertation, Universiteit Leuven.

Dekeukeleire, D., & Steelandt, P. (2003). *Autimatically: 61233 images about autism.* Gent, Belgium: Autisme Centraal/Viko.

Delis, D., Kaplan, E., & Kramer, J. (2001). *Delis-Kaplan executive function system.* San Antonio, TX: The Psychological Corporation, Harcourt Brace & Company.

De Martino, B., Harrison, N. A., Knafo, S., Bird, G., & Dolan, R. J. (2008). Explaining enhanced logical consistency during decision making in autism. *The Journal of Neuroscience, 28*(42), 10746-10750.

Dennet, D. (1984). Cognitive wheels: The frame problem in AI. In C. Hookway (Ed.), *Minds, machines, and evolution* (pp. 128-151. Cambridge, MA: Cambridge University Press.

Dennis, M., Lazenby, A. L., & Lockyer, L. (2001). Inferential language in high-functioning children with autism. *Journal of Autism and Developmental Disorders, 31*, 47-54.

Dennis, M., Lockyer, L., & Lazenby, A. L. (2000). How high-functioning children with autism understand real and deceptive emotion. *Autism, 4*, 370-381.

Denteneer, W., & Verpoorten, R. (2007). *Autisme Spectrumstoornissen, Basisbegrippen en inleiding tot Concept Ondersteunende Communicatie* [Autism spectrum disorders: Basic concepts and introduction to concept supporting communication]. Retrieved from Uitgeverij Viataalshop@Viataal.nl

Derntl, B., Seidel, E.M., Eickhoff, S.B., Kellermann, T., Gur, R.C., Schneider, F., & Habel, U. (2011). Neural correlates of social approach and withdrawal in patients with major depression. *Social Neuroscience, IFirst*, 1-20.

de Vignemont, F., & Singer, T. (2006). The empathic brain: How, when and why? *Trends in Cognitive Sciences, 10*(10), 435-441.

Dewey, M. (1991). Living with Asperger's syndrome. In U. Frith (Ed.), *Autism and Asperger Syndrome* (pp. 184-206). Cambridge/New York, NY: Cambridge University Press.

Dewey, M. A., & Everard, M. P. (1974). The near-normal autistic adolescent. *Journal of Autism and Childhood Schizophrenia, 4*(4), 347-356.

Diehl, J. J., Bennetto, L., Watson, D., Gunlogson, C., & McDonough, J. (2008). Resolving ambiguity: A psycholinguistic approach to prosody processing in high-functioning autism. *Brain and Language, 106,* 144-152.

Dijksterhuis, A. (2008). *Het slimme onbewuste* [The smart unconscious]. Amsterdam, Netherlands: Bert Bakker.

Dijksterhuis, A., Aarts, H., & Smith, P. K. (2005). The power of the subliminal: Perception and possible applications. In R. Hassin, J. Uleman, & J. A. Bargh (Eds.), *The new unconscious* (pp. 77-106). New York, NY: Oxford University Press.

Dijksterhuis, A., & Nordgren, L. F. (2006). A theory of unconscious thought. *Perspectives on Psychological Science, 1*(2), 95-109.

Dolan, R. J., Fletcher, P. C. McKenna, P., Friston, K. J., & Frith, C. D. (1999). Abnormal neural integration related to cognition in schizophrenia. *Acta Psychiatrica Scandinavica, 99*, 58-67.

Eco, U. (2001). *Kant en het vogelbekdier* [Kant and the platypus]. Amsterdam, Netherlands: Bert Bakker.

Egan, G. J., Brown, R. T., Goonan, L., Goonan, B. T., & Celano, M. (1998). The development of decoding of emotions in children with externalising behavioural disturbances and their normally developing peers. *Archives of Clinical Neuropsychology, 13*, 383-396.

Ekbia, H. R., & Maguitman, N. (2001, July). Context and relevance: A pragmatic approach. In V. Akman, P. Bouquet, R. Thomason, & R. Young (Eds.), Modeling and using context. *Vol. 2116 of Lecture Notes in Artificial Intelligence* (pp. 156-169). Proceedings of CONTEXT 2001 – Third International and Interdisciplinary Conference on Modeling and Using Context, Dundee, Scotland. Heidelberg, Germany: Springer Verlag.

Ekman, P. (2003). *Emotions revealed: Recognizing faces and feelings to improve communication and emotional life.* New York, NY: Times Books.

Ekman, P., Huang, T., Sejnowski, T., & Hager, J. (Eds.) (1993). *Final report to National Science Foundation of the planning workshop on facial expression understanding* (Technical Report). San Francisco, CA: University of California, Human Interaction Lab.

Epstein, R. A., & Higgins, J. S. (2007). Differential parahippocampal and retrosplenial involvement in three types of visual scene recognition. *Cerebral Cortex, 17*, 1680-1693.

Erickson, M. A., & Kruschke, J. K. (1998). Rules and exemplars in category learning. *Journal of Experimental Psychology: General, 127*, 107-140.

Ernestus, M., Baayen, H., & Schreuder, R. (2002). The recognition of reduced word forms. *Brain and Language, 81*, 162-173.

Evans, J.S.B.T. (2008). Dual-processing accounts of reasoning, judgment and social cognition. *Annual Review of Psychology, 59*, 255-278.

Faubert, J., & Bertone, A. (2004). A common link between aging, schizophrenia, and autism? *Behavioral and Brain Sciences, 27*, 593-594.

Fay, W., & Schuler, A. L. (1980). *Emerging language in autistic children.* London, UK: Edward Arnold.

Fein, D., Lucci, D., Braverman, M., & Waterhouse, L. (1992). Comprehension of affect in context in children with pervasive developmental disorders. *Journal of Child Psychology and Psychiatry, 33*, 1157-1167.

Fernández-Dols, J. M., Carrera, P., & Russell, J. A. (2002). Are facial displays social? Situational influences in the attribution of emotion to facial expressions. *Spanish Journal of Psychology, 5*, 119-124.

Fiebach, C. J., & Friederici, A. D. (2004). Processing concrete words: fMRI evidence against a specific right-hemisphere involvement. *Neuropsychologia, 42*, 62-70.

Fine, J., Bartolucci, G., Szatmari, P., & Ginsberg, G. (1994). Cohesive discourse in pervasive developmental disorders. *Journal of Autism and Developmental Disorders, 24*, 315-329.

Fletcher-Watson, S., Leekam, S. R., Turner, M. A., & Moxon, L. (2006). Do people with autism spectrum disorders show normal selection for attention? Evidence from change blindness. *British Journal of Psychology, 97*(4), 537-554.

Frances A. (2010, July 6) Normality is an endangered species: psychiatric fads and overdiagnosis. *Psychiatric Times.* Retrieved from http://www.psychiatrictimes.com/dsm-5/content/article/10168/1598676

Friston, K. J. (1998). The disconnection hypothesis. *Schizophrenia Research, 30*(2), 115-125.

Frith, U. (1989). *Autism: explaining the enigma.* Oxford, UK: Blackwell Publishing.

Frith, C. D. (1991). In what context is latent inhibition relevant to the symptoms of schizophrenia? *Behavioral and Brain Sciences, 14*, 28-29.

Frith, U. (2003). *Autism: Explaining the enigma. Second edition.* Oxford, UK: Blackwell Publishing.

Frith, C. (2003). What do imaging studies tell us about the neural basis of autism? *Novartis Foundation Symposium, 251*, 149-166.

Frith, U. (2004). Emmanuel Miller lecture: Confusions and controversies about Asperger Syndrome. *Journal of Child Psychology and Psychiatry, 4*(4), 672-686.

Frith, C. D., & Frith, U. (2006a). The neural basis of mentalizing. *Neuron, 50*(4), 531-534.

Frith, C. D., & Frith, U. (2006b). How we predict what other people are going to do. *Brain Research, 1079*(1), 36-46.

Frith, U. (2008). *Autism: A very short introduction.* Oxford, UK: Oxford University Press.

Frith, U., & Snowling, M. (1983). Reading for meaning and reading for sound in autistic and dyslexic children. *British Journal of Developmental Psychology, 1*, 329-342.

Froehlich, A., Miller, J. N., DuBray, M., Bigler, E., & Lainhart, J. E. (2008, May). *Learning of well-defined and ill-defined categories in autism.* Poster session presented at the 7th International Meeting for Autism Research, London.

Gabora, L., Rosch, E., & Aerts, D. (2008). Toward an ecological theory of concepts. *Ecological Psychology, 20*(1), 84-116.

Gaigg, S. B., Bowler, D. M., & Gardiner, J. M. (2008). Free recall in autism spectrum disorder: The role of relational and item-specific encoding. *Neuropsychologia, 46*, 986-992.

Galli, G., Feurra, M., & Viggiano, M. P. (2006). "Did you see him in the newspaper?" Electrophysiological correlates of context and valence in face processing. *Brain Research, 1119*, 190-202.

Ganis, G., & Kutas, M. (2003). An electrophysiological study of scene effects on object identification. *Brain Research: Cognitive Brain Research, 16*(2), 123-144.

Ganong, W. F. (1980). Phonetic categorization in auditory word perception. *Journal of Experimental Psychology: Human Perception and Performance, 6*, 110-125.

Gastgeb, H., Strauss, M. S., & Minshew, N. J. (2006) Do individuals with autism process categories differently: The effect of typicality and development. *Child Development*, *77*, 1717-1729.

Gauthier, I., Skudlarski, P., Gore, J. C., & Anderson, A. W. (2000). Expertise for cars and birds recruits brain areas involved in face recognition. *National Neuroscience*, *3*(2), 191-197.

Gentaz, E., Moroni, C., & Luyat, M. (2005). The role of contextual cues in the haptic perception of orientations and the oblique effect. *Psychonomic Bulletin & Review*, *12*(4), 760-766.

Gibbs, R. W. (1984). Literal meaning and psychological theory. *Cognitive Science*, *8*(3), 275-304.

Gibbs, R. W., Jr. (2002). A new look at literal meaning in understanding what is said and implicated. *Journal of Pragmatics*, *34*(4), 457-486.

Gilbert, C., Ito, M., Kapadia, M., & Westheimer, G. (2000). Interactions between attention, context and learning in primary visual cortex. *Vision Research*, *40*(10-12), 1217-1226.

Giora, R. (1999). On the priority of salient meanings: Studies of literal and figurative language. *Journal of Pragmatics*, *31*(7), 919-929.

Goddard, L., Howlin, P., Dritschel, B., & Patel, T. (2007). Autobiographical memory and social problem-solving in Asperger Syndrome. *Journal of Autism and Developmental Disorders*, *37*(2), 291-300.

Goh, J.O.S., Siong, S. C., Park, D., Gutchess, A., Hebrank, A., & Chee, M.W.L. (2004). Cortical areas involved in object, background, and object-background processing revealed with functional magnetic resonance adaptation. *The Journal of Neuroscience*, *24*(45), 10223-10228.

Golan, O., Baron-Cohen, S., Hill, J. J., & Golan, Y. (2006). The "Reading the Mind in Films" task: Complex emotion recognition in adults with and without autism spectrum conditions. *Social Neuroscience*, *1*(2), 111-123.

Golan, O., Baron-Cohen, S., & Golan, Y. (2008). The "Reading the Mind in Films" task [Child Version]: Emotion and mental state recognition in children with and without Autism Spectrum Disorders. *Journal of Autism and Developmental Disorders*, *38*(8), 1534-1541.

Goldstein, G., Allen, D. N., Minshew, N. J., Williams, D. L., Volkmar, F., Klin, A., et al. (2008). The structure of intelligence in children and adults with high functioning autism. *Neuropsychology*, *22*(3), 301-312.

Goldstone, R. L., & Kersten, A. (2003). Concepts and categorization. In A. F. Healy & R. W. Proctor (Eds.), *Comprehensive handbook of psychology, Vol. 4. Experimental psychology* (pp. 599-621). Hoboken, NJ: Wiley.

Goldwater, S., Griffiths, T. L., & Johnson, M. (2007). Distributional cues to word boundaries: Context is important. In D. Bamman, T. Magnitskaia, & C. Zaller (Eds.), *Proceedings of the 31st Annual Boston University Conference on Language Development* (pp. 239-250). Somerville, MA: Cascadilla Press.

Goodarzi, M. A., Wykes, T., & Hemsley, D. R. (2000). Cerebral lateralization of global-local processing in people with schizotypy. *Schizophrenia Research, 45*, 115-121.

Grandin, T. (2000, November). My mind is a web browser: How people with autism think. In Geneva Centre for Autism (Ed.), *International Symposium on Autism 2000. Conference proceedings* (pp. 37-44). Toronto, ONT: Geneva Centre for Autism.

Grandin, T. (2009). How does visual thinking work in the mind of a person with autism? A personal account. *Philosophical Transactions of the Royal Society B, 364*, 1437-1442.

Grant, H. M., Bredahl, L. C., Clay, J., Ferrie, J., Groves, J. E., McDorman, T. A., et al. (1998). Context-dependent memory for meaningful material: Information for students. *Applied Cognitive Psychology, 12*, 617-623.

Gray, C. A. (1998). Social stories and comic strip conversations with students with Asperger Syndrome and high-functioning autism. In E. Schopler & G. B. Mesibov (Eds.), *Asperger Syndrome or high-functioning autism? Current issues in autism* (pp. 167-198). New York, NY: Plenum Press.

Green, M. J., Uhlhaas, P. J., & Coltheart, M. (2005). Context processing and social cognition in schizophrenia. *Current Psychiatry Reviews, 1*(1), 11-22.

Green, M. J., Waldron, J. H., Simpson, I., & Coltheart, M. (2008). Visual processing of social context during mental state perception in schizophrenia. *Journal of Psychiatry and Neuroscience, 33*(1), 34-42.

Grice, P. (1989) *Studies in the way of words*. Cambridge, MA: Harvard University Press.

Gronau, N., Neta, M., & Bar, M. (2008). Integrated contextual representation for objects' identities and their locations. *Journal of Cognitive Neuroscience, 20*(3), 371-388.

Grossman, J. B., Klin, A., Carter, A. S., & Volkmar, F. R. (2000). Verbal bias in recognition of facial emotions in children with Asperger syndrome. *Journal of Child Psychology and Psychiatry and Allied Disciplines, 41*, 369-379.

Gruppuso, V., Lindsay, D. S., & Masson, M.E.J. (2007). I'd know that face anywhere! *Psychonomic Bulletin & Review, 14*, 1085-1089.

Haddon, M. (2003). *The curious incident with the dog in the night-time.* New York, NY: Knopf Doubleday Publishing Group.

Hadwin, J., Baron-Cohen S., Howlin, P., & Hill, K. (1996). Can we teach children with autism to understand emotions, belief or pretence? *Development and Psychopathology, 8*(2), 345-365.

Hala, S., Pexman, P. M., & Glenwright, M. (2007). Priming the meaning of homographs in typically developing children and children with autism. *Journal of Autism and Developmental Disorders, 37,* 329-340.

Hamilton, A.F.D.C., Brindley, R. M., & Frith, U. (2007). Imitation and action understanding in autistic spectrum disorders: How valid is the hypothesis of a deficit in the mirror neuron system? *Neuropsychologia, 45*(8), 1859-1868.

Hampton, J. A. (2003). Abstraction and context in concept representation. *Philosophical Transactions of the Royal Society of London* [Special issue: The Abstraction Paths: From Experience to Concept], *358*, 1251-1259.

Hampton, J. A. (2007). Typicality, graded membership and vagueness. *Cognitive Science, 31*(3), 355-384.

Hampton, J. A., Dubois, D., & Yeh, W. (2006). The effects of pragmatic context on classification in natural categories. *Memory & Cognition 34,* 1431-1443.

Happé, F. (1993). Communicative competence and theory of mind in autism: A test of relevance theory. *Cognition, 48*, 101-119.

Happé, F. (1994). *Autism: An introduction to psychological theory.* London, UK: UCL Press.

Happé, F.G.E. (1994). An advanced test of theory of mind: Understanding of story characters' thoughts and feelings by able autistic, mentally handicapped, and normal children and adults. *Journal of Autism and Developmental Disorders, 24*(2), 129-154.

Happé, F. (1996). Studying weak central coherence at low levels: Children with autism do not succumb to visual illusions. A research note. *Journal of Child Psychology and Psychiatry, 37*, 873-877.

Happé, F.G.E. (1997). Central coherence and theory of mind in autism: Reading homographs in context. *British Journal of Developmental Psychology, 15*(1), 1-12.

Happé, F.G.E., & Booth, R.D.L. (2008). The power of the positive: Revisiting weak coherence in autism spectrum disorders. *The Quarterly Journal of Experimental Psychology, 61*(1), 50-63.

Happé, F., & Frith, U. (2006). The weak coherence account: Detail-focused cognitive style in autism spectrum disorders. *Journal of Autism and Developmental Disorders, 36*(1), 5-25.

Happé, F., Ronald, A., & Plomin, R. (2006). Time to give up on a single explanation for autism. *Nature Neuroscience, 9*, 1218-1220.

Hardin, S., Cooke, M., & König, P. (2008). Auditory gist perception: An alternative to attentional selection of auditory streams? *Lecture Notes in Computer Science, 4840*, 399-416.

Harris, P. L. (1989). *Children and emotion: The development of psychological understanding.* New York, NY: Cambridge University Press.

Hayashi, M., Kato, M., Igarashi, K., & Kashima, H. (2008). Superior fluid intelligence in children with Asperger's disorder. *Brain and Cognition, 66*(3), 306-310.

Heaton, R. K., Chelune, G. J., Talley, J. L., Kay, G. G., & Curtiss, G. (1993). *Wisconsin Card Sorting Test manual: Revised and expanded.* Odessa, FL: Psychological Assessment Resources.

Hemsley, D. R. (1993) A simple (or simplistic?) cognitive model for schizophrenia. *Behaviour Research and Therapy, 31*, 633-646.

Hemsley, D. R. (2005a). The development of a cognitive model of schizophrenia: Placing it in context. *Neuroscience and Biobehavioral Reviews, 29*, 977-988.

Hemsley, D. R. (2005b). The schizophrenic experience: Taken out of context? *Schizophrenia Bulletin, 31*(1), 43-53.

Hemsley, D. R., & Richardson, P. H. (1980). Shadowing by context in schizophrenia. *Journal of Nervous and Mental Disease, 168*, 141-145.

Henderson, J. M., & Hollingworth, A. (1999). High-level scene perception. *Annual Review of Psychology, 50*, 243-271.

Hermelin, B., & O'Connor, N. (1970). *Psychological experiments with autistic children*. London, UK: Pergamon Press.

Higgins, E. T. (1996). Knowledge activation: Accessibility, applicability, and salience. In E. T. Higgins & A. W. Kruglanski (Eds.), *Social psychology: Handbook of basic principles* (pp. 133-168). New York, NY: Guilford.

Hill, E. L. (2004). Evaluating the theory of EF deficits in autism. *Developmental Review, 24*, 189-233.

Hillier, A., & Allinson, L. (2002). Beyond expectations. Autism, understanding embarrassment, and the relationship with theory of mind. *Autism: The International Journalof Research and Practice, 6*, 299-314.

Hobson, R. P. (1986a). The autistic child's appraisal of expressions of emotion. *Journal of Child Psychology and Psychiatry, 27*, 321-342.

Hobson, R. P. (1986b). The autistic child's appraisal of expressions of emotion: A further study. *Journal of Child Psychology and Psychiatry, 27*, 671-680.

Hobson, R. P., Ouston, J., & Lee, A. (1988a). What's in a face? The case of autism. *British Journal of Psychology, 79*, 441-453.

Hobson, R. P., Ouston, J., & Lee, A. (1988b). Emotion recognition in autism: Coordinating faces and voices. *Psychological Medicine*, 911-923.

Hobson, R. P., Ouston, J., & Lee, A. (1989). Naming emotion in faces and voices: Abilities and disabilities in autism and mental retardation. *British Journal of Developmental Psychology, 7*, 237-250.

Hochstein, S., & Ahissar, M. (2002). View from the top: Hierarchies and reverse hierarchies in the visual system. *Neuron, 36*, 791-804.

Hoffner, C., & Badzinski, D. M. (1989). Children's integration of facial and situational cues to emotion. *Child Development, 60*(2), 411-422.

Hofstadter, D. R. (1985). *Metamagical themas: Questing for the essence of mind and pattern.* New York, NY: Basic Books.

Hönig, H., & Kussmaul, P. (1982). *Strategie der Uebersetzung* [Strategy of translation]. Tübingen, Germany: Gunter Narr Verlag.

Howlin, P. (1998). Practitioner review: Psychological and educational treatments for autism. *Journal of Child Psychology and Psychiatry, 39*(3), 307-322.

Hoy, R. (2007). *Autism and me* [DVD]. London, UK: Jessica Kingsley Publishers.

Huang, H. C. (2007). *Lexical context effects on speech perception in Chinese people with autistic traits.* Unpubished manuscript, University of Edinburgh, Developmental Linguistics. Retrieved from http://hdl.handle.net/1842/1927

Huart, J., Corneille, O., & Becquart, E. (2005). Face-based categorization, context-based categorization, and distortions in the recollection of gender ambiguous faces. *Journal of Experimental Social Psychology, 41*, 598-608.

Iacoboni, M., Molnar-Szakacs, I., Gallese, V., Buccino, G., Mazziotta, J. C., & Rizzolatti, G. (2006). Grasping the intentions of others with one's own mirror neuron system. *PLoS Biology, 3*(3), e79, 0529-0535.

Iarocci, G., Burack, J. A., Shore, D. I., Mottron, L., & Enns, J. T. (2006). Global-local visual processing in high functioning children with autism: Structural versus implicit task biases. *Journal of Autism and Developmental Disorders, 36*(1), 117-129.

Iarocci, G., & McDonald, J. (2006). Sensory integration and the perceptual experience of persons with autism. *Journal of Autism and Developmental Disorders, 36*(1), 77-90.

Irwin, J. R. (2007). Auditory and audiovisual speech perception in children with autism spectrum disorders. *Acoustics Today*, 8-15.

Jastrezembski, J. E. (1981). Multiple meanings, number of related meanings, frequency of occurrence, and the lexicon. *Cognitive Psychology, 13*, 278-305.

Jemel, B., Mottron, L., & Dawson, M. (2006). Impaired face processing in autism: Fact or artifact? *Journal of Autism and Developmental Disorders, 36*(1), 91-106.

Jessen, F., Heun, R., Erb, M., Granath, D. O., Klose, U., Papassotiropoulos, A., et al. (2000). The concreteness effect: Evidence for dual coding and context availability. *Brain & Language, 7*, 103-112

Jeste, S., & Nelson, C. A. (2009). Event Related Potentials in the understanding of autism spectrum disorders: An analytical review. *Journal of Autism and Developmental Disorders, 39*(3), 594-510.

Jolliffe, T. (1997). *Central coherence dysfunction in autistic spectrum disorder*. Cambridge, MA: University of Cambridge Press.

Jolliffe, T., & Baron-Cohen, S. (1999a). Linguistic processing in high-functioning adults with autism or Asperger syndrome: Is local coherence impaired? *Cognition, 71*, 149-185.

Jolliffe, T., & Baron-Cohen, S. (1999b).The strange stories test: A replication with high-functioning adults with autism or Asperger Syndrome. *Journal of Autism and Developmental Disorders, 29*(5), 395-406.

Jolliffe, T., & Baron-Cohen, S. (2000). Linguistic processing in high-functioning adults with autism or Asperger Syndrome: Can global coherence be achieved? A further test of central coherence theory. *Psychological Medicine, 30*, 1169-1187.

Jordan, R., & Powell, S. (1995) *Understanding and teaching children with autism.* Chichester, UK: Wiley.

Joseph, R. M., & Tanaka, J. R. (2003). Holistic and part-based face recognition in children with autism. *Journal of Child Psychology and Psychiatry, 44*, 529-542.

Just, M. A., Cherkassky, V. L., Keller, T. A., Kana, R. K., & Minshew, N. J. (2007). Functional and anatomical cortical underconnectivity in autism: Evidence from an fMRI study of an executive function task and corpus callosum morphometry. *Cerebral Cortex, 17*(4), 951-961.

Just, M. A., Cherkassky, V. L., Keller, T. A., & Minshew, N. J. (2004). Cortical activation and synchronization during sentence comprehension in high-functioning autism: Evidence of underconnectivity. *Brain, 127*, 1811-1821.

Just, M. A., Newman, S. D., Keller, T. A., McEleney, A., & Carpenter, P. A. (2004). Imagery in sentence comprehension: An fMRI study. *NeuroImage, 2*(1), 112-124.

Kaland, N., Smith, L., & Mortensen, E. L. (2007). Response times of children and adolescents with Asperger syndrome on an "advanced" test of theory of mind. *Journal of Autism and Developmental Disorders, 37*, 197-209.

Kaland, N., Callesen, K., Møller-Nielsen, A., Mortensen, E. L., & Smith, L. (2008). Performance of children and adolescents with Asperger Syndrome or high-functioning autism on advanced theory of mind tasks. *Journal of Autism and Developmental Disorders, 38*(6), 1112-1123.

Kaland, N., Mortensen, E. L., & Smith, L. (2007). Disembedding performance in children and adolescents with Asperger Syndrome or high-functioning autism. *Autism, 11*(1), 81-92.

Kaldy, Z., & Kovacs, I. (2003). Visual context integration is not fully developed in 4-yearold children. *Perception, 32*, 657-666.

Kambe, G., Rayner, K., & Duffy, S. A. (2001). Global context effects on processing lexically ambiguous words: Evidence from eye fixations. *Memory & Cognition, 29*(2), 363-372.

Kanner, L. (1943). Autistic disturbances of affective contact. *Nervous Child, 2*, 217-250.

Kappas, A. (2002). What facial activity can and cannot tell us about emotions. In M. Katsikitis (Ed.), *The human face: Measurement and meaning* (pp. 215-234). Dordrecht, Netherlands: Kluwer.

Karmiloff-Smith, A. (1986). Some fundamental aspects of language acquisition after five. In P. Fletcher, & M. Garman (Eds.), *Language acquisition – Studies in first language development* (2nd ed., pp. 306-323). Cambridge, MA: Cambridge University Press.

Kemps, R., Ernestus, M., Schreuder, R., & Baayen, R. H. (2004). Processing reduced word forms: The suffix restoration effect. *Brain and Language, 90*, 117-127.

Kilts, C. D., Egan, G., Gideon, D. A., Ely, T. D., & Hoffman, J. M. (2003). Dissociable neural pathways are involved in the recognition of emotion in static and dynamic facial expressions. *Neuroimage, 18*(1), 156-168.

Kim, H., Somerville, L. H., Johnstone, T., Polis, S., Alexander, A. L., Shin, L. M., et al. (2004). Contextual modulation of amygdala responsivity to surprised faces. *Journal of Cognitive Neuroscience, 16*, 1730-1745.

Kirshner, D., & Whitson, J. A. (1997). *Situated cognition: Social, semiotic, and psychological perspectives.* Mahwah, NJ: Erlbaum.

Klin, A., & Jones, W. (2006). Attributing social and physical meaning to ambiguous visual displays in individuals with higher-functioning autism spectrum disorders. *Brain and Cognition, 61*, 40-53.

Klin, A., & Jones, W. (2008). Altered face scanning and impaired recognition of biological motion in a 15-month-old infant with autism. *Developmental Science, 11*(1), 40-46.

Klin, A., Jones, W., Schultz, R., Volkmar, F., & Cohen, D. (2002). Visual fixation patterns during viewing of naturalistic social situations as predictors of social competence in individuals with autism. *Archives of General Psychiatry, 59*, 809-816.

Klinger, L., & Dawson, G. (2001). Prototype formation in children with autism and Down Syndrome. *Development and Psychopathology, 13*, 111-124.

Klinger, L. G., & Dawson, G. (1995). A fresh look at categorization abilities in persons with autism. In E. Schopler & G. B. Mesibov (Eds.), *Learning and cognition in autism* (pp. 119-136). New York/London, UK: Plenum Press.

Klinger, M. R., Klinger, L. G., Travers, B. G., & Mussey, J. L. (2008, May). *Contextual learning in persons with ASD.* Poster session presented at the International Meeting for Autism Research, London.

Kokinov, B. (1994). The context-sensitive cognitive architecture DUAL. In A. Ram & K. Eiselt (Eds.), *Proceedings of the 16th Annual Conference of the Cognitive Science Society* (pp. 502-507). Hillsdale, NJ: Erlbaum.

Kokinov, B., & Raeva, D. (2004). Can an incidental picture make us more or less willing to risk? *Proceedings of the 1st European Conference on Cognitive Economics,* Gif-sur-Ydette, France.

Koning, C., & Magill-Evans, J. (2001). Social and language skills of adolescent boys with Asperger Syndrome. *Autism: International Journal of Research and Practice, 5,* 23-36.

Kooijman, V., Hagoort, P., & Cutler, A. (2005). Electrophysiological evidence for prelinguistic infants' word recognition in continuous speech. *Cognitive Brain Research, 24,* 109-116.

Kourkoulou, A., Findlay, J. M., & Leekam, S. (2008, May). *Enhanced visual attention and implicit learning of local context in autism spectrum disorders (ASD).* Poster session presented at the International Meeting for Autism Research, London.

Kourkoulou, A., Findlay, J. M., & Leekam, S. R. (2008). Implicit memory of visual context is intact in autism spectrum disorders (ASDs). *Perception, 37*(6), 959-968.

Kourkoulou, A., Leekam, S. R., & Findlay, J. M. (2011). Implicit learning of local context in autism spectrum disorder. *Journal of Autism and Developmental Disorders.*

Kunar, M. A., Flusberg, S. J., Horowitz, T. S., & Wolfe, J. M., (2007). Does contextual cueing guide the deployment of attention? *Journal of Experimental Psychology: Human Perception and Performance, 33,* 816-828.

Kuschner, E. S., Bodner, K. E., & Minshew, N. J. (2009). Local vs. global approaches to reproducing the Rey Osterrieth Complex Figure by children, adolescents, and adults with high-functioning autism. *Autism Research, 2,* 348-358.

Lahaie, A., Mottron, L., Arguin, M., Berthiaume, C., Jemel, B., & Saumier, D. (2006). Face perception in high-functioning autistic adults: Evidence for superior processing of face parts, not for a configural face processing deficit. *Neuropsychology, 20*(1), 30-41.

Laurent J. P., Denhières, G., Passerieux, C., Iakimova, G., & Hardy-Baylé, M. C. (2006). On understanding idiomatic language: The salience hypothesis assessed by ERPs. *Brain Research, 1068*(1), 151-160.

Lawson, J. (2003). Depth accessibility difficulties: An alternative conceptualisation of autism spectrum conditions. *Journal for the Theory of Social Behaviour, 33*(2), 189-202.

Lawson, J., Baron-Cohen, S., & Wheelwright, S. (2004). Empathising and systemising in adults with and without Asperger Syndrome. *Journal of Autism and Developmental Disorders, 34*(3), 301-310.

Lee, T. S. (2002). Top-down influence in early visual processing: A Bayesian perspective. *Physiology and Behaviour, 77*, 645-650.

Le Sourn-Bissaoui, S., Caillies, S., Gierski, F., & Motte, J. (2011). Ambiguity detection in adolescents with Asperger syndrome: is central coherence or theory of mind impaired. *Research in Autism Spectrum Disorders, 5*(1), 648-656.

Levitan, C. (1996). *Cognitive event related potential and neuroanatomical correlates of auditory hallucinations in schizophrenia*. Kensington, AU: University of New South Wales.

Liebscher, R., & Groppe, D. (2003). Rethinking context availability for concrete and abstract words: A corpus study. In D. Archer, P. Rayson, A. Wilson, & T. McEnery (Eds.), *Proceedings of the Corpus Linguistics 2003 Conference* (pp. 449-456). Lancaster, UK: Lancaster University.

Lincoln, A. J., Courchesne, E., Kilman, B. A., Elmasian, R., & Allen, M. (1988). A study of intellectual abilities in high-functioning people with autism. *Journal of Autism and Developmental Disorders, 18*(4), 505-524.

Lind, S., & Bowler, D. (2008). Episodic memory and autonoetic consciousness in autism spectrum disorders: The roles of self-awareness, representational abilities, and temporal cognition. In J. M. Boucher, & D. M. Bowler (Eds.), *Memory in autism: Theory and evidence* (pp. 166-187). Cambridge, MA: Cambridge University Press.

Lopez, B., & Leekam, S. R. (2003). Do children with autism fail to process information in context? *Journal of Child Psychology and Psychiatry, 44*(2), 285-300.

Lopez, B., Donnelly, N., Hadwin, J., & Leekam, S. R. (2004). Face processing in high functioning adolescents with autism: Evidence for weak central coherence. *Visual Cognition, 11*, 673-688.

Lord, C., Rutter, M., Goode, S., et al. (1989). Autism diagnostic observation schedule: a standardized observation of communicative and social behavior. *Journal of Autism and Developmental Disorders, 19*(2), 185–212.

Losh, M., & Capps, L. (2003). Narrative ability in high-functioning children with autism or Asperger syndrome. *Journal of Autism and Developmental Disorders, 33*, 239-251.

Loth, E., Gomez, J. C., & Happé, F. (2008). Event schemas in autism spectrum disorders: The role of theory of mind and weak central coherence. *Journal of Autism and Developmental Disorders, 38*(3), 449-463.

Loth, E., Gómez, J. C., & Happé, F. (2008, May). *Detecting changes in naturalistic scenes: Contextual inconsistency does not influence spontaneous attention in high-functioning people with autism spectrum disorder.* Poster session presented at the International Meeting for Autism Research, London.

Loth, E., Gomez, J. C., & Happé, F. (2011). Do high-functioning people with autism spectrum disorder spontaneously use event knowledge to selectively attend to and remember context-relevant aspects in scenes? *Journal of Autism and Developmental Disorders, 41*(7), 945-961.

Loukusa, S., Leinonen, E., Jussila, K., Ryder, N., Ebeling, H., & Moilanen, I. (2007). Answering contextually demanding questions: Pragmatic errors produced by children with Asperger syndrome or high-functioning autism. *Journal of Communication Disorders, 40*(5), 357-381.

Loukusa, S., Leinonen, E., Kuusikko, S., Jussila, K., Ryder, N., Ebeling, H., et al. (2007). Use of context in pragmatic language comprehension by children with Asperger Syndrome or high-functioning autism. *Journal of Autism and Developmental Disorders, 37*(6), 1049-1059.

Loveland, K. A., Pearson, D. A., Tunali-Kotoski, B., Ortgeon, J., & Gibbs, M. C. (2001). Judgments of social appropriateness by children and adolescents with autism. *Journal of Autism and Developmental Disorders, 31*(4), 367-376.

Loveland, K. A., Tunali-Kotoski, B., Chen, R., & Brelsford, K. A. (1995). Intermodal perception of affect in persons with autism or Down syndrome. *Development & Psychopathology*, 7(3), 409-418.

Machery, E. (2007). 100 years of psychology of concepts: The theoretical notion of concept and its operationalization. *Studies in History and Philosophy of Biological and Biomedical Sciences, 38*, 63-84.

Magneé, M.J.C.M., de Gelder B., van Engeland, H., & Kemner, C. (2008). Atypical processing of fearful face-voice pairs in pervasive developmental disorder: An ERP study. *Clinical Neurophysiology, 119*, 2004-2010.

Mandler, G. (1980). Recognizing: The judgment of previous occurrence. *Psychological Review, 87*, 252-271.

Maras, K. L., & Bowler, D. M. (2011). Context reinstatement effects on eyewitness memory in autism spectrum disorder. *British Journal of Psychology*. (Article first published online Sep 26, 2011.)

Mareschal, D., & Tan, S. H. (2007). Flexible and context-dependent categorisation by eighteen-month-olds. *Child Development, 78*, 19-37.

Marks, L. E., & Arieh, Y. (2006). Differential effects of stimulus context in sensory processing. *European Review of Applied Psychology, 56*, 213-221.

Marslen-Wilson, W. D. (1990). Activation, competition, and frequency in lexical access. In G.T.M. Altmann (Ed.). *Cognitive models of speech processing: Psycholinguistic and computational perspectives* (pp. 148-172). Cambridge, MA: MIT Press.

Marslen-Wilson, W. D., & Welsh, A. (1978). Processing interactions and lexical access during word-recognition in continuous speech. *Cognitive Psychology, 10*(1), 29-63.

Martin, I., & McDonald, S. (2003). Weak coherence, no theory of mind, or executive dysfunction? Solving the puzzle of pragmatic language disorders, *Brain and Language, 85*(3), 451-466.

Massaro, D. W. (1987). *Speech perception by ear and eye: A paradigm for psychological enquiry.* Hillsdale, NJ: Lawrence Erlbaum Associates.

Massaro, D. W., & Boesseler, A. (2003). Perceiving speech by ear and eye: Multimodal integration by children with autism. *Journal of Developmental and Learning Disorders, 7*, 111-146.

Matson, J. L., & Kozlowski, A. M. (2011) The increasing prevelance of autism spectrum disorders. *Research in Autism Spectrum Disorders, 5*(1), 418-425.

McClelland, J. L., & Rumelhart, D. E. (1981). An interactive activation model of context effects in letter perception: Part 1. An account of basic findings. *Psychological Review, 88*, 375-407.

McCloskey, M., & Glucksberg, S. (1978). Natural categories: Well-defined or fuzzy sets? *Memory & Cognition, 6*, 462-472.

McGurk, H., & MacDonald, J. (1976). Hearing lips and seeing voices, *Nature, 264*(5588), 746-748.

Medin, D. L., & Schaffer, M. (1978). Context theory of classification learning. *Psychological Review, 85*, 207-238.

Meeren, H.K.M., van Heijnsbergen, C., & de Gelder, B. (2005). Rapid perceptual integration of facial expression and emotional body language. *Proceedings of the National Academy of Sciences of the USA, 102*(45), 16518-16523.

Mervis, C., & Crisafi , M. (1982). Order of acquisition of subordinate, basic, and superordinate level categories. *Child Development, 53*, 258-266.

Mervis, C. B., & Rosch, E. (1981). Categorization of natural objects. *Annual Review of Psychology, 32*, 89-115.

Meyer, D. E., & Schvaneveldt, R. W. (1971). Facilitation in recognising pairs of words: Evidence of a dependence between retrieval operations. *Journal of Experimental Psychology, 90*, 227-234.

Miller, G. A. (1999). On knowing a word. *Annual Review of Psychology, 50,* 1-19.

Miller, G. A., & Charles, W. G. (1991). Contextual correlates of semantic similarity. *Language and Cognitive Processes*, *6*(1), 1-28.

Milne, E., & Scope, A. (2008). Are children with autistic spectrum disorders susceptible to contour illusions? *British Journal of Developmental Psychology, 26*, 91-102.

Minshew, N. J., Meyer, J., & Goldstein, G. (2002). Abstract reasoning in autism: A dissociation between concept formation and concept identification. *Neuropsychology, 16*, 327-334.

Molesworth, C. J., Bowler, D. M., & Hampton, J. A. (2005). The prototype effect in recognition memory: Intact in autism? *Journal of Child Psychology and Psychiatry, 46*, 664-672.

Molesworth, C. J., Bowler, D. M., & Hampton, J. A. (2008). When prototypes are not best: Judgments made by children with autism. *Journal of Autism and Developmental Disorders, 38*(9), 1721-1730.

Mongillo, E. A., Irwin, J. R., Whalen, D. H., Klaiman, C., Carter, A. S., & Schultz, R. T. (2008). Audiovisual processing in children with and without autism spectrum disorders. *Journal of Autism and Developmental Disorders, 38*(7), 1349-1358.

Morsanyi, K., Handley, S. J., & Evans, J.S.B.T. (2010). Decontextualised minds: Adolescents with autism are less susceptible to the conjunction fallacy than typically developing adolescents. *Journal of Autism and Developmental Disorders, 40*(11), 1378-1388.

Moss, H. E., McCormick, S. F., & Tyler, L. K. (1997). The time course of activation of semantic information during spoken word recognition. *Language and Cognitive Processes, 12*, 695-731.

Murphy, G. L., & Wisniewski, E. J. (1989). Categorizing objects in isolation and in scenes: What a superordinate is good for. *Journal of Experimental Psychology: Learning, Memory, and Cognition, 15,* 572-586.

Myers, E. B., & Blumstein, S. E. (2008). The neural bases of the lexical effect: An fMRI investigation. *Cerebral Cortex, 18*, 346-355.

Nah, Y.-H., & Poon, K.K. (2011). The perception of social situations by children with autism spectrum disorders. *Autism, 15*(2), 185-203.

Nakahachi, T., Yamashita, K., Iwase, M., Ishigami, W., Tanaka, C., Toyonaga, K., et al. (2008). Disturbed holistic processing in autism spectrum disorders verified by two cognitive tasks requiring perception of complex visual stimuli. *Psychiatry Research, 159,* 330-338.

Navon, D. (1977). Forest before the trees: The precedence of global features in visual perception. *Cognitive Psychology*, 9, 353-383.

Neider, M. B., & Zelinsky, G. J. (2006). Scene context guides eye movements during visual search. *Vision Research, 46,* 614-621.

Neisser, U. (1976). *Cognition and reality: principles and implications of cognitive psychology*. San Francisco, CA: W. H. Freeman.

Neisser, U. (1987). From direct perception to conceptual structure. In U. Neisser (Ed.), *Concepts and conceptual development: Ecological and intellectual factors in categorization* (pp. 101-140). Cambridge/London, UK: Cambridge University Press.

Noens, I., van Berckelaer-Onnes, I., Verpoorten, R., & Van Duijn, G. (2006). The ComFor: An instrument for the indication of augmentative communication. *Journal of Intellectual Disability Research, 50*, 621-632.

Noens, I.L.J., & van Berckelaer-Onnes, I. A. (2005). Captured by details: Sense-making, language and communication in autism. *Journal of Communication Disorders, 38,* 123-141.

Noens, I.L.J., & van Berckelaer-Onnes, I. A. (2007). The central coherence account in autism revisited: Evidence from the ComFor study. *Research in Autism Spectrum Disorder, 2,* 209-222.

Norbury, C. F. (2004). Factors supporting idiom comprehension in children with communication disorders. *Journal of Speech, Language and Hearing Research, 47,* 1179-1193.

Norbury, C. F. (2005). Barking up the wrong tree? Lexical ambiguity resolution in children with language impairments and autistic spectrum disorders. *Journal of Experimental Child Psychology, 90,* 142-171.

Norbury, C. F., & Bishop, D.V.M. (2002). Inferential processing and story recall in children with communication problems: A comparison of specific language impairment, pragmatic language impairment and high functioning autism. *International Journal of Language & Communication Disorders, 37,* 227-251.

Nosofsky, R. M. (1986). Attention, similarity, and the identification-categorization relationship. *Journal of Experimental Psychology: General, 115,* 39-57.

Oberman, L. M., Hubbard, E. M., McCleery, J. P., Altschuler, E. L., Ramachandran, V. S., & Pineda, J. A. (2005). EEG evidence for mirror neuron dysfunction in autism spectrum disorders. *Cognitive Brain Research, 24*(2), 190-198.

Oi, M., & Tanaka, S. (2011). When do Japanese children with autism spectrum disorder comprehend ambiguous language overliterally or overnonliterally? *Asia Pacific Journal of Speech, Language, and Hearing, 14*(1), 1-12.

Oliva, A. (2005). Gist of the scene. In L. Itti, G. Rees, & J. K. Tsotsos (Eds.), *The encyclopedia of neurobiology of attention* (pp. 251-256). San Diego, CA: Elsevier.

Oliva, A., & Schyns, P. G. (2000). Diagnostic colors mediate scene recognition. *Cognitive Psychology, 41,* 176-210.

Oliva, A., & Torralba, A. (2001). Modeling the shape of the scene: S holistic representation of the spatial envelope. *International Journal of Computer Vision, 42*(3), 145-175.

Oliva, A., & Torralba, A. (2006). Building the gist of a scene: The role of global image features in recognition. *Visual Perception, Progress in Brain Research, 155*, 23-35.

O'Loughlin, C., & Thagard, P. (2000). Autism and coherence: A computational model. *Mind and Language, 15*(4), 375-392.

O'Riordan, M. A., Plaisted, K. C., Driver, J., & Baron-Cohen, S. (2001). Superior visual search in autism. *Journal of Experimental Psychology: Human Perception and Performance, 27*(3), 719-730.

O'Riordan, M.A.F. (2004). Superior visual search in adults with autism. *Autism, 8*, 229-248.

Palmer, S. E. (1975). The effects of contextual scenes on the identification of objects. *Memory and Cognition, 3*, 519-526.

Park, S., Lee, J., Folley, B. F., & Kim, J. (2003). Schizophrenia: Putting context in context. *Behavioral and Brain Science, 26*(1), 98-99.

Pascalis, O., & Slater, A. (Eds.). (2003). *The development of face processing in infancy and early childhood: Current perspectives.* New York, NY: Nova Science Publishers.

Pelphrey, K. A., Sasson, N. J., Reznick, J. S., Paul, G., Goldman, B. D., & Piven, J. (2002). Visual scanning of faces in autism. *Journal of Autism and Developmental Disorders, 32*, 249-261.

Pelphrey, K. A., Singerman, J. D., Allison, T., & McCarthy, G. (2003). Brain activation evoked by perception of gaze shifts: The influence of context. *Neuropsychologia, 41*(2), 156-170.

Penn, D. L., Ritchie, M., Francis, J., Combs, D., & Martin, J. (2002). Social perception in schizophrenia: The role of context. *Psychiatry Research, 109*(2), 149-159.

Phillips, W. A., & Silverstein, S. M. (2003). Convergence of biological and psychological perspectives on cognitive coordination in schizophrenia. *Behavioral and Brain Sciences, 26,* 65-138.

Phillips, W. A., & Singer, W. (1997). In search of common foundations for cortical computation. *Behavioral and Brain Sciences 20*(4), 657-722.

Pijnacker, J., Geurts, B., van Lambalgen, M., Kan, C. C., Buitelaar, J. K., & Hagoort, P. (2009). Defeasible reasoning in high-functioning adults with autism: Evidence for impaired exception-handling. *Neuropsychologia, 47*(3), 644-651.

Pijnacker, J., Geurts, B., van Lambalgen, M., Buitelaar, J. K., & Hagoort, P. (2010). Exceptions and anomalies: An ERP study on context sensitivity in autism. *Neuropsychologia, 48*(10), 2940-2951.

Pinker, S. (1997). *How the mind works.* New York, NY: W.W. Norton & Company.

Plaisted, K., O'Riordan, M., & Baron-Cohen, S. (1998). Enhanced discrimination of novel, highly similar stimuli by adults with autism during a perceptual learning task. *Journal of Child Psychology and Psychiatry, 39,* 765-775.

Plaisted, K. C. (2000). Aspects of autism that theory of mind cannot explain. In S. Baron-Cohen, H. Tager-Flusberg, & D. J. Cohen (Eds.), *Understanding other minds: Perspectives from developmental cognitive neuroscience* (pp. 222-250). New York, NY: Oxford University Press.

Ponnet, K., Roeyers, H., Buysse, A., De Clercq, A., & Van der Heyden, E. (2004). Advanced mind-reading in adults with Asperger syndrome. *Autism, 8,* 249-266.

Porter, P. B. (1954). Another picture puzzle. *American Journal of Psychology, 67,* 550-551.

Potter, M. C. (1975). Meaning in visual search. *Science, 187*(4180), 965-966.

Premack, D. G., & Woodruff, G. (1978). Does the chimpanzee have a theory of mind? *Behavioral and Brain Sciences, 1,* 515-526.

Rankin, K. M., & Marks, L. E. (1992). Effects of context on sweet and bitter tastes: Unrelated to sensitivity to PROP (6-n-propylthiouracil). *Perception and Psychophysics, 52,* 479-486.

Rayner, K., Cook, A. E., Juhasz, B. J., & Frazier, L. (2006). Immediate disambiguation of lexically ambiguous words during reading: Evidence from eye movements. *British Journal of Psychology, 97*(4), 467-482.

Reed, P., Broomfield, L., McHugh, L., McCausland, A., & Leader, G. (2009). Extinction of over-selected stimuli causes emergence of under-selected cues in higher-functioning children with autistic spectrum disorders. *Journal of Autism and Developmental Disorders, 39*(2), 290-298.

Reicher, G. M. (1969). Perceptual recognition as a function of meaningfulness of stimulus material. *Journal of Experimental Psychology, 81,* 275-280.

Rensink, R. A., O'Regan, J. K., & Clark, J. J. (1997). To see or not to see: The need for attention to perceive changes in scenes. *Psychological Science, 8,* 368-373.

Righart, R., & de Gelder, B. (2006). Context influences early perceptual analysis of faces. An electrophysiological study. *Cerebral Cortex, 16,* 1249-1257.

Righart, R., & de Gelder, B. (2008a). Recognition of facial expressions is influenced by emotional scene gist *Cognitive, Affective, & Behavioral Neuroscience, 8*(3), 264-272.

Righart, R., & de Gelder, B. (2008b). Rapid influence of emotional scenes on encoding of facial expressions. An ERP study. *Social Cognitive and Affective Neuroscience, 3,* 270-278.

Ring, H., Sharma, S., Wheelwright, S., & Barrett, G. (2007). An electrophysiological investigation of semantic incongruity processing by people with Asperger's syndrome. *Journal of Autism and Developmental Disorders, 37,* 281-290.

Rizzolatti, G., Fadiga, L., Fogassi, L., & Gallese, V. (1996). Premotor cortex and the recognition of motor actions. *Cognitive Brain Research, 3,* 131-141.

Roediger, H. L., & McDermott, K. B. (1995). Creating false memories: Remembering wordsnot presented in lists. *Journal of Experimental Psychology: Learning, Memory, & Cognition, 21,* 803-814.

Roeyers, H., Buysse, A., Ponnet, K., & Pichal, B. (2001). Advancing advanced mindreading tests: Empathic accuracy in adults with a pervasive developmental disorder. *Journal of Child Psychology and Psychiatry, 42,* 271-278.

Roeyers, H., & Demurie, E. (2010). How impaired is mind-reading in high-functioning adolescents and adults with autism? *European Journal of Developmental Psychology, 7*(1), 123-134.

Ropar, D., & Mitchell, P. (1999). Are individuals with autism and Asperger's syndrome susceptible to visual illusions? *Journal of Child Psychiatry and Psychology, 40,* 1283-1293.

Ropar, D., & Mitchell, P. (2001). Susceptibility to illusions and performance on visuospatial tasks in individuals with autism. *Journal of Child Psychiatry and Psychology*, 42, 539-549.

Ropar, D., & Mitchell, P. (2002). Shape constancy in autism: The role of prior knowledge and perspective cues. *Journal of Child Psychology and Psychiatry, 43*(5), 647-653.

Ropar, D., Mitchell, P., & Ackroyd, K. (2003). Do children with autism find it difficult to offer alternative interpretations to ambiguous figures? *British Journal of Developmental Psychology, 21*, 387-395.

Rosch, E. (1975). Cognitive representations of semantic categories. *Journal of Experimental Psychology: General, 104*(3), 192-33.

Rosenblum, L. D., Schmuckler, M. A., & Johnson, J. A. (1997). The McGurk effect in infants. *Perception & Psychophysics, 59*(3), 347-357.

Roth, E. M., & Shoben, E. J. (1983). The effect of context on the structure of categories. *Cognitive Psychology, 15,* 346-378.

Rousselet, G. A., Joubert, O. R., & Fabre-Thorpe, M. (2005). How long to get to the "gist" of real-world natural scenes? *Visual Cognition, 12*(6), 852-877.

Rumsey, J. M. (1985). Conceptual problem-solving in highly verbal, nonretarded autistic men. *Journal of Autism and Developmental Disorders, 15*(1), 23-26.

Russell, J. A., & Fehr, B. (1987). Relativity in the perception of emotion in facial expressions. *Journal of Experimental Psychology: General, 116*, 223-237.

Russell, J. A., Bachorowski, J-A., & Fernández-Dols, J. M. (2003). Facial and vocal expressionsof emotion. *Annual Review of Psychology, 54*, 329-349.

Rutherford, M. D., & Towns, A. M. (2008). Scan path differences and similarities during emotion perception in those with and without autism spectrum disorders. *Journal of Autism and Developmental Disorders, 38*(7), 1371-1381.

Saldaña, D., & Frith, U. (2007). Do readers with autism make bridging inferences from world-knowledge? *Journal of Experimental Child Psychology, 96*, 310-319.

Sato, W., Uono, S., Okada, T., & Toichi, M. (2010). Impairment of unconscious, but not conscious, gaze-triggered attention orienting in Asperger's Disorder. *Research in Autism Spectrum Disorders, 4*(4), 782-786.

Schwanenflugel, P. J., & Stowe, R. W. (1989). Context availability and the processing of abstract and concrete words in sentences. *Reading Research Quarterly, 24*, 114-126.

Serra, M., Loth, F. L., van Geert, P. L., Hurkens, E., & Minderaa, R. B. (2002). Theory of mind in children with lesser variants of autism: A longitudinal study. *Journal of Child Psychology and Psychiatry, 43*(7), 885-900.

Serra, M., Minderaa, R. B., van Geert, P. L., Jackson, A. E., Althaus, M., & Til, R. (1995). Emotional role-taking abilities of children with a pervasive developmental disorder not otherwise specified. *Journal of Child Psychology and Psychiatry, 36*(3), 475-490.

Servan-Schreiber, D., Cohen, J. D., & Steingard, S. (1996). Schizophrenic deficits in the processing of context: A test of a theoretical model. *Archives of General Psychiatry, 53*, 1105-1113.

Shantz, C. U. (1983). Social cognition. In J. H. Flavell & E. M. Markman (Eds.), P. H. Mussen (Series Ed.), *Handbook of child psychology, Vol. III: Cognitive development* (pp. 495-555). New York, NY: Wiley and Sons.

Shin, Y. W., Na, M. H., Ha, T. H., Kang, D. H., Yoo, S. Y., & Kwon, J. S. (2008). Dysfunction in configural face processing in patients with schizophrenia. *Schizophrenia Bulletin, 34*(3), 538-543.

Silverstein, S. M., & Schenkel, L. S. (1997). Schizophrenia as a model of context deficient cortical computation. *Behavioral and Brain Sciences, 20*, 696-697.

Simons, D. J., & Chabris, C. F. (1999). Gorillas in our midst: Sustained inattentional blindness for dynamic events. *Perception, 28*, 1059-1074.

Simons, D. J., & Levin, D. T. (1998). Failure to detect changes to people in a real-world interaction. *Psychonomic Bulletin and Review, 5*(4), 644-649.

Simpson, G. B., Peterson, R. R., Casteel, M. A., & Burgess, C. (1989). Lexical and sentence context effects in word recognition. *Journal of Experimental Psychology: Learning, Memory, and Cognition, 15*, 88-97.

Skellern, C., Schluter, P., & McDowell, M. (2005). From complexity to category: responding to diagnostic uncertainties of autism spectrum disorders. *Journal of Paediatrics and Child Health, 41*(8), 407-412.

Skoyles, J. R. (2011). Autism, context/noncontext information processing, and atypical development. *Autism Research and Treatment*.

Smith, M. L., Cottrell, G. W., Gosselin, F., & Schyns, P. G. (2005). Transmitting and decoding facial expressions. *Psychological Science, 16*, 184-189.

Smith, S. (1988). Environmental context-dependent memory. In G. M. Davies & D. M. Thomson (Eds.), *Memory in context: Context in memory* (pp. 13-34). Chichester, UK: Wiley.

Snowling, M., & Frith, U. (1986). Comprehension in "hyperlexic" readers. *Journal of Experimental Child Psychology, 42*, 392-415.

Sobel, D. M., Capps, L., & Gopnik, A. (2005). Ambiguous figure perception and theory of mind understanding in children with autistic spectrum disorders. *British Journal of Developmental Psychology, 23*, 159-174.

Soulières, I., Mottron, L., Saumier, D., & Larochelle, S. (2007). Atypical categorical perception in autism: Autonomy of discrimination? *Journal of Autism and Developmental Disorders, 37*(3), 481-490.

Speer, L. L., Cook, A. E., McMahon, W. M., & Clark, E. (2007). Face processing in children with autism: Effects of stimulus contents and type. *Autism, 11*(3), 265-277.

Spek, A. A., Scholte, E. M., & van Berckelaer-Onnes, I. A. (2010). Theory of mind in adults with HFA and Asperger Syndrome. *Journal of Autism and Developmental Disorders, 40*(3), 280-289.

Sperber, D., & Wilson, D. (1995). *Relevance: Communication and cognition* (2nd ed.). Oxford, UK: Blackwell.

Spiro, R., & Jehng, J. (1990). Cognitive flexibility and hypertext: Theory and technology for the nonlinear and multidimensional traversal of complex subject matter. In D. Nix & R. Spiro (Eds.), *Cognition, education and multimedia: Exploring ideas in high technolog* (pp. 163-205). Hillsdale, NJ: Lawrence Erlbaum Associates.

Spivey, M. J., Tanenhaus, M. K., Eberhard, K. M., & Sedivy, J. C. (2002). Effects of visual context in the resolution of temporary syntactic ambiguities in spoken language comprehension. *Cognitive Psychology, 45*, 447-481.

Spivey-Knowlton, M. J., Trueswell, J. C., & Tanenhaus, M. K. (1993). Context effects in syntactic ambiguity resolution. *Canadian Journal of Experimental Psychology, 47*, 276-309.

Stanovich, K., & West, F. (2002) Individual differences in reasoning: Implications for the rationality debate. In T. Gilovich, D. Griffin, & D. Kahneman (Eds.), *Heuristic and biases: The psychology of intuitive judgment* (pp. 421-440). Cambridge, MA: Cambridge University Press.

Sternberg, R. J. (1987). Most vocabulary is learned from context. In M. G. McKeown, & M. E. Curtis (Eds.), *The nature of vocabulary acquisition* (pp. 89-106). Hillsdale, NJ: Erlbaum.

Stewart, M. E., & Ota, M. (2008). Lexical effects on speech perception in individuals with "autistic" traits. *Cognition, 109*(1), 157-162.

Strauss, M., Newell, L., Best, C. A., Rump, K. M., Gastgeb, H., & Minshew, N. (2005, April). *Discrimination of facial gender by typically developing children and individuals with autism.* Poster session presented at the 32nd Society for Research in Child Development Biennial Meeting, Atlanta.

Swettenham, J. (2000). Teaching theory of mind to individuals with autism. In S. Baron-Cohen, H. Tager-Flusberg, & D. J. Cohen (Eds.), *Understanding other minds: Perspectives from developmental cognitive neuroscience* (2nd ed., pp. 442-456). Oxford/New York, NY: Oxford University Press.

Tager-Flusberg, H. (1991). Semantic processing in the free recall of autistic children: Further evidence for a cognitive deficit. *British Journal of Developmental Psychology, 9*, 417-430.

Tager-Flusberg, H. (2000). Language and understanding minds: Connections in autism. In S. Baron-Cohen, H. Tager-Flusberg, & D. J. Cohen, *Understanding other minds: Perspectives from developmental cognitive neuroscience* (2nd ed., pp.124-149). Oxford, UK: Oxford University Press.

Tanenhaus, M. K., Spivey-Knowlton, M., Eberhard, K., & Sedivy, J. (1995). Integration of visual and linguistic information during spoken language comprehension. *Science, 268*, 1632-1634.

Teunisse, J. P., & de Gelder, B. (2001). Impaired categorical perception of facial expressions in high-functioning adolescents with autism. *Neuropsychology, Development and Cognition, Section C, Child Neuropsychology. 7*, 1-14.

Teunisse, J. P., & de Gelder, B. (2003). Face processing in adolescents with autistic disorder: The inversion and composite effects. *Brain and Cognition, 52*(3), 285-294.

Titone, D., & Debruille, J. B. (2003). Guarding against over-inclusive notions of "context": Psycholinguistic and electrophysiological studies of specific context functions in schizophrenia. *Behavioral and Brain Sciences, 26*, 108-109.

Torralba, A. (2003). Contextual priming for object detection. *International Journal of Computer Vision, 53,* 169-191.

Torralba, A. (2009). How many pixels make an image? *Visual Neuroscience, 26*(1), 123-131.

Torralba, A., Oliva, A., Castelhano, M. S. & Henderson, J. M. (2006). Contextual guidance of eye movements and attention in real-world scenes: The role of global features in object search. *Psychological Review, 113*(4), 766-786.

Trillingsgaard, A. (1999). The script model in relation to autism. *European Journal of Adolescent Psychiatry, 8*(1), 45-49.

Tsatsanis, K. D., Noens, I. L. J., Illmann, C. L., Pauls, D. L., Volkmar, F. R., Schultz, R. T., & Klin, A. (2011). Managing complexity: Impact of organization and processing style on nonverbal memory in autism spectrum disorders. *Journal of Autism and Developmental Disorders, 41*(1), 135-147.

Tversky, A., & Kahneman, D. (1974). Judgment under uncertainty: Heuristics and biases. *Science, 185,* 1124-1131.

Tversky, A., & Kahneman, D. (1983). Extension versus intuitive reasoning: The conjunction fallacy in probability judgment. *Psychological Review, 90*(4), 293-315.

Ungerer, J., & Sigman, M. (1987). Categorization skills in autistic children. *Journal of Autism and Developmental Disorders, 17,* 3-16.

Van Berckelaer-Onnes, I. A. (1992). *Leven naar de letter* [Living to the letter]. Groningen, Netherlands: Wolters-Noordhoff.

Van Berckelaer-Onnes, I. A. (2007, June). *Ook op 29 juni bestaat Sinterklaas* [Santa Claus also exists on June 29th]. Valedictory celebration speech, University of Leiden, Netherlands.

Van Berkum, J., Brown, C., & Hagoort, P. (1999). Early referential context effects in sentence processing: Evidence from event-related brain potentials. *Journal of Memory and Language, 41,* 147-182.

Vandenbroucke, M. W., Scholte, H. S., van Engeland, H., Lamme, V. A., & Kemner, C. (2008). A neural substrate for atypical low-level visual processing in autism spectrum disorder. *Brain, 131,* 1013-1024.

Van den Stock, J., Righart, R., & de Gelder, B. (2007). Body expressions influence recognition of emotions in the face and voice. *Emotion, 7*(3), 487-494.

Van der Gaag, R. J., & van Berckelaer-Onnes, I. (2000). *Protocol autisme en aan autisme verwante contactstoornissen* [Protocol autism and autism related contact disorders]. In P. Prins & N. Pameijer (Eds.), *Protocollen in de jeugdzorg: Richtlijnen voor diagnostiek, indicatiestelling en interventie* [Protocols for youth care: Guidelines for diagnosis, allocation and interventions] (pp. 135-155). Lisse, Belgium: Swets & Zeitlinger.

Vermeulen, P. (1996a). *Dit is de titel: Over autistisch denken.* Gent/Antwerpen, Netherlands: Vlaamse Dienst Autisme/Epo. English version: Vermeulen, P. (2001). *Autistic thinking.* London, UK: Jessica Kingsley Publishers.

Vermeulen, P. (1996b). Autistisch kijken naar autisme [Looking at autism in an autistic way)]. *Autisme, 15*(6), 31-32.

Vermeulen, P. (1998). *Brein bedriegt. Als autisme niet op autisme lijkt* [Brain deceives: When autism doesn't look like autism]. Berchem/ Gent, Belgium: EPO/Vlaamse Dienst Autisme.

Vermeulen, P. (2002). *Beter vroeg dan laat en beter laat dan nooit: De onderkenning van autisme bij normaal tot hoogbegaafde personen* [The sooner the better and better late than never. Diagnosis of autism in people with an average or high intelligence]. Antwerpen/ Gent, Belgium: EPO/ Vlaamse Dienst Autisme.

Vermeulen, P. (2003). *Dialogica. Autisme < = > Kunst* [Dialogue: Autism versus art]. Antwerpen/Gent, Belgium: EPO/Autisme Centraal.

Vermeulen, P. (2005a). *Het gesloten boek: Autisme en emoties* [A closed book: On autism and emotions]. Leuven, Belgium: Acco.

Vermeulen, P. (Ed.) (2005b). *Ik ben speciaal - 2. Handboek psycho-educatie voor mensen met autisme*. Antwerpen/Gent, Belgium: EPO/Vlaamse Dienst Autisme. English version: Vermeulen, P. (2012). *I am special-2. A workbook to help children, teens and adults with Autism to understand their diagnosis, gain confidence and thrive.* London, UK: Jessica Kingsley Publishers.

Verpoorten, R., Noens, I., & van Berckelaer-Onnes, I. (2007). *ComVoor: Voorlopers in communicatie (Herziene versie)* [ComFor: Forerunners in communication, rev. ed.]. Leiden, Netherlands: Pits-online.

Verpoorten, R.A.W. (1996). Communicatie met verstandelijk gehandicapte autisten: Een multidimensioneel communicatiemodel [Communication with learning disabled people with autism: A multi-dimensional model of communication]. *Nederlands Tijdschrift Voor Zorg Aan Verstandelijk Gehandicapten, 22,* 106-120. (Dutch Journal of Care for People with Learning Disabilities).

Volden, J., & Johnston, J. (1999). Cognitive scripts in autistic children and adolescents. *Journal of Autism and Developmental Disorders, 29*(3), 203-211.

Volkmar, F., Sparrow, S., Rende, R. D., & Cohen, D. J. (1989). Facial perception in autism. *Journal of Child Psychology and Psychiatry, 30*, 591-598.

Walenski, M., Mostofsky, S. H., Larson, J.C.G., & Ullman, M. T. (2008). Enhanced picture naming in autism. *Journal of Autism and Developmental Disorders, 38*, 1395-1399.

Walenski, M., Tager-Flusberg, H., & Ullman, M. T. (2006). Language in autism. In S. O. Moldin & J.L.R. Rubenstein (Eds.), *Understanding autism: From basic neuroscience to treatment* (pp. 175-203). Boca Raton, FL: Taylor and Francis Books.

Wallace, S., Coleman, M., & Bailey, A. (2008). An investigation of basic facial expression recognition in autism spectrum disorders. *Cognition and Emotion, 22*(7), 1353-1380.

Walton, G. E., & Bower, T.G.R. (1993). Newborns form "prototypes" in less than 1 minute. *Psychological Science, 4,* 203-205.

Wang, A. T., Lee, S. S., Sigman, M., & Dapretto, M. (2006). Neural basis of irony comprehension in children with autism: The role of prosody and context. *Brain, 129*(4), 932-943.

Warren, R. M. (1970). Restoration of missing speech sounds. *Science, 167*, 392-393.

Warren, R. M., & Warren, R. P. (1970). Auditory illusions and confusions. *Scientific American, 223,* 30-36.

Waterhouse, L., & Fein, D. (1982). Language skills in developmentally disabled children. *Brain and Language, 15*, 307-333.

Watt, R. J., & Phillips, W. A. (2000). The function of dynamic grouping in vision. *Trends in Cognitive Sciences, 4*, 447-454.

Wechsler, D. (1991). *The Wechsler intelligence scale for children – third edition.* San Antonio, TX: The Psychological Corporation.

Wickelgren, I. (2005). Neurology: Autistic brains out of synch? *Science, 308*(5730), 1856-1858.

Witkin, H. A., Dyk, R. B., Faterson, H. F., Goodenough, D. R., & Karp, S. K. (1962). *Psychological differentiation.* New York, NY: Wiley.

Witkin, H. A., Oltman, P. K., Raskin, E., & Karp, S. A. (1971). *A manual for the Embedded Figures Test.* Palo Alto, CA: Consulting Psychologists Press.

Wright, B., Clarke, N., Jordan, J., Young, A. W., Clarke, P., Miles, J., et al. (2008). Emotion recognition in faces and the use of visual context in young people with high-functioning autism spectrum disorders. *Autism, 12*(6), 607-626.

Wu, L. L., & Barsalou, L. W. (2009). Perceptual simulation in conceptual combination: Evidence from property generation. *Acta Psychologica.*

Zalla, T., Sav, A. M., Ahade S., & Leboyer, M. (2009). Faux pas detection and intentional action in Asperger Syndrome. A replication on a French sample. *Journal of Autism and Developmental Disorders, 39*(2), 373-382.

Zwitserlood, P. (1989). The locus of the effects of sentential-semantic context in spoken word processing. *Cognition, 32*

## *What Others Are Saying....*

"In this excellent followup to *Autistic Thinking,* Peter Vermeulen reinforces the importance of context in our understanding of social behaviors in autism. The well-known cognitive models relating to theory of mind, central coherence, and executive function help us to understand behaviors in autism but may lack practical utility if they fail to take account of context. As few social encounters have absolute meaning, the concept of context is critical. Without a grasp of context, effective social discourse is impossible, and although it has long been recognized in the psychological literature, its importance in autism has largely been overlooked. Vermeulen provides a scholarly and lucid account of autism and the instinctive nature of context blindness as a core component of the condition, impacting on all aspects of social behavior, including emotions affecting self-esteem and self-confidence.

This book will inform our approach to communication, teaching, and intervention and is bound to enjoy a wide appeal. I commend it to researchers interested in the social cognition of autism, to practitioners seeking to develop appropriate interventions, and to anyone who wishes to learn more about why individuals with autism tend to see the world the way they do and the challenges they face."

– Richard Mills, director of research, The National Autistic Society, UK

"Peter Vermeulen presents a theoretical framework with which we can better understand the autistic brain and improve intervention planning. His writing is incredibly interesting and easy to comprehend. He provides specific examples that are immediately recognizable and can be easily applied to the reader's own experiences with individuals with ASD. This is a remarkable, innovative book from the theoretical and the clinical perspective that can help develop more effective therapeutic goals. I encourage every type of professional who works with persons on the autism spectrum to add *Autism as Context Blindness* to their library."

– Aileen Zeitz Collucci, MA, CCC, speech-language pathologist, and author of *Big Picture Thinking – Using Central Coherence Theory to Support Social Skills, A Book for Students*

"Dr. Vermeulen has produced a brilliant work that demands attention. *Autism as Context Blindness* provides a unique glance into the minds of individuals with ASD. It is at once simple but groundbreaking, challenging but accessible. Application of Vermeulen's insights into the mind of autism will help individuals with ASD to become ready for the contexts in which they live. In his own words, 'The essence of autism is in the mind, not in the behavior.'"

– Ruth Aspy, PhD, and Barry G. Grossman, PhD, The Ziggurat Group

"This book changes our conceptualization of the perception and thinking of people with autism and provides a logical explanation of behavior and abilities that have previously been confusing for parents, teachers, therapists, and clinicians. Vermeulen's style is engaging and highly informative, creating a bridge between theory and research and the everyday experiences of someone with autism. It is essential reading for anyone who wants to understand the autistic mind."

– Tony Attwood, PhD, international speaker, writer, and researcher on autism spectrum disorders

PUBLISHING

P.O. Box 23173
Shawnee Mission, Kansas 66283-0173
www.aapcpublishing.net

CPSIA information can be obtained at www.ICGtesting.com
Printed in the USA
LVOW04s0411021214

416641LV00003B/3/P

9 781937 473006